Framework 7

MATHS C

David Capewell — Formerly Westfield School, Sheffield

Marguerite Comyns — Queen Mary's High School, Walsall

Gillian Flinton — All Saints Catholic High School, Sheffield

Geoff Fowler — Maths Strategy Manager, Birmingham

Kam Grewal-Joy — Mathematics Consultant

Derek Huby — Mathematics Consultant, West Sussex

Peter Johnson — Wellfield High School, Leyland, Lancashire

Penny Jones — Waverley School, Birmingham

Jayne Kranat — Langley Park School for Girls, Bromley

Ian Molyneux — St. Bedes RC High School, Ormskirk

Peter Mullarkey — Netherhall School, Maryport, Cumbria

Nina Patel — Ifield Community College, West Sussex

OXFORD
UNIVERSITY PRESS

OXFORD
UNIVERSITY PRESS

Great Clarendon Street, Oxford OX2 6DP

Oxford University Press is a department of the University of Oxford.
It furthers the University's objective of excellence in research,
scholarship, and education by publishing worldwide in

Oxford New York

Auckland Cape Town Dar es Salaam Hong Kong Karachi
Kuala Lumpur Madrid Melbourne Mexico City Nairobi
New Delhi Shanghai Taipei Toronto

With offices in

Argentina Austria Brazil Chile Czech Republic France Greece
Guatemala Hungary Italy Japan Poland Portugal Singapore
South Korea Switzerland Thailand Turkey Ukraine Vietnam

Oxford is a registered trade mark of Oxford University Press
in the UK and in certain other countries

British Library Cataloguing in Publication Data

Data available

ISBN: 978-0-19-914849-3

20 19 18 17 16 15 14 13

Typeset by Mathematical Composition Setters Ltd.

Printed in Singapore by KHL Printing Co. Pte Ltd

Acknowledgements

The photograph on the cover is reproduced courtesy of Pictor.

The publisher and authors would like to thank the following for permission
to use photographs and other copyright material: Stock Market Picture
Library, page 1, Pictor International (UK), page 79, Corbis UK, pages 166 and
246, J. Arnold, page 235.

Figurative artwork by Jeff Anderson.

About this book

This book has been written specifically for Year 7 of the Framework for Teaching Mathematics. It is aimed at students who are following the Year 7 teaching programme from the Framework and have gained a Level 4 at the end of KS2.

The authors are experienced teachers and maths consultants who have been incorporating the Framework approaches into their teaching for many years and so are well qualified to help you successfully meet the Framework objectives.

The book is made up of units based on the sample medium term plans which complement the Framework document, thus maintaining the required pitch, pace and progression. The units are:

Each unit comprises double page spreads that should take a lesson to teach. These are shown on the full contents list.

Problem solving is integrated throughout the material as suggested in the Framework.

How to use this book

This book is made up of units of work which are colour coded into: Algebra (Blue), Data (Pink), Number (Orange) and Shape, space and measures (Green).

Each unit of work starts with an overview of the content of the unit, as specified in the Framework document, so that you know exactly what you are expected to learn.

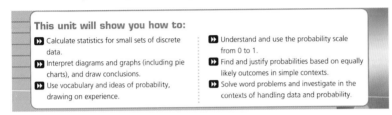

This unit will show you how to:
- Calculate statistics for small sets of discrete data.
- Interpret diagrams and graphs (including pie charts), and draw conclusions.
- Use vocabulary and ideas of probability, drawing on experience.
- Understand and use the probability scale from 0 to 1.
- Find and justify probabilities based on equally likely outcomes in simple contexts.
- Solve word problems and investigate in the contexts of handling data and probability.

The first page of a unit also highlights the skills and facts you should already know and provides Check in questions to help you revise before you start so that you are ready to apply the knowledge later in the unit:

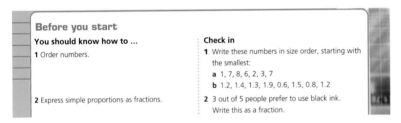

Before you start

You should know how to ...

1 Order numbers.

2 Express simple proportions as fractions.

Check in

1 Write these numbers in size order, starting with the smallest:
 a 1, 7, 8, 6, 2, 3, 7
 b 1.2, 1.4, 1.3, 1.9, 0.6, 1.5, 0.8, 1.2

2 3 out of 5 people prefer to use black ink. Write this as a fraction.

Inside each unit, the content develops in double page spreads which all follow the same structure.

The spreads start with a list of the learning outcomes and a summary of the keywords:

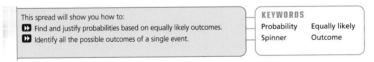

This spread will show you how to:
- Find and justify probabilities based on equally likely outcomes.
- Identify all the possible outcomes of a single event.

KEYWORDS
Probability   Equally likely
Spinner   Outcome

The keywords are summarised and defined in a Glossary at the end of the book so you can always check what they mean.

Key information is highlighted in the text so you can see the facts you need to learn.

▶ Area of a rectangle = length × width

Examples showing the key skills and techniques you need to develop are shown in boxes. Also hint boxes show tips and reminders you may find useful:

Peter has £1 and spends 35p on chocolate.
What fraction of his money has he spent?

....

Divide his money into equal-sized parts: £1 = 100p
He has spent 35p.
He has spent $\frac{35}{100}$ of his money.

Notice that the units have to be the same before you can compare them using fractions.

Each exercise is carefully graded, set at three levels of difficulty:

» The first few questions provide lead-in questions, revising previous learning.
» The questions in the middle of the exercise provide the main focus of the material.
» The last few questions are challenging questions that provide a link to the Year 8 learning objectives.

At the end of each unit is a summary page so that you can revise the learning of the unit before moving on.

Check out questions are provided to help you check your understanding of the key concepts covered and your ability to apply the key techniques.

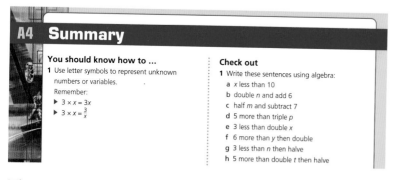

A4 Summary

You should know how to ...
1 Use letter symbols to represent unknown numbers or variables.
   Remember:
   ▶ $3 \times x = 3x$
   ▶ $3 \div x = \frac{3}{x}$

Check out
1 Write these sentences using algebra:
   a x less than 10
   b double n and add 6
   c half m and subtract 7
   d 5 more than triple p
   e 3 less than double x
   f 6 more than y then double
   g 3 less than n then halve
   h 5 more than double t then halve

The answers to the Check in and Check out questions are produced at the end of the book so that you can check your own progress and identify any areas that need work.

Contents

This unit will show you how to:

 Generate and describe simple integer sequences.

 Generate terms of a simple sequence, given a term-to-term rule.

 Generate sequences from practical contexts.

 Express simple functions in words, then using symbols.

 Represent functions in mappings.

 Use letter symbols to represent unknown numbers or variables.

 Solve word problems and investigate in the context of algebra.

 Suggest extensions to problems by asking 'What if ...?'.

 Begin to generalise and to understand the significance of a counter-example.

The spirals in this sunflower follow a sequence.

Before you start

You should know how to ...

1 Count on or back in steps.

2 Know multiplication facts up to 10 × 10.

Check in

1 For each question continue for six steps.

  a Count on from 2 in steps of 3.
    Write: 2, _, _, _, _, _

  b Count back from 20 in steps of 4.
    Write: 20, _, _, _, _, _

  c Count back from 10 in steps of 0.5.
    Write: 10, 9.5, _, _, _, _

  d Count back from 3 in steps of 0.1.
    Write: 3, 2.9, _, _, _, _

2 Copy and complete these multiplications.

  a $3 \times 9 = $ _   **b** $4 \times 8 = $ _

  c $7 \times 6 = $ _   **d** $9 \times 7 = $ _

  e $8 \times $ _ $ = 72$ **f** $5 \times $ _ $ = 30$

  g $7 \times $ _ $ = 49$ **h** _ $ \times 9 = 54$

  i _ $ \times 7 = 28$ **j** _ $ \times 5 = 45$

Introducing sequences

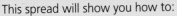

This spread will show you how to:

▶▶ Generate and describe sequences.

KEYWORDS

Sequence   Consecutive

Term   Finite

Rule   Infinite

Joe lives at number 6.

His neighbours are at number 4 and number 8.
The last house in the street is number 12.

The house numbers on Joe's side of the street
form the even numbers up to 12:
2, 4, 6, 8, 10, 12

▶ When numbers or pictures follow a rule or pattern they
form a **sequence**.

This packet contains 8 chocolate wafers.

Two packets would contain 8 × 2 = 16 wafers.
Three packets would contain 8 × 3 = 24 wafers.

The number of wafers forms a sequence: 8, 16, 24, 32, 40, 48, ...

▶ Each number in the sequence is
called a **term**.

Terms next to each other, like 40
and 48 are **consecutive**.

The first term is 8,   the third term is 24.

House numbers form a **finite** sequence
because they have a definite end:
2, 4, 6, 8, 10, 12

Even numbers form an **infinite** sequence
because they go on and on and on:
2, 4, 6, 8, 10, 12, ...

The dots show the sequence
goes on for ever.

▶ You can describe a sequence using a **rule**.
The sequence 3, 7, 11, 15, 19, ... starts with a 3 and goes up in 4's.

Hint: when you are finding a
rule, it often helps to look at the
difference between terms.

example

Describe these sequences in words.

a	2, 5, 8, 11, 14, ...	**b**	2, 4, 8, 16, 32, ...	**c**	21, 19, 17, 15, ...

a	Starts at 2 Goes up by 3	**b**	Starts at 2 Doubles each time	**c**	Starts at 21 Goes down by 2

Exercise A1.1

1 Copy these sequences and add the next three terms.
  a 6, 12, 18, __, __, __
  b 5, 11, 17, 23, __, __, __
  c 43, 40, 37, 34, __, __, __
  d 1.5, 3, 4.5, 6, __, __, __
  e 3, 6, 12, __, __, __

2 Describe these sequences in words:
  a 25, 21, 17, 13, ...
  b 3, 10, 17, 24, ...
  c 16, 19, 22, 25, ...
  d 1.2, 1.8, 2.4, 3, ...
  e 5, 10, 20, 40, ...

3 Copy and complete the first 6 terms of these sequences.
  a 1, __, 5, __, 9, __
  b 3, 6, __, __, 15, __
  c 45, __, 35, __, 25, __
  d 2, 5, __, __, 14, __
  e 6, __, 20, __, 34, __

4 These sequences all start 1, 2, ... but after this they differ.
  Copy each sequence.
  Add two more terms.
  Describe each sequence in words.
  a 1, 2, 3, 4, __, __
  b 1, 2, 4, 8, __,
  c 1, 2, 4, 7, __, __
  d 1, 2, 5, 10, 17, __, __

5 The sequence of odd numbers starts:
  1, 3, 5, 7, ...
  Write down four other sequences that contain the terms 3 and 5.
  Describe each of your sequences in words.

6 **Investigation**
  The postman often gets confused on Joe's street because the house numbers are arranged like this:

2	4	6	8	10	12
11	9	7	5	3	1

  Joe lives at number 6.
  a Describe the sequence formed on the opposite side of the street to Joe.
    The street is extended and the odd-numbered houses are renumbered like this:

2	4	.....	....	18	20
19	17		...	3	1

  b What number does Joe live opposite now?
  c How long would the street need to be for Joe to live opposite number 55? Investigate.

7 There are two sequences jumbled up together here:

  31, 15, 24, 7, 18, 22,
  47, 16, 20, 23, 26, 39

  a One sequence goes up in 8s.
    Write this sequence in numbers.
    Describe the sequence in words.
  b List the second sequence and describe it in words.

Sequences and rules

This spread will show you how to:
⏩ Generate terms of a sequence given a rule for finding each term from the previous term.

KEYWORDS

Generate Rule
Sequence Continue
Term Unknown

▶ You can use a **rule** to continue or find unknown terms in a sequence.

example

Describe these sequences in words.
Use the rule to continue the sequence for the next two terms.
a 1, 5, 9, 13, 17, ___, ___   **b** 16, 13, 10, 7, ___, ___

a The sequence starts at 1, and goes up by 4 each time.
  1,   5,   9,   13,   17,   21,   25
    +4   +4   +4   +4

  To find the next two terms: add 4 ...   ... and add 4 again.

b The sequence starts at 16, and goes down by 3 each time.
  16,   13,   10,   7,   4,   1
    −3   −3   −3

  To find the next two terms: subtract 3 ...   and subtract 3 again.

In these examples you find the next term from the previous term.

▶ A term-to-term rule tells you how to find the next term from the previous term.

You can use a term-to-term rule to generate a sequence.

'Generate' means 'make'.

example

Generate the first 5 terms of these sequences:
a 1st term 2, term-to-term rule add 5   **b** 1st term 4, term-to-term rule multiply by 3

a You start at 2 and keep adding 5:
  2, 7, 12, 17, 22

b You start at 4 and keep multiplying by 3:
  4, 12, 36, 108, 324

Exercise A1.2

1 Copy each of these sequences and continue for the next two terms.

    a 3, 5, 7, 9, __, __   **b** 1, 6, 11, 16, __, __

    c 2, 4.5, 7, 9.5, __, __   **d** 11, 34, 57, 80, __, __

    e 8, 11, 14, 17, __, __   **f** 70, 66, 62, 58, __, __

    g $1\frac{1}{2}$, $2\frac{3}{4}$, 4, $5\frac{1}{4}$, __, __   **h** 4, 6, 9, 13, 18, __, __

2 Write down the first five terms of these sequences:

    a Starting at 4, each term is 2 bigger than the one before.

    b The first term is 7 and each term is 4 larger than the previous term.

    c The first term is 19 and each term is 3 smaller than the previous term.

    d The first term is 6 and each term is 1.3 larger than the previous term.

    e The second term is 13 and each term is 7 larger than the previous term.

3 Write down the first five terms of each of these sequences.
Describe the sequences in words in another way.

    a Each term is one more than the 4 times table.

    b Each term is two less than the 6 times table.

    c The third term is 9. Each term is 4 larger than the previous term.

    d The second term is 17. Each term is 3 smaller than the previous term.

4 Write down the first five terms of each of these sequences:

    a The second term is 6. Each term is double the previous term.

    b The first term is 12. Each term is half the previous term.

    c The second term is 0. Each term is 6 more than the previous term.

    d The second, fourth and sixth terms are the first three terms of the 8 times table.

    e The first two terms are 2 and 3. The difference between two consecutive terms is one greater than the difference between the previous consecutive terms.

5 **Investigation**
Copy and complete this sequence:
1, __, __, 10, __
How many different sequences can you find that will fit?

6 There are three sequences jumbled up here:
1, 4, 5, 8, 8, 8, 11, 14, 15, 16, 17, 22, 29, 32, 64
Find the three sequences. Describe them in words.
These clues may help:

    ▸ The second term in each sequence is the same.

    ▸ One of the sequences doubles each time.

    ▸ One of the sequences adds 7 each time.

Sequences in diagrams

This spread will show you how to:
▶▶ Generate sequences from simple practical contexts.

KEYWORDS
Rule   Predict
Sequence   Term

You can describe picture patterns using sequences.

example

a Find the rule for this pattern:

b How many matchsticks will the next pattern have?

....

a Start with 4 and add 3 each time.

b 13 + 3 = 16

The next pattern will have 16 matchsticks.

You can use a table to help spot the sequence:

Number of squares	1	2	3	4	5
Number of matchsticks	4	7	10	13	16

▶ When you understand how a sequence grows you can predict unknown terms.

example

a Draw the next two patterns in this sequence:
b Explain how to get the next pattern.
c Draw the 10th pattern.
d Explain how to predict the number of counters in the 18th pattern.
   (You don't need to draw it.)

....

a The next two patterns look like this:

b For the next pattern you add a counter to each 'arm' of the Y shape.

c

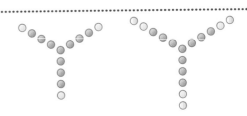

d For the 18th pattern there would be 18 counters on each 'arm' plus the one in the centre.
$18 \times 3 + 1 = 55$
There would be 55 counters.

Exercise A1.3

1 a Draw the next two patterns in this sequence.

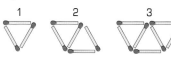

b How many matches are there in each of the five patterns?

c Predict how many matches will be in the 10th pattern.

2 For each of these sequences:
- ▶ Draw the next two patterns.
- ▶ Describe in words how the pattern grows.
- ▶ Complete this table for the number of counters.

Pattern number	Number of counters
1	
2	
3	
4	
5	
10	
17	
20	

a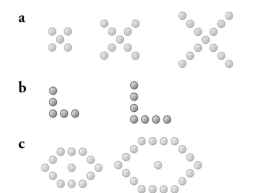

b

c

3 Copy and complete the patterns in this grid:

7	9	11	
10			
	15	17	
16			

4 Look at this sequence of tile patterns.

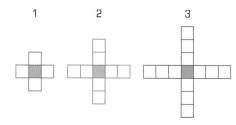

a How many white tiles are needed in each of the first five patterns?

b How many white tiles would be needed in the 10th pattern?

c How many **tiles** are needed in the 10th pattern?

d How many tiles are needed in the 100th pattern?

5 Game
- ▶ Each player writes down the first four terms of a sequence.
- ▶ Players then swap sequences.
- ▶ Each player draws a pattern for the sequence they are given.
- ▶ Players score 1 point for each correct pattern and 1 point for predicting the 10th term of the sequence.
- ▶ The winner is the player with the most points after 10 rounds.

This spread will show you how to:
▶▶ Express simple functions at first in words and then using symbols.

KEYWORDS
Function machine
Input   Output
Function   Rule

You can process numbers using a **function**.

Here are some functions:
'turn hours into minutes'

'convert degrees Centigrade to Fahrenheit'

'cook for 30 mins per kilo'

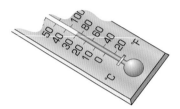

You can show a function using a **function machine**.

This function machine multiplies everything by 2:

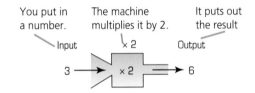

You put in a number.   The machine multiplies it by 2.   It puts out the result

Input   × 2   Output

3 ⟶ × 2 ⟶ 6

Using a function machine is like using a calculator:

Input	Function	Output
3	× 2 =	6

▶ In a function machine:
  ▶ The **input** value is the value you put in to the machine.
  ▶ The machine performs the **function**.
  ▶ The **output** value is the result that the machine puts out.

You can have more than one function in a function machine.

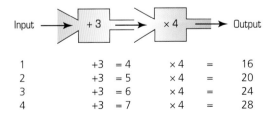

Input ⟶ + 3 ⟶ × 4 ⟶ Output

1	+3 = 4	× 4	=	16
2	+3 = 5	× 4	=	20
3	+3 = 6	× 4	=	24
4	+3 = 7	× 4	=	28

The output numbers form a sequence: it starts at 16 and the rule is 'add 4'.

▶ A function machine is a rule.
  When you input the counting numbers it will generate a sequence.

Exercise A1.4

1 For these function machines, find the outputs for each of the inputs 1, 2 and 3.

a

b
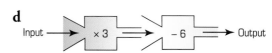

c
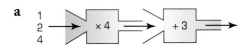

d
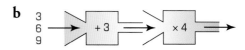

2 For these function machines, find the outputs for the inputs given.

a

b
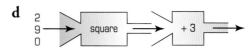

c
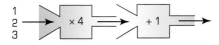

d

3 a Work out the outputs for this function.

b Reverse the order of the functions (add 1 first).
Work out the outputs.
Are they the same as in **a**?

4 This function machine has no functions!

Choose any two of these functions to put into the machine:

| × 3 | + 5 | − 4 | ÷ 2 |

There are 12 different combinations you can use.
a Which order of functions gives the largest outputs?
b Which order of functions gives the smallest outputs?
c Are there any combinations that give the same outputs?

5 Use these three functions: ... in this function machine:

| × 4 | + 3 | ÷ 2 |

a Which order give the largest outputs?
b Which order gives the smallest outputs?

Finding the function

This spread will show you how to:
- ▶▶ Express simple functions in words.
- ▶▶ Given inputs and outputs, find the function.

KEYWORDS

Input   Output
Function Mapping
Function machine

You can work out problems using a function machine.

example

What input gives an output of 10 for this machine?

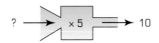

Input × 5 = 10 2 × 5 = 10 so input = 2

In these machines you know a few input and output values but not the function:

example

Find the functions for these machines:

a
5	1
7	3
10	6
13	9

b
1		4
2		7
3		10
8		25

a 5 – 4 = 1
  7 – 4 = 3
  10 – 4 = 6
  13 – 4 = 9

The function is: 'subtract 4'.

b 1 × 3 + 1 = 4
  2 × 3 + 1 = 7
  3 × 3 + 1 = 10
  8 × 3 + 1 = 25

The difference between the first two terms is 3 so try ×3!

The function is: 'multiply by 3, then add 1'.

In the example, there is more than one input and output.

▶ You can show more than one input and output using a **mapping diagram**.

This function machine uses the inputs 1, 2, 3 and 4.

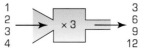

Redraw the inputs and outputs as number lines:

This is a mapping diagram for the function 'multiply by 3'.

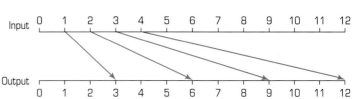

Exercise A1.5

1 For each of these function machines, work out the inputs for the given output.

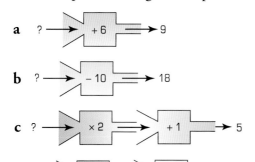

a ? → + 6 → 9

b ? → − 10 → 18

c ? → × 2 → + 1 → 5

d ? → × 3 → − 4 → 8

2 In these function machines, you are given three pairs of inputs and outputs.
Find the function.

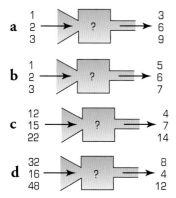

a 1 2 3 → ? → 3 6 9

b 1 2 3 → ? → 5 6 7

c 12 15 22 → ? → 4 7 14

d 32 16 48 → ? → 8 4 12

3 For each of these mapping diagrams, draw a function machine, showing clearly **i** the inputs, **ii** the function and **iii** the outputs.

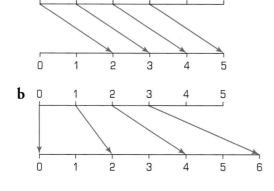

a 0 1 2 3 4 5 → 0 1 2 3 4 5

b 0 1 2 3 4 5 → 0 1 2 3 4 5 6

4 For the function machines in questions 2a and 2b, draw a mapping diagram.

5 **Function challenge**
Find the missing functions in each of these machines.
Explain the strategies you use.

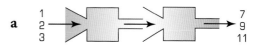

a 1 2 3 → ☐ → ☐ → 7 9 11

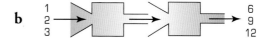

b 1 2 3 → ☐ → ☐ → 6 9 12

c 1 2 3 → ☐ → ☐ → 3 8 13

d 2 4 6 → ☐ → ☐ → 3 4 5

e 3 1 2 → ☐ → ☐ → 33 13 23

6 **Investigation**
a Write down the outputs for this function machine.

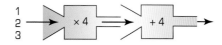

1 2 3 → × 4 → + 4 →

b Write down the outputs for this function machine.

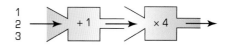

1 2 3 → + 1 → × 4 →

c What do you notice?
d **Challenge**
Can you find another pair of functions that give the same outputs?

This spread will show you how to:
- ▶▶ Reinforce the idea of an unknown.
- ▶▶ Use letter symbols.
- ▶▶ Begin to recognise algebraic conventions.

KEYWORDS

Variable	Function
Algebra	Term
Value	Expression

▶ A **variable** is a value that can change.

For example, the number of days until your birthday changes each day.

The input of this function machine is variable:

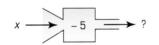

$$1 \quad 2 \quad 3 \quad 4 \xrightarrow{\;} \boxed{+2} \xrightarrow{\;} 3 \quad 5 \quad 7 \quad 9$$

You could use a letter instead to represent the numbers:

$$x \qquad\qquad x + 2$$

▶ You can use a letter to stand for a variable.

Algebra is the branch of maths where letters stand for variables.
There are a few conventions or rules that you must follow:

- ▶ $3n$ means $3 \times n$ this is the same as $n \times 3$, or 3 lots of n
- ▶ n^2 means $n \times n$ so $3n^2$ means 3 lots of n^2
- ▶ $\frac{n}{2}$ means $n \div 2$ so $\frac{3n}{2}$ means 3 lots of $\frac{n}{2}$

In algebra, $3n$, $3n^2$ and $\frac{3n}{2}$ are all examples of algebraic **terms**.

> Leave out the × sign so it's not confused with the letter x!

example

Write the outputs for these function machines as algebraic terms:

a

$$x \xrightarrow{\;} \boxed{-5} \xrightarrow{\;} ?$$

b

$$p \xrightarrow{\;} \boxed{\times 7} \xrightarrow{\;} ?$$

c

$$n \xrightarrow{\;} \boxed{\div 4} \xrightarrow{\;} ?$$

a   The output is $x - 5$
    You can write $x \rightarrow x - 5$

b   The output is $p \times 7$, or $7p$
    You can write $p \rightarrow 7p$

c   The output is $n \div 4$, or $\frac{n}{4}$
    You can write $n \rightarrow \frac{n}{4}$

$n + 2$, $a + b$ and $3f + 1$ are algebraic **expressions**.

▶ An algebraic expression is a collection of terms.

> When you know the value of the expression you have an equation. You will learn about equations in A4.

Exercise A1.6

1 Write the outputs for these function machines as algebraic expressions.

For example:

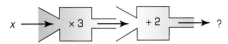

The output is $x \times 3 + 2$, or $3x + 2$

a

b
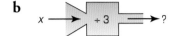

c
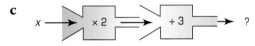

d
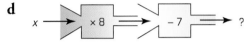

e
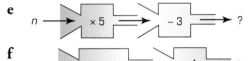

f
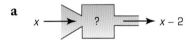

2 In these questions you are given the input and the output.
Work out the operations in each function machine.

a

b
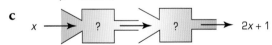

c
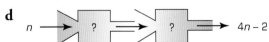

d
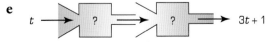

e
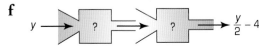

f

3 Write these functions as function machines.
For example, $x \rightarrow 3x - 4$ is

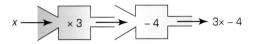

a $x \rightarrow 4x + 1$
b $y \rightarrow 3y - 8$
c $d \rightarrow \frac{d}{4} + 6$
d $p \rightarrow p^2 + 6$

4 Write each of these terms using the correct algebraic conventions:

a $p4$ **b** $6 \times e$
c $x \div 3$ **d** $2 \times t \times t$
e $3 \times y \div 4$ **f** $2 \times a + 3$

5 Puzzle
Here is a function machine with three operations.

a Complete the function machine using each of these symbols once: +, −, ×, 1, 2 and 3.
b Starting with an input of 7, and using the same signs and numbers as in **a**, how many different outputs can you find?

6 Challenge

Using the numbers 1, 2, 3, 4 and 5, and the operations +, −, × once and only once, find the input, output and the three functions that will make the function machine work.

You should know how to ...

1 Generate and describe sequences.

2 Use letter symbols to represent unknown numbers or variables.

Remember:

▶ 3*n* means 3 × *n*.

▶ $\frac{n}{2}$ means *n* ÷ 2.

Check out

1 For each of these sequences:

▶ Copy and continue the sequence for the next three terms.

▶ Describe the sequence in words.

▶ Predict the value of the 10th term of the sequence.
Check your prediction.

a 3, 8, 13, __, __, __

b 2, 6, 10, __, __, __

c 18, 15, 12, __, __, __

d 2, 4, 8, 16, __, __, __

e

2 For each of these function machines:

▶ Find the output when the input value is 8.

▶ Write an expression for the output when the input value is *x*.

a Input ⟶ + 3 ⟶ Output

b Input ⟶ − 5 ⟶ Output

c Input ⟶ × 2 ⟶ Output

d Input ⟶ ÷ 4 ⟶ Output

e Input ⟶ × 2 ⟶ + 3 ⟶ Output

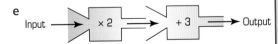

f Input ⟶ × 3 ⟶ − 4 ⟶ Output

This unit will show you how to:

▶▶ Understand and use decimal notation and place value.

▶▶ Compare and order decimals.

▶▶ Order, add and subtract positive and negative numbers.

▶▶ Consolidate and extend mental methods of calculation, accompanied where appropriate by suitable jottings.

▶▶ Make and justify estimates and approximations of calculations.

▶▶ Use efficient column methods for addition and subtraction of whole numbers, and extend to decimals.

▶▶ Interpret the display on a calculator in different contexts.

▶▶ Solve word problems and investigate in the context of number.

> I owe Justine £3.50 for the cinema ticket, but Dionne still owes me £4.60 and it's okay because I'll get £4 pocket money tomorrow so I can get a £5 top-up card for my phone.

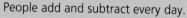

People add and subtract every day.

Before you start

You should know how to ...

1 Read and write whole numbers in words and figures.

2 Use mental strategies for addition and subtraction of whole numbers.

3 Use written methods for addition and subtraction of whole numbers.

Check in

1 a Write these numbers in words:
   i 13 206
   ii 130 206

  b Write these numbers in figures:
   i four hundred thousand and eight
   ii four hundred and eight thousand

2 Work out in your head:
  a 123 + 49
  b 412 – 395

3 Work out:
  a 2168 + 2431
  b 2487 – 1298

This spread will show you how to:
▶▶ Understand and use decimal notation and place value.
▶▶ Compare and order decimals.
▶▶ Add or subtract 0.1 and 0.01.

▶ Each digit in a number has a value that depends on its place in the number: its **place value**.

For example: 452.945

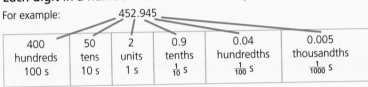

400	50	2	0.9	0.04	0.005
hundreds	tens	units	tenths	hundredths	thousandths
100 s	10 s	1 s	$\frac{1}{10}$ s	$\frac{1}{100}$ s	$\frac{1}{1000}$ s

You say four hundred and fifty two point nine four five

▶ A zero holds place value in a number.

For example: 40.07

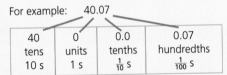

40	0	0.0	0.07
tens	units	tenths	hundredths
10 s	1 s	$\frac{1}{10}$ s	$\frac{1}{100}$ s

You say zero tenths as they hold the place value – forty point zero seven.

If you forget the zeros you get 4.7 which is four units and seven tenths

▶ Every number can be represented as a position on a number line.

For example: 6.37 = 6 + 0.3 + 0.07

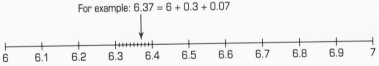

▶ To compare two or more numbers first compare the place value of the first non-zero digit then the second digit and so on.

For example: the most significant digit in 243.14 is the 2 which is 200.

The first non-zero digit in a number is the most significant.

example

Place these numbers in size order, starting with the largest.   0.56 0.6 0.616 0.66 0.62

▶ There are no units in any of the numbers so first arrange by comparing the first decimal place:

0.6   0.616   0.66   0.62   0.56

▶ The first four numbers all have the same first decimal place so look at the second decimal place:

0.66   0.62   0.616   0.60   0.56

The numbers are now in size order.

Hint
Use a number line:

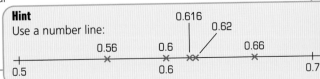

Exercise N1.1

1 Write these numbers in words:
   a 423 603
   b 71 005
   c 102 070
   d 72.4

2 Write these numbers in figures:
   a two hundred and seven
   b four thousand and twenty-three
   c eight hundred and three thousand, six hundred and two
   d thirty and one tenth

3 **a** Write this list of numbers in order of size, smallest first:
   6.3   6.8   7   6.1   6
   b Draw a number line from 5 to 8 and label the numbers on it.

4 Place > or < between these numbers:
   (**Remember**: < means 'less than' and > means 'greater than'.)
   a 12 436   ☐   12 300
   b 1.76   ☐   1.67
   c 2.6   ☐   2.62

5 **Game** Each player rolls a 0–9 dice and writes the digit in one of the spaces beside the first target number. This continues until all the spaces are filled.
   The player with the number closest to the target wins the round.
   The players complete five rounds.
   Round   Target
   i   Highest number   ☐☐☐.☐☐
   ii Smallest number   ☐☐☐.☐☐
   iii Nearest to 400   ☐☐☐.☐☐
   iv Farthest away from 400   ☐☐☐.☐☐
   v   Nearest to a square number
                                     ☐☐☐.☐☐
   The player who wins the most rounds is the overall winner.

6 Copy and complete these number patterns:

a

6.7		6.9			7.2	7.3

b

25.38				35.38	

c

12.32					11.72

d

4.132							4.402

7 Write these numbers in words:
   a 5.479
   b 0.25
   c 148.03

8 Write these numbers using decimals:
   a five and seventeen hundredths
   b fourteen and twelve thousandths

9 What number lies halfway between:
   a 13 and 14
   b 1.9 and 2
   c 0.4 and 0.41?

10 These are the results of the 100 metres race at Veryfast School:
   Anton   13.3 s
   Barnabas   14.15 s
   Cedric   13.43 s
   Dominico   13.19 s
   Edwardio   14.03 s
   Put the runners in order from fastest to slowest.

11 In a recent exam paper, students were asked which is the smallest:
   A 0.625   B 0.25   C 0.375
   D 0.125   E 0.5
   The answer is 0.125 – answer D.
   Most students answered A, D or E.
   a Try to explain why a student might have chosen A as the answer.
   b Try to explain why a student might have chosen E as the answer.

This spread will show you how to:

▶▶ Order integers and position them on a number line.

▶▶ Use positive and negative numbers in context.

KEYWORDS

Positive	Add
Negative	Subtract
Difference	Integer

You use negative numbers in many situations in real life ...

... describing the temperature   ... storing frozen food   ... describing depths

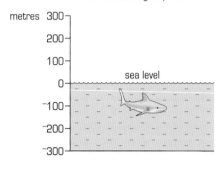

⁻4°C is a temperature of 4°C below zero

These fish fingers must be stored below ⁻20°C to stay frozen

⁻100 m is a depth of 100 m below sea level

▶ Negative numbers can be represented on a number line.

Numbers below 0 are **negative** numbers   Numbers above 0 are **positive** numbers

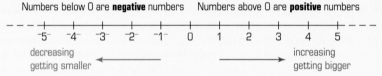

decreasing
getting smaller

increasing
getting bigger

▶ As you move to the left the numbers get smaller.

For example: ⁻5 is smaller than ⁻2.

You can use a number line to help solve problems involving negative numbers.

example

Vicky dives from a diving board which is 12 metres above the water level.
The pool is 4 metres deep.
How far is it from the diving board to the bottom of the pool?

The diving board is 12 metres above water level, or 12 metres.

The bottom of the pool is 4 metres below water level, or ⁻4 metres.

Using a number line you can see that the difference between the height of the board and the bottom of the pool is 16 metres.

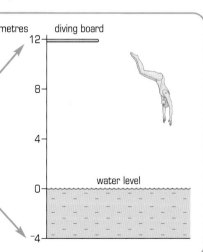

Exercise N1.2

1 a Which is colder:
⁻8 °C or ⁻4 °C?

b Write down the temperatures marked A, B, C, D and E.

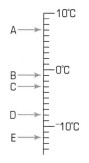

2 What temperature is 12 degrees colder than ⁻13 °C?

3 What temperature is exactly halfway between
   a ⁻7 degrees and 3 degrees?
   b ⁻32 degrees and ⁻15 degrees?

4 Put these integers in order, lowest first:
   a ⁻1, 6, 5, ⁻5, ⁻8, 19, ⁻13, ⁻7
   b ⁻28, 39, 16, 107, ⁻58, ⁻3, 72, ⁻26, ⁻19

5 Copy and complete these number patterns.

a | | | | 0 | 8 | |

b | | | ⁻3 | | | 5 | |

c | | ⁻71 | | | | | ⁻11 |

d | ⁻53 | | | | | | 3 |

e | | | | ⁻20 | ⁻10 | | |

6 If ⁻11 < △ < ⁻6, what integer values could △ be?

7 Put these sets of numbers in order from lowest to highest.

Set A

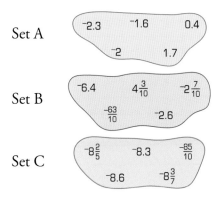

Set B

Set C

8 The following statistics were taken from a Geography book.
Find the range of temperatures in these cities. (The range is the difference between the mid-summer and mid-winter temperatures.)

Location	Mid-summer temperature °C	Mid-winter temperature °C
Dawson	17	⁻30
Verkhoyunsk	15	⁻45
Montreal	21	⁻9
London	20	4
Rangoon	30	25
Buenos Aires	25	10
Moscow	20	⁻12
Vienna	21	⁻2
Marseilles	22	8
Helsinki	18	⁻8
Bucharest	22	⁻3
Reykjavik	11	⁻1
Barnaul	20	⁻20

9 a Cillio was born in 18BC and died in 49AD. For how many years did he live?

b Mr. Ghetti has £1427 and spends £2639 on a vase. How much money does he need to borrow?

c A bird is flying at 62 feet. It dives into the sea, to catch a fish swimming 7 feet below sea level. How many feet did the bird dive?

10 a The points (1, 0) (2, ⁻4) and (⁻3, ⁻1) are three of the four vertices of a square. What are the coordinates of the fourth vertex?

b The points (⁻2, 2) and (4, ⁻2) are two of the four vertices of a square. What are the coordinates of the other two vertices?
Find as many possibilities as you can.

This spread will show you how to:

▶▶ Begin to add and subtract integers.

▶▶ Use positive and negative numbers in context.

example

You can use a number line to help you add to or subtract from a negative number.

Calculate:

a $^-2 + 10$ **b** $^-10 - 20$

a Draw a number line.
You are adding so the answer will be bigger than the first number and the line should extend to the right.

Start at $^-2$ and add on 10:

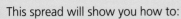

$^-2 + 10 = 8$

b Draw a number line.
You are subtracting so the answer will be smaller than the first number and the line should extend to the left.

Start at $^-10$ and subtract 20:

$^-10 - 20 = ^-30$

▶ **Adding a negative number is the same as subtracting a positive number.**
For example, $2 + (^-3) = 2 - 3 = ^-1$

example

John owes £60 on his Alpha credit card. This is $^-$£60 credit.
He also owes £40 on his Beta credit card. This is $^-$£40 credit.

a How much credit does he have altogether?
b Due to an error the bank takes away the amount he owes on the Beta credit card. How much credit does he have now?

a Altogether he has $^-$£60 + $^-$£40.
Remember that adding a negative number is the same as subtracting a positive number so
$^-$£60 + $^-$£40 = $^-$£60 − £40 = $^-$£100

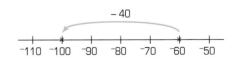

b The bank takes away the $^-$£40 credit with Beta – they give him £40 credit back.
Now he has $^-$£100 − $^-$£40 = $^-$£100 + £40.
$^-$£100 − $^-$£40 = $^-$£100 + £40 = $^-$£60
John now has $^-$£60 credit.

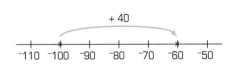

▶ **Subtracting a negative number is the same as adding a positive number.**
For example, $3 - ^-2 = 3 + 2 = 5$.

Remember you are taking away what you owe!

Exercise N1.3

1 Write an addition or a subtraction to solve each of the following:

  a The temperature is $^-7$ degrees.
It rises by 10 degrees.
What is the new temperature?

  b The temperature is $^-7$ degrees.
It falls by 10 degrees.
What is the new temperature?

  c The temperature is $^-12$ degrees.
It rises by 8 degrees.
What is the new temperature?

  d The temperature is 17 degrees.
It falls by 20 degrees.
What is the new temperature?

2 **Investigation**
Extend these patterns:

  a $8 + 4 = 12$ **b** $8 - 4 = 4$
      $8 + 3 = 11$ $8 - 3 = 5$
      $8 + 2 = 10$ $8 - 2 = 6$
      $8 + 1 = 9$ $8 - 1 = 7$
      $8 + 0 = 8$ $8 - 0 = 8$
      $8 + {}^-1 = 7$ $8 - {}^-1 = 9$

Write down what you notice.

3 Calculate:

  a $4 + {}^-2$ **b** $11 + {}^-8$
  c ${}^-9 + {}^-6$ **d** $38 + {}^-47$
  e ${}^-118 + {}^-127$ **f** $221 + {}^-428$

4 In a Pyramid the brick which sits directly above two bricks is the sum of those two bricks.

Copy and complete the following Pyramids:

  a

  b

  c

  d

5 **a** Copy and complete these complements of 100:

    i $63 + ? = 100$ **ii** $27 + ? = 100$
    iii $132 + ? = 100$ **iv** $? + {}^-87 = 100$

  b Copy and complete these complements of 50:

    i $68 + ? = 50$ **ii** $? + {}^-37 = 50$

6 Calculate the following (you will be subtracting negative numbers in some of these questions):

  a $9 - 4$ **b** $13 - {}^-6$
  c ${}^-8 - {}^-10$ **d** ${}^-16 - 11$
  e ${}^-26 - {}^-16$ **f** ${}^-41 - {}^-83$
  g ${}^-93 - {}^-216$ **h** $48 - 137$

7 In Negative Countdown you can add or subtract the numbers given to make the target number. You must use all of the numbers.

  a target = $^-5$

  b target = 2

  c target = $^-4$

8 If $a = 5$, $b = {}^-8$, $c = 10$ and $d = {}^-3$ find the value of:

  a $a + b$ **b** $a + b - c$
  c $c - b$ **d** $a + d - c + b$
  e $c - a$ **f** $b - d$
  g $a - b - d$ **h** $c - a - b$

9 Copy and complete this Pyramid:

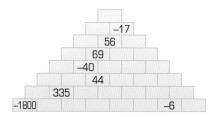

21

This spread will show you how to:

▶▶ Partition and deal with the most significant numbers first.

▶▶ Use compensation.

KEYWORDS

Difference   Complement

Total   Partition

Calculating mentally means working calculations out in your head.

There are many different ways of working out a calculation mentally. Here you will learn about two of them: partitioning and compensation.

Partitioning

▶ Partitioning involves breaking a number down into parts that are easier to work with in your head.

The size of the parts depends on the calculation. A number line can help you decide what size parts to use.

example

Use partitioning to calculate mentally:

a 55 + 437

b 12.2 − 7.6

a Rearrange so that you are adding the smaller number: 437 + 55

Now break 55 down into 50 + 5 and deal with the most significant part first:
Picture a number line:

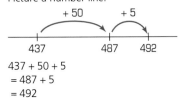

437 + 50 + 5
= 487 + 5
= 492

b Work with the whole numbers first:

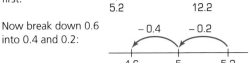

Now break down 0.6 into 0.4 and 0.2:

12.2 − 7 − 0.2 − 0.4
= 5.2 − 0.2 − 0.4
= 5 − 0.4
= 4.6

Compensation

▶ Compensation involves rounding a number up or down and then compensating by adding or subtracting the extra amount.

example

Use compensation to calculate mentally:

a 520 − 266

b 5.7 + 3.8

a Round 266 up to 300 then compensate by adding back the extra 34:
   520 − 266
= 520 − 300 + 34
= 220 + 34
= 254

b Round 3.8 up to 4 and then compensate by subtracting the extra 0.2:
   5.7 + 3.8
= 5.7 + 4 − 0.2
= 9.7 − 0.2
= 9.5

Exercise N1.4

1 Calculate the following. You should be able to work them out mentally.
- **a** $64 + 29$
- **b** $172 - 96$
- **c** $123 + 44$
- **d** $270 + 186$
- **e** $382 + 163$
- **f** $382 - 120$

2 Identify the unknown number in each of the following:
- **a** $0.3 + \square = 1$
- **b** $7.2 + \square = 10$
- **c** $0.38 + \square = 1$
- **d** $\square + 4.7 = 10$
- **e** $1.7 + \square = 1$

3 **Making Numbers Game**
- ▶ Each player has a 0–9 dice. The players take it in turns to roll their dice and write their number in one of their boxes in Round 1.
- ▶ After all the boxes have been filled the players calculate their answer.
- ▶ The player with the highest score wins the round.
- ▶ The game is repeated for each of the other rounds.
- ▶ The player who wins most rounds is the winner.

Round 1 $\square.\square + \square.\square =$
Round 2 $\square.\square - \square.\square =$
Round 3 $\square\square.\square + \square.\square =$
Round 4 $\square\square.\square - \square.\square =$
Round 5 $\square.\square\square + \square.\square\square =$

4 Two numbers have a sum of 5.8 and a difference of 3.2. What are the two numbers?
Explain how you worked out your answer.

5 **Investigation**
Here are three cards. Each card has a number on both sides. These are the numbers on the front:

The total of the cards at the moment is:
$0.6 + 0.7 + 0.8 = 2.1$
Here are all the possible totals of the cards.
1.5   1.6   1.7   1.8   2   2.1   2.2   2.3
Work out what number is on the back of each of the three cards.

6 In an arithmagon the number in a square must be the sum of the numbers on each side.
Solve these arithmagons.

a   **b**
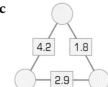 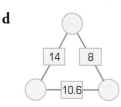

c   **d**
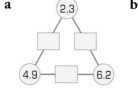

7 In a Pyramid the brick which sits directly above two bricks is the sum of the two bricks. Copy and complete the following Pyramids.

a   **b**

c   **d**
 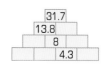

This spread will show you how to:
▶▶ Extend methods to include decimals with up to two decimal places.
▶▶ Make and justify estimates and approximates.
▶▶ Use rounding to approximate and judge whether the answer is the answer is the correct order of magnitude.

KEYWORDS

Add   Estimate
Subtract   Approximate

When numbers are too difficult to calculate in your head you need to use a written method.

The first lap was 74.2 seconds, then 78.35, then 81.97. So that adds up to … now where's a pen and paper?

▶ In column addition and subtraction you must always line up the units. This keeps all the digits in the correct place order.

$$74.2 + 78.35 = \begin{array}{r} 74.2 \\ + 78.35 \\ \hline \end{array}$$

You line up the units

Remember: you should always estimate the answer first so you have an idea of how big the answer should be.

example

Calculate:

a $175.9 + 253.7$ b $613.4 + 28.1 + 0.67$ c $982.4 - 75.3$ d $25.1 - 3.52$

a $175.9 + 253.7 \approx 180 + 250 = 430$

$\approx$ means 'is approximately equal to'

$$\begin{array}{r} 175.9 \\ 253.7 \\ \hline 429.6 \end{array}$$

b $613.4 + 28.1 + 0.67 \approx 610 + 30 \, (+1) = 640$

$$\begin{array}{r} 613.4 \\ 28.1 \\ + \ 0.67 \\ \hline 642.17 \end{array}$$

c $982.4 - 75.3 \approx 980 - 75 = 905$

$$\begin{array}{r} 982.4 \\ -75.3 \\ \hline 907.1 \end{array}$$

d $25.1 - 3.52 \approx 25 - 4 = 21$

$$\begin{array}{r} 25.1 \\ -3.52 \\ \hline 21.58 \end{array}$$

Exercise N1.5

1 Calculate the following. You will need to use a mixture of mental and written methods.

   a 84 − 57   **b** 135 − 77
   c 168 + 273   **d** 369 − 299
   e 202 − 89   **f** 395 + 403
   g 266 − 108   **h** 3002 − 1995

2 **a** The attendances at four football matches were:

      3503   8271   12 643   6487

    What was the total attendance at these matches?

   b A car is due for a service at 90 000 miles. It has currently travelled 82 643 miles. How many more miles is it until a service is due?

   c A theatre has 1484 seats. On Monday 637 seats were taken. How many seats were empty?

   d Calculate the perimeter of this garden.

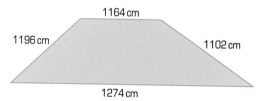

3 **Investigation**
A palindromic number is one which has the same value when its digits are reversed. Examples are 353 or 17 971.

  ▶ Write down a two-digit number, for example   85
  ▶ Reverse it   58
  ▶ Add the numbers together   143
  ▶ Reverse it   341
  ▶ Add the numbers together   484
  ▶ STOP when you reach a palindromic number

Investigate different two-digit numbers to see how many steps it takes for them to become a palindromic number.

4 Calculate the following. (You should be able to use a mental method for some questions.)

   a 14.2 + 12.5   **b** 4.56 + 6.27
   c 13.8 − 6.9   **d** 24.3 − 11.7
   e 27.5 + 8.73   **f** 35.73 − 18.6
   g 28.05 − 19.3 **h** 121.9 − 76.25

5 This map shows nine towns with the distance (in km) along roads between them.

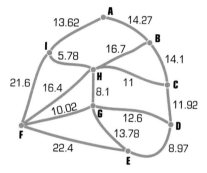

Calculate the shortest distance to get from:

   a A to E
   b I to D
   c A to A visiting each town
   d B to B visiting all the towns which are *not* vowels.

6 Copy and complete this addition pyramid.

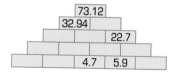

7 Calculate the following (some of the numbers are negative numbers).

   a 13.5 + ⁻12.9
   b 12.64 − 19.73 − ⁻2.4
   c ⁻132.7 + 268.2
   d 17.5 − 12.3 − ⁻6.2
   e 167.4 + ⁻78.35

Using a calculator

This spread will show you how to:

▶▶ Use rounding to approximate and judge whether the answer is the correct order of magnitude.

▶▶ Carry out more complex calculations using a calculator.

▶▶ Interpret the display on a calculator in different contexts.

When calculations become too difficult to do in your head it makes sense to use a calculator. You should first approximate so you can judge whether the answer you get is reasonable.

▶ To make a good approximation round a number to the nearest 100, 10 or whole number.

example

a Round 323 to the nearest 100 and the nearest 10.

b Round 38.7 to the nearest 10 and the nearest whole number.

a 323 is 300 to the nearest 100

323 is 320 to the nearest 10

b 38.7 is 40 to the nearest 10

38.7 is 39 to the nearest whole number

example

Karen wants to check her bank balance for July. She adds up all the transactions on her calculator.

The display on the calculator shows 562.8
This means she has £562.80 in her account.

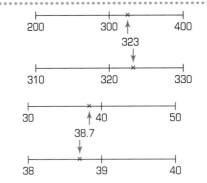

562.8

You can enter a negative number using the [+/–] key on a calculator or using the memory

key: [M⁺]

Check you can input 2 – ⁻3 = 5

Date	Transaction	Amount
1/7	balance	£232.26
1/7	deposit	£738.59
4/7	cash	⁻£100.00
5/7	cheque	⁻£11.99
5/7	switch	⁻£28.97
6/7	switch	⁻£38.42
8/7	bank transfer	£250.00
11/7	cash	⁻£80.00
12/7	cheque	⁻£330.00
14/7	cash	⁻£40.00
17/7	cheque	⁻£28.67

Exercise N1.6

1 Solve these problems using a mental or written method, or using a calculator where appropriate.

Write your answer in the correct units.

a A shirt costs £14.80, a tie costs £13.79 and a book costs £5.99. Is £35 sufficient to pay for all these items? Explain your answer.

b In one month Mr. Big spends the following amounts on petrol:
£28.72, £31.13, £32.04, £29.16, £27.65
Calculate the total amount he spent on petrol during the month.

c A recipe uses these ingredients:

flour	425 g
sugar	120 g
1 tsp vanilla	0.62 g
1 egg	24.5 g
1 litre milk	228.7 g

  i What is the total weight?

  ii How much less than 1 kg is this?

d Peter is rewiring his house. For upstairs he needs a length of 9.34 m, for downstairs he needs a length of 6.8 m. He has a length of 16.2 m. Will this be enough for the two pieces he requires? Calculate how much short or how much extra cable there will be.

2 Calculate the following using a mental or written method, or where appropriate using your calculator.

Carry out a mental approximation to check the answer on the calculator.

a $4.564 + 2.37$

b $17.6 - (3.82 + 4.7 + 6.34 + 4.9 + 2.37)$

c $368.72 + {}^-28.392$

d $328.1 - 199.5$

e $17.438 - {}^-23.597$

f $13.97 + 16.22 + 14.83 + 12.91 + \frac{16.23}{5}$

g $16.2 + 14.39 - {}^-22.6 + {}^-13.85 - 12.6$

3 **Make me zero**

This a game for 2 players.

▸ The first player enters a number into the calculator.

▸ The players take it in turns to subtract a number from this, but only one digit can be changed at a time.

▸ For example, $3.\mathbf{6}25 - 0.6 = 3.\mathbf{0}25$ is allowed because only the 6 has changed.

▸ The display must never show a negative number.

▸ The winner is the person who makes the display on the calculator zero.

Here is an example of a game:

Player	Button	Display
1		83.625
2	−80	3.625
1	−0.6	3.025
2	−3	0.025
1	−0.01	0.015
2	−0.004	0.011
1	−0.01	0.001
2	−0.001	0

Player 2 wins.

a Play the game a few times.
Who wins when there are four non-zero digits?
Investigate for other numbers of digits.

b Explain why the game would not work if the display could be a negative number.

> **Hint**
> You can use the [+/−] key on your calculator for this question.
> You could also use the memory keys.

You should know how to ...

1 Extend mental methods of addition and subtraction to include decimals.

2 Add and subtract positive and negative numbers. Remember:
$2 + {}^-3 = 2 - 3 = {}^-1$
$2 - {}^-3 = 2 + 3 = 5$

3 Use column methods for addition and subtraction of decimals with up to 2 decimal places.

4 Solve word problems in the context of number.

Check out

1 Work out these calculations in your head:
  a $4.2 + 2.9$
  b $15 - 3.7$

2 Calculate:
  a $13 - 23$
  b ${}^-8 + 17$
  c $-15 + {}^-6$
  d $3.5 - {}^-6$

3 Calculate, showing all your working:
  a $26.5 + 9.46$
  b $131.4 - 85.72$

4 **a** A TV costs £216.85.
    A video recorder costs £149.27.
    How much more expensive is the TV than the video recorder?
  b A drink and a sandwich cost £3.28.
    Two drinks and a sandwich cost £4.11.
    How much is a sandwich?
  c Copy and complete this magic square:

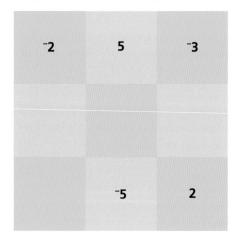

1 Perimeter and area

This unit will show you how to:

▶▶ Use names and abbreviations of units of measurement to measure, estimate, calculate and solve problems in everyday contexts involving length and area.

▶▶ Know and use the formula for the area of a rectangle.

▶▶ Use 2-D representations to visualise 3-D shapes and deduce some of their properties.

▶▶ Calculate the perimeter and area of shapes made from rectangles.

▶▶ Calculate the surface area of cubes and cuboids.

▶▶ Solve word problems and investigate in the context of perimeter and area.

▶▶ Suggest extensions to problems by asking 'What if ...?'.

Hmm, the perimeter of the room is 4.5m and the height is 2.2m. I'll need enough gloss for 4.5m and paint for 4.5m × 2.2m – now where is my calculator?

It helps to know about area and perimeter when you are decorating.

Before you start

You should know how to ...

1 Use, read and write standard metric units, including their abbreviations.

2 Understand the formula for the area of a rectangle:

Area = length × width

Check in

1 Suggest something you would measure in:

a kilometres, km   b metres, m

c centimetres, cm   d millimetres, mm

2 Find the area of this rectangle.

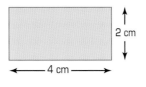

Area = _____ cm^2

Perimeter and area

This spread will show you how to:
- ⏩ Use standard metric units of measure.
- ⏩ Deduce and use formulae for the perimeter and area of a rectangle.
- ⏩ Calculate the perimeter and area of shapes made from rectangles.

KEYWORDS

Area	Length
Perimeter	Width
Distance	Factor

This rectangle measures 3 cm by 4 cm.

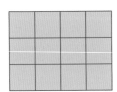

It has an area of 12 cm^2.
Notice that the area of the rectangle is length × width.
3 cm × 4 cm = 12 cm^2

Area is measured in squared units: mm^2, cm^2, etc.

▶ **Area of a rectangle = length × width**

You can write this formula using shorthand:

▶ $A = l \times w$ or $A = lw$

The perimeter of the rectangle is the distance around the outside of it.

4 cm

3 cm

Perimeter
= 3 cm + 4 cm + 3 cm + 4 cm
= 14 cm

Perimeter is a length so it is measured in cm, mm, m etc.

Notice that the perimeter of the rectangle can be written as 3 cm + 3 cm + 4 cm + 4 cm which is 2 × length + 2 × width

▶ **Perimeter of a rectangle = 2 × length + 2 × width**   or $P = 2l + 2w$

example

A rectangle has an area of 24 mm^2. What could the dimensions of the rectangle be? Give two examples and find the perimeter for each example.

The length and the width must multiply to 24 mm^2.

A = 24 mm²

The dimensions could be any pair of factors of 24:
1 × 24, 2 × 12, 3 × 8 or 4 × 6

The units must match:
mm^2 = mm × mm

Using   1 mm × 24 mm   and   8 mm × 3 mm
The perimeter is: 2 × 1 mm + 2 × 24 mm   or   2 × 8 mm + 2 × 3 mm
                          = 50 mm   = 22 mm

Exercise S1.1

Find the area of the shapes in questions 1 to 5.

1

3 cm — 2 cm

2

4 in — 1½ in

3

50 mm — 20 mm

4

25 ft — 15 ft

5

12 m — 5 m, B, A, 5 m, 5 m

6 Find the missing lengths in these diagrams:

a

8 cm — x cm — A = 24 cm²

b

y mm — 3 mm — A = 420 mm²

7 Find the area of this shape:

60 m, 30 m, 20 m, 20 m, 20 m, 30 m, 30 m

8

54 m, 42 m, 12 m, 24 m

Find the area of the shaded region.

9 The area of a rectangle is 3.76 m².
It is 2.5 m long. What is its width?

10 Find the perimeter of each shape in questions 1 to 4.

11 Does the biggest perimeter give the biggest area?
Investigate for different rectangles.

12 Draw a rectangle with an area of 20 cm².
What is its perimeter?
  a Can you draw a rectangle with the same area but a different perimeter?
  b Can you draw a rectangle with the same perimeter but a different area?
  c Draw a rectangle twice as big. Is the perimeter twice as big too?

S1.2 More perimeter and area

This spread will show you how to:
- ▶▶ Use standard metric units of measure.
- ▶▶ Calculate the area of shapes made from rectangles.
- ▶▶ Derive and use a formula for the area of a right-angled triangle.

KEYWORDS

Base	Height
Perimeter	Area
Distance	Triangle

Here is a shape made out of rectangles.

You can find the area of the shaded part like this:

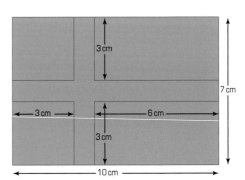

1 Find the area of the horizontal strip:
   10 cm × 1 cm = 10 cm²
2 Find the area of the vertical strip:
   7 cm × 1 cm = 7 cm²
3 Find the area of the part you've counted twice:
   1 cm × 1 cm = 1 cm²
4 Calculate the shaded area – take away the part you counted twice:
   10 cm² + 7 cm² – 1 cm² = 16 cm²

You can use the area of a rectangle to help you find the area of a right-angled triangle.

Draw a right-angled triangle on squared paper

Complete the surrounding rectangle

Cut out the two triangles. They should match

The area of a right-angled triangle is half the area of the surrounding rectangle.

▶ Area of a right-angled triangle $= \frac{1}{2}$ (area of rectangle)
$= \frac{1}{2}$ (base × height)

example

Find the area of each triangle.

a

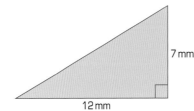

7 mm

12 mm

b

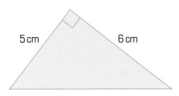

5 cm   6 cm

....

a   Area $= \frac{1}{2}$ (base × height)

$= \frac{1}{2}$ (12 mm × 7 mm) = 42 mm²

b   Area $= \frac{1}{2}$ (base × height)

$= \frac{1}{2}$ (5 cm × 6 cm) = 15 cm²

Exercise S1.2

1 Find the area of these triangles by measuring.

a

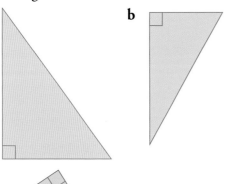

b

c

b

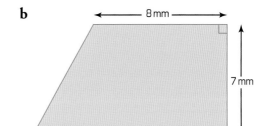

Hint
Split these shapes up into rectangles and triangles.

c

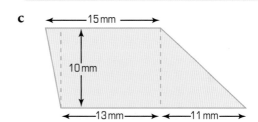

2 Using the measurements given, find the area of these shapes.

a

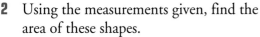
2 cm
5 cm

b
1 in   2 in

c

3 mm
6 mm

d

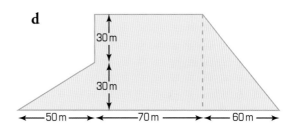
30 m
30 m
50 m   70 m   60 m

3 Find the area of these compound shapes.

a

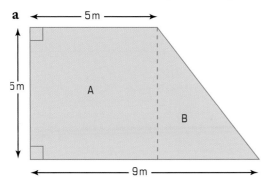
5 m
5 m
A
B
9 m

4 Here is a parallelogram.

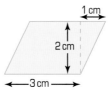
1 cm
2 cm
3 cm

Copy the parallelogram onto squared paper.
Cut the triangle off one of the ends.
Attach it to the other triangle.
What shape do you get?
Does this always happen?
Use your findings to write down the formula for the area of a parallelogram.

S1.3 Measurement and scales

This spread will show you how to:
- ▶▶ Use standard metric units and rough imperial equivalents.
- ▶▶ Suggest appropriate units and methods to estimate or measure length, capacity and mass.

KEYWORDS

Length	Area
Mass	Width
Capacity	

▶ You measure lengths and distances using metric units ...

millimetres (mm)

1 mm is about the width of a grain of sand

centimetres (cm)

1 cm is about the width of your finger nail

metres (m)

1 m is about the width of a door

kilometres (km)

1 km takes about 15 minutes to walk

or imperial units ...

inches

1 inch ≈ 2.5 cm

feet

1 foot is 12 inches ≈ 30 cm

yards

1 yard is 3 feet, which is slightly smaller than 1 metre

miles

1 mile ≈ 1.6 km
Aeroplanes often fly at a height of 1 mile

▶ You measure areas using square metric units ...

The ^{2} shows that area has two dimensions.

square millimetres (mm^2)
1 mm^2 is about the size of a sugar granule

square centimetres (cm^2)
1 cm^2 is smaller than a stamp

square metres (m^2)
1 m^2 is about half the area of a door

square kilometres (km^2)
1 km^2 is about the size of a field

You can also use square inches, square feet and square miles.

example

What are the most suitable metric and imperial units to measure:
- **a** the thickness of a hair
- **b** the length of a river
- **c** the area of a leaf
- **d** your height?

....

- **a** A hair is very thin so mm are best. Inches are too big and so would not be useful.
- **b** A river is very long so km or miles are best.
- **c** A leaf is about the size of your hand so cm^2 or square inches are best.
- **d** You are shorter than a door but longer than its width so metres or feet (and yards) are best.

Exercise S1.3

1 Copy and complete the table.

▶ First choose the most sensible units to use.
▶ Then estimate the length and width. Use these estimates to work out an estimate for the area.
▶ Decide on the equipment you will use.
▶ Measure each object and find the actual area.

Object	Equipment I will use	Units for area	Length Estimate	Length Actual	Width Estimate	Width Actual	Area = length × width Estimate	Area = length × width Actual
Window								
Desk								
Door								
Ruler								
Pencil								
Blackboard (or whiteboard)								
Classroom								
Calculator screen								

Choose from ruler, meter rule, tape measure, trundle wheel

Choose from cm², mm², m², ft² or in²

Remember to include the units!

2 Here are some metric and imperial equivalents:

Length	Mass	Capacity
1 inch ≈ 2.5 cm 1mile ≈ 1.6 km	1 kg ≈ 2.2 pounds	1 litre ≈ 1.76 pints

Use these equivalents to convert:
a 6 inches to cm
b 5 miles to km
c 12 kg to pounds
d 3 litres to pints
e the capacity of a soft drink bottle, 1.5 litres to pints
f 5 km to miles
g 33 pounds to kg
h 15 inches to cm
i 8 pints to litres
j your weight in pounds to kg
k your height in inches to cm

Capacity is the measure of how much liquid something will hold.

Three-dimensional shapes

This spread will show you how to:

➤➤ Use 2-D representations to visualise 3-D shapes and deduce some of their properties.

➤➤ Find the surface area of cuboids.

KEYWORDS

3-D	Vertex
Net	Face
Base	Edge
Surface area	Solid

Most everyday objects have three dimensions ... length, width and height. Some common 3-D shapes are:

Cubes

All its faces are the same size squares.

Cuboids

Opposite faces are equal sized rectangles.

Prisms

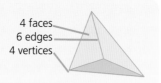

End faces are the same and remain constant throughout the length. You name the prism by its end face.

Pyramids

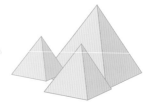

The base tapers to a point called the apex. You name the pyramid by its base.

▶ You describe a 3-D shape by its faces, edges and vertices. For example, this pyramid has

4 faces
6 edges
4 vertices

Hint
A vertex is a corner.

▶ A net is a flat shape that folds up into a 3-D shape.
The area of the net of a 3-D shape is called the **surface area**.

You find the surface area by adding together the area of the faces.

---

example

Find the surface area of a cuboid measuring 3 cm by 5 cm by 2 cm.

Lay the shape out flat – draw a net:

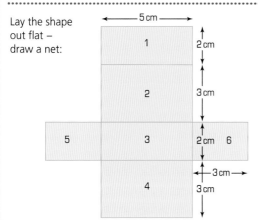

Find the area of each face:

⇒ ① and ③ = 2 × 5 = 10

⇒ ② and ④ = 3 × 5 = 15

⇒ ⑤ and ⑥ = 2 × 3 = 6

Add the areas up:

10 + 15 + 10 + 15 + 6 + 6 = 62

The surface area is 62 cm^2.

Exercise S1.4

1 Which of the following nets will make a cube?

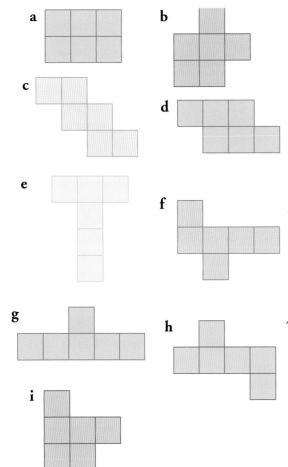

a

b

c

d

e

f

g

h

i

If you don't know, make up the nets and test them.

2 Make these shapes using multilink cubes. For each shape write down the surface area.

a

b

3 Construct the net of a cube with dimensions 4 cm by 4 cm by 4 cm.

4 Construct the net of a cuboid with dimensions 4 cm by 3 cm by 6 cm.

5 For each of the nets constructed in questions 3 and 4 calculate the surface area of the shape.

6 What are the dimensions of the faces of these shapes?

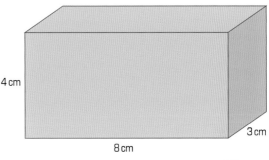

4 cm
8 cm
3 cm

b

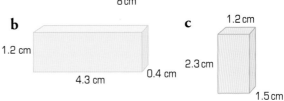

1.2 cm
4.3 cm
0.4 cm

c

1.2 cm
2.3 cm
1.5 cm

7 Find the surface area of the shapes in question 6.

8 **Investigation**
Use four multilink cubes.
Make as many different shapes as you can.
For example:

Sketch each of your shapes and write down its surface area.
a What is the greatest surface area you can make with four cubes?
b What is the smallest surface area you can make with four cubes?
Investigate for different numbers of cubes.

You should know how to ...

Solve word problems and investigate in a range of contexts: length, perimeter and area.

Remember these formulae for a rectangle:
▶ Area = length × width
  $A = l \times w$
▶ Perimeter = 2 × length + 2 × width
  $P = 2l \times 2w$

Check out

1 Draw four different rectangles which all have a perimeter of 24 cm.
For example:

8 cm

4 cm   4 cm

8 cm

2 Draw three different rectangles which all have an area of 24 cm².

3 a Draw at least four rectangles which have a perimeter of 16 cm.
  b What is the area of each rectangle?
  c Which dimensions give you the largest area?

4 This diagram shows the plan of a hall. The hall is to be carpeted using carpet tiles.
A carpet tile is 40 cm square.

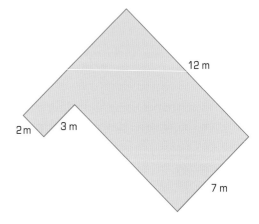

12 m

2 m   3 m

7 m

  a What is the area of each tile?
  b What is the area of the hall?
  c How many tiles are needed to carpet the hall?

This unit will show you how to:

▶▶ Use fraction notation to describe parts of shapes.

▶▶ Recognise the equivalence of percentages, fractions and decimals.

▶▶ Calculate simple fractions of quantities and measurements.

▶▶ Begin to add and subtract simple fractions.

▶▶ Understand percentage as the 'number of parts per 100'.

▶▶ Simplify fractions by cancelling all common factors and identify equivalent fractions.

▶▶ Calculate simple percentages.

▶▶ Consolidate and extend mental methods of calculation to include decimals, fractions and percentages.

▶▶ Solve word problems and investigate in the context of number.

▶▶ Break a complex calculation into simpler steps, choosing and using appropriate and efficient operations, methods and resources.

▶▶ Explain and justify methods and conclusions.

15 minutes left, that's $\frac{1}{6}$ of the game. There's a quarter of an hour left, which is 25% of an hour ...

You can use decimals, percentages or fractions to say the same thing.

Before you start

You should know how to ...

1 Read fractions.

2 Write fractions.

3 Find factors of numbers.

Check in

1 Write these fractions using words:

a $\frac{1}{5}$　b $\frac{3}{5}$　c $\frac{2}{3}$　d $\frac{3}{10}$

2 Write these fractions using digits:

a two fifths

b three eighths

c a third

d seven tenths

3 What factors do these numbers have in common?

a 2 and 8　　b 3 and 12

c 6 and 10　　d 20 and 50

This spread will show you how to:

▶▶ Use fraction notation to describe a proportion of a shape.

▶▶ Express a smaller number as a fraction of a larger one.

KEYWORDS

Part   Divide

Whole   Numerator

Fraction   Denominator

You use fractions when you ...

... cut a slice from a cake

Here is 1 out of the 6 pieces.
This is $\frac{1}{6}$ of the cake

... colour part of a shape red

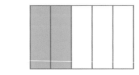

2 out of 5 parts is red.
$\frac{2}{5}$ is red

... tell the time

The minute hand is $\frac{1}{4}$ of the way round.
It's quarter past 6

▶ A fraction describes part of a whole.

▶ In a fraction:

The top number shows how many parts you have	$\frac{2}{3}$	The top number is the numerator
The bottom number shows how many parts there are		The bottom number is the denominator

▶ To use fractions the whole must be divided into equal-sized parts.

---

example

What fraction of this shape is shaded?

First divide the triangle into equal pieces.
There are 8 equal parts.
3 parts are shaded.
$\frac{3}{8}$ of the shape is shaded.

---

example

Peter has £1 and spends 35p on chocolate.
What fraction of his money has he spent?

Divide his money into equal-sized parts: £1 = 100p
He has spent 35p.
He has spent $\frac{35}{100}$ of his money.

Notice that the units have to be the same before you can compare them using fractions.

Exercise N2.1

1 Write down the fraction of each shape that is shaded.

a
b

c

2 Copy these shapes and shade the fraction indicated.

a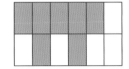
b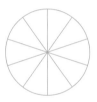

shade $\frac{1}{3}$ shade $\frac{2}{5}$

3 Use fractions to label the readings marked on each of these number lines:

a

b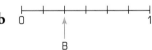

4 What fraction of:
  a £1 is 20p
  b £10 is £3
  c 60 mm is 20 mm
  d 1 kg is 400 g
  e 24 laps is 7 laps
  f 1 km is 150 m
  g 60 mm is 3 cm
  h 250 cm is 2 m
  i 1 foot is 4 inches
  j 2 metres is 200 mm
  k 1 year is 72 hours?

5 Here is a set of 10 cuisinnaire rods.

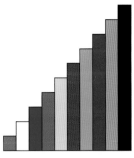

  a Red is 1 unit long, white is 2 units long, blue is 3 units long and so on. Write down the colour of the rod given by each of these clues.
   i 'I am $\frac{2}{3}$ of the blue rod.'
   ii 'I am $\frac{1}{2}$ of one rod and $\frac{1}{3}$ of another.'
   iii 'I am $\frac{4}{5}$ of one rod and $\frac{1}{2}$ of another.'
  b Make up three clues of your own.

6 Here is a picture of Jakob's flag.

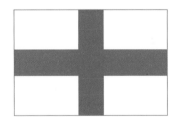

Drawn to scale

  a What fraction of Jakob's flag is red? You will need to measure the lengths on the picture with a ruler.

  b Design your own flag with 4 colours – each colour must be a different fraction of the flag.
  Describe what fraction of the flag is made from each colour.

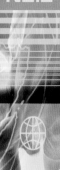

This spread will show you how to:
▶▶ Simplify fractions by cancellation and recognise equivalent fractions.
▶▶ Compare two or more simple fractions.
▶▶ Use strategies for finding equivalent fractions.

KEYWORDS

Lowest terms   Equivalent
Fraction   Simplest form
Numerator   Cancel
Denominator

You can write the same fraction in different ways:

$\frac{1}{2}$ is shaded

$\frac{2}{4}$ is shaded

$\frac{3}{6}$ is shaded

$\frac{12}{24}$ is shaded

▶ The fractions $\frac{1}{2}, \frac{2}{4}, \frac{3}{6}$ and $\frac{12}{24}$ are all equivalent. You can write: $\frac{1}{2} = \frac{2}{4} = \frac{3}{6} = \frac{12}{24}$

▶ You can write a fraction in its simplest form by **cancelling**.
You divide the numerator and denominator by the highest common factor.

example

Write these fractions in their simplest form:

a $\frac{3}{6}$

b $\frac{12}{24}$

Simplest form is also called lowest terms.

The highest common factor is 3:

$$\frac{3}{6} \overset{\div 3}{\underset{\div 3}{=}} \frac{1}{2}$$

The highest common factor is 12:

$$\frac{12}{24} \overset{\div 12}{\underset{\div 12}{=}} \frac{1}{2}$$

Note that you can do this in stages:
$\frac{12}{24} = \frac{6}{12} = \frac{1}{2}$

▶ You can find equivalent fractions by multiplying the numerator and denominator by the same number.

example

Find three equivalent fractions for $\frac{2}{3}$:

Multiply by 2:

$$\frac{2}{3} \overset{\times 2}{\underset{\times 2}{=}} \frac{4}{6}$$

Multiply by 3:

$$\frac{2}{3} \overset{\times 3}{\underset{\times 3}{=}} \frac{6}{9}$$

Multiply by 4:

$$\frac{2}{3} \overset{\times 4}{\underset{\times 4}{=}} \frac{8}{12}$$

You can compare the size of fractions using this fraction wall:

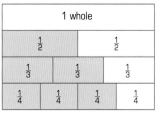

$\frac{1}{2}$ is greater than $\frac{1}{3}$; $\frac{1}{3}$ is greater than $\frac{1}{4}$; $\frac{1}{2} > \frac{1}{3} > \frac{1}{4}$

$\frac{1}{2}$ is smaller than $\frac{2}{3}$; $\frac{2}{3}$ is smaller than $\frac{3}{4}$; $\frac{1}{2} < \frac{2}{3} < \frac{3}{4}$

Exercise N2.2

1 Cancel down each of these fractions to their simplest form by dividing the top and bottom number by a common factor.

a $\frac{2}{4}$ **b** $\frac{6}{30}$ **c** $\frac{3}{9}$ **d** $\frac{4}{16}$ **e** $\frac{3}{24}$

f $\frac{9}{90}$ **g** $\frac{7}{63}$ **h** $\frac{5}{40}$ **i** $\frac{16}{36}$ **j** $\frac{24}{60}$

2 What fraction of each shape is shaded? Give each fraction in its lowest terms.

a 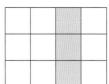 **b**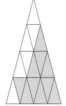

c 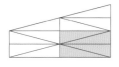 **d**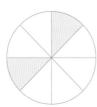

3 This number line has been split into 30 equal parts, so that each part is $\frac{1}{30}$.

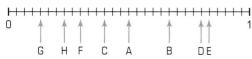

Match each of these fractions to the letters indicated on the number line.

$\frac{1}{2}$ $\frac{2}{3}$ $\frac{2}{5}$ $\frac{2}{15}$
$\frac{5}{6}$ $\frac{4}{5}$ $\frac{3}{10}$ $\frac{7}{30}$

4 Here is a box of fractions.
For each of the fractions **a** to **i**, find two equivalent fractions from the box.

$\frac{30}{100}$	$\frac{64}{72}$	$\frac{30}{40}$	$\frac{100}{380}$	$\frac{60}{165}$	$\frac{35}{60}$
$\frac{56}{96}$	$\frac{35}{56}$	$\frac{50}{190}$	$\frac{50}{175}$	$\frac{63}{210}$	$\frac{100}{160}$
$\frac{18}{63}$	$\frac{11}{22}$	$\frac{12}{33}$	$\frac{24}{27}$	$\frac{21}{28}$	$\frac{84}{168}$

a $\frac{3}{4}$ **b** $\frac{2}{7}$ **c** $\frac{5}{8}$ **d** $\frac{4}{11}$ **e** $\frac{3}{10}$

f $\frac{8}{9}$ **g** $\frac{7}{12}$ **h** $\frac{5}{19}$ **i** $\frac{1}{2}$

5 Copy and complete these equivalent fractions.

a $\frac{3}{4} = \frac{\square}{12}$

b $\frac{2}{5} = \frac{\square}{30}$

c $\frac{6}{10} = \frac{\square}{100}$

d $\frac{4}{25} = \frac{16}{\square}$

e $\frac{\square}{5} = \frac{6}{15}$

f $\frac{\square}{8} = \frac{20}{32}$

6 What fraction of:
a 1 metre is 70 cm
b 1 kg is 350 g
c 1 hour is 42 minutes
d 1 turn is 80°
e 1 week is 750 minutes
f £3.60 is 81p?

7 For each pair of fractions insert one of the signs: >, < or = between them.

a $\frac{1}{2}$ $\frac{3}{6}$

b $\frac{1}{2}$ $\frac{7}{10}$

c $\frac{1}{2}$ $\frac{2}{3}$

d $\frac{5}{12}$ $\frac{1}{4}$

8 Rearrange these fractions in order starting with the smallest:

$\frac{1}{3}$ $\frac{1}{4}$ $\frac{2}{5}$ $\frac{1}{2}$ $\frac{4}{15}$ $\frac{3}{10}$

9 **a** Use the digits 1, 2, 3, 4 and 8 to complete this equivalent fraction:

$$\frac{\square}{7} = \frac{\square\square}{\square\square}$$

b Use the digits 3, 5, 6, 8 and 9 to make two equivalent fractions:

$$\frac{\square}{\square 4} = \frac{\square 1}{2 0 0 \square}$$

43

This spread will show you how to:
- ▶▶ Add and subtract simple fractions.
- ▶▶ Relate fractions to division.
- ▶▶ Recall fraction facts.

KEYWORDS

Mixed number   Convert

Improper   Equivalent

▶ **You can add fractions with the same denominator by just adding the numerators.**
For example, $\frac{1}{8} + \frac{3}{8} = \frac{4}{8}$

You can use equivalent fractions to add fractions with different denominators together.
For example: $\frac{1}{4} + \frac{1}{8} = \frac{2}{8} + \frac{1}{8} = \frac{3}{8}$

 + =

You subtract in the same way:
$\frac{3}{8} - \frac{1}{8} = \frac{2}{8} = \frac{1}{4}$

You often need to use numbers bigger than 1 which include fractions.

▶ **Numbers with a whole number part and a fraction part are called mixed numbers.**

You convert a mixed number into a single fraction like this:

$3\frac{2}{5}$ means 3 whole numbers and 2 fifths.

☐ 5 fifths	☐ 5 fifths
☐ 5 fifths	☐ 2 fifths

There are 17 fifths in total

A short way is to say:
3 wholes = 15 fifths.
So $3\frac{2}{5} = 15 + 2$ fifths $= \frac{17}{5}$.

So $3\frac{2}{5} = \frac{17}{5}$

▶ **A single fraction that is greater than 1, like $\frac{5}{3}$, is called an improper fraction.**
It is sometimes called a top-heavy fraction because the numerator is bigger than the denominator.

example

Convert these improper fractions to mixed numbers:

a $\frac{12}{7}$ **b** $\frac{7}{3}$

$\frac{12}{7} = \frac{7}{7} + \frac{5}{7}$ $\frac{7}{3} = \frac{3}{3} + \frac{3}{3} + \frac{1}{3}$
$= 1\frac{5}{7}$ $= 2\frac{1}{3}$

A quick way to convert $\frac{7}{3}$ is to
divide by 3:
7 ÷ 3 = 2 remainder 1
$\frac{7}{3} = 2\frac{1}{3}$
Can you explain why?

▶ **You can add or subtract mixed numbers when the fraction parts have the same denominator.**
Just change to improper fractions and add the numerators:
$3\frac{3}{5} + 1\frac{4}{5} = \frac{18}{5} + \frac{9}{5} = \frac{27}{5}$

$\frac{27}{5} = 5\frac{2}{5}$ so $3\frac{3}{5} + 1\frac{4}{5} = 5\frac{2}{5}$

Exercise N2.3

1 Convert each of these improper fractions into mixed numbers.

Work out the answers in your head.

a $\frac{5}{2}$ **b** $\frac{11}{4}$ **c** $\frac{12}{5}$ **d** $\frac{8}{2}$ **e** $\frac{18}{4}$ **f** $\frac{31}{9}$

2 Convert these mixed numbers into improper fractions.

Work out the answers in your head.

a $1\frac{1}{3}$ **b** $1\frac{5}{6}$ **c** $3\frac{1}{4}$

d $3\frac{5}{8}$ **e** $4\frac{9}{10}$ **f** $7\frac{1}{4}$

3 Convert each of these improper fractions to mixed numbers. You may need to use a written method.

a $\frac{68}{10}$ **b** $\frac{77}{8}$ **c** $\frac{43}{3}$ **d** $\frac{180}{17}$ **e** $\frac{148}{15}$

f $\frac{42}{30}$ **g** $\frac{72}{16}$ **h** $\frac{63}{45}$ **i** $\frac{217}{84}$ **j** $\frac{370}{50}$

4 Convert these mixed numbers to improper fractions. You may need to use a written method.

a $8\frac{2}{3}$ **b** $5\frac{5}{9}$ **c** $9\frac{3}{7}$ **d** $3\frac{8}{13}$

e $14\frac{7}{11}$ **f** $18\frac{7}{15}$ **g** $17\frac{5}{12}$ **h** $10\frac{4}{15}$

i $13\frac{23}{35}$ **j** $7\frac{3}{8}$ **k** $12\frac{5}{9}$ **l** $8\frac{12}{25}$

5 For each pair of fractions insert the appropriate sign.

Choose from: <, > or =

a $4\frac{1}{3}$ ____ $\frac{15}{3}$

b $\frac{37}{5}$ ____ $5\frac{2}{5}$

c $\frac{43}{5}$ ____ $\frac{87}{10}$

d $3\frac{3}{4}$ ____ $\frac{50}{12}$

e $3\frac{2}{3}$ ____ $\frac{44}{12}$

f $\frac{100}{15}$ ____ $6\frac{3}{5}$

g $\frac{14}{3}$ ____ $4\frac{3}{4}$

h $7\frac{1}{2}$ ____ $\frac{23}{5}$

6 This number line has been split into 12 equal parts, so each part is $\frac{1}{12}$.

Match each of these fractions to the points indicated on the number line.

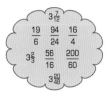

7 Work out the following, leaving your answers as mixed numbers where appropriate.

a $\frac{1}{5} + \frac{2}{5} =$

b $\frac{4}{5} + \frac{4}{5} =$

c $\frac{3}{4} + \frac{3}{4} + \frac{3}{4} =$

d $\frac{7}{4} - \frac{5}{4} =$

e $1\frac{1}{5} - \frac{3}{5} =$

f $1\frac{1}{6} + 1\frac{1}{6} =$

g $2\frac{2}{5} + \frac{14}{5} =$

h $3\frac{1}{4} + \frac{11}{4} + 3\frac{3}{4} =$

i $3\frac{3}{5} - \frac{6}{5} =$

j $2\frac{1}{3} + \frac{17}{3} =$

8 Using each of the digits 1, 2, 3, 4 and 5 once in each question:

a What is the smallest improper fraction you can make?

b What is the smallest mixed number you can make?

c What is the largest improper fraction you can make?

d What is the largest mixed number you can make?

This spread will show you how to:

▶▶ Convert terminating decimals to fractions and fractions to decimals.

▶▶ Use strategies for finding equivalent fractions and decimals.

KEYWORDS

Equivalent   Convert

Decimal fraction   Cancel

Lowest terms

A fraction describes part of a whole. A decimal also describes part of a whole. Decimals are often called decimal fractions.

▶ You can write a terminating decimal as a fraction:

  ▶ Write the decimal as a fraction.

  ▶ Cancel the fraction to its lowest terms.

A terminating decimal terminates or stops.

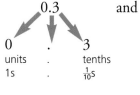

0.3   and   2.48   are decimal fractions.

0	.	3		2	.	4	8
units	.	tenths		units	.	tenths	hundredths
1s	.	$\frac{1}{10}$s		1s	.	$\frac{1}{10}$ s	$\frac{1}{100}$ s

$0.3 = \frac{3}{10}$

$2.48 = 2 + \frac{4}{10} + \frac{8}{100}$

$2.48 = 2 + \frac{40}{100} + \frac{8}{100}$

$\frac{4}{10} = \frac{40}{100}$

$2.48 = 2\frac{48}{100} = 2\frac{12}{25}$

0.48 is $\frac{48}{100}$ and the common factor is 4 so use 25ths.

▶ You can write any fraction as a decimal.

▶ You should know these common fractions and their decimal equivalents:

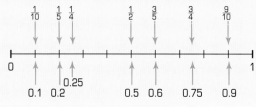

$\frac{1}{10}$ $\frac{1}{5}$ $\frac{1}{4}$ $\frac{1}{2}$ $\frac{3}{5}$ $\frac{3}{4}$ $\frac{9}{10}$

0   0.25   1

0.1   0.2   0.5   0.6   0.75   0.9

example

Convert to decimals:

a $\frac{2}{5}$ **b** $\frac{13}{10}$ **c** $\frac{1}{8}$ **d** $\frac{3}{20}$

a $\frac{1}{5}$ is 0.2
so $\frac{2}{5}$ is
$0.2 + 0.2 = 0.4$

b $\frac{1}{10}$ is 0.1
$\frac{10}{10} = 1$ and
$\frac{3}{10} = 0.3$
so $\frac{13}{10}$ is 1.3

c $\frac{2}{8} = \frac{1}{4} = 0.25$
so
$\frac{1}{8} = 0.25 \div 2 = 0.125$

d $\frac{3}{20} = \frac{15}{100}$
so $\frac{3}{20} = 0.15$

Exercise N2.4

1 This number line is split into tenths.

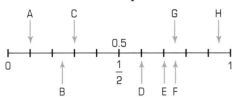

a Match each of the fractions and decimals to the points indicated on the number line.

$\frac{7}{10}$ $\frac{3}{5}$ $\frac{3}{4}$ 0.3 0.1 0.95 0.75 $\frac{1}{4}$

b Write each fraction as its decimal equivalent and each decimal as its fraction equivalent, for example $0.5 = \frac{1}{2}$.

2 Use the numbers in the boxes to make up fractions and decimals that are equal to each other.

a $\frac{\square}{\square} = \square . \square$

3	3
0	10

b $\frac{\square}{\square} = \square . \square$

3	6
0	5

c $\frac{\square}{\square} = \square . \square \square$

0	3	7
4	5	

d $\frac{\square}{\square} = \square . \square$

7	3
5	2

3 Convert these decimals to fractions in their simplest form, writing them as mixed numbers where appropriate.

a 0.1 **b** 0.35 **c** 0.48
d 0.64 **e** 0.82 **f** 1.25
g 2.3 **h** 4.72 **i** 10.75
j 23.6 **k** 14.44 **l** 7.6

4 Convert these fractions into their decimal equivalents.

a $\frac{3}{5}$ **b** $\frac{17}{20}$ **c** $\frac{3}{4}$
d $\frac{7}{5}$ **e** $\frac{13}{10}$ **f** $2\frac{3}{4}$
g $\frac{7}{4}$ **h** $\frac{9}{12}$ **i** $\frac{56}{40}$
j $3\frac{10}{40}$ **k** $4\frac{4}{5}$ **l** $\frac{76}{25}$

5 Put these fractions and decimals in order from lowest to highest.

$\frac{1}{2}$ $\frac{9}{20}$ 0.42 $\frac{2}{5}$ $\frac{22}{50}$.

6 **Challenge: Making the square magic**
In this magic square each row, each column and both diagonals should add up to $1\frac{1}{2}$. Unfortunately someone has muddled up the numbers. Can you rearrange the numbers to make the square magic again?

$\frac{1}{2}$	$\frac{3}{10}$	$\frac{4}{40}$
$\frac{81}{90}$	$\frac{1}{5}$	$\frac{9}{15}$
$\frac{16}{20}$	$\frac{700}{1000}$	$\frac{20}{50}$

7 **Investigation**
$\frac{1}{5} = 0.2$ and $\frac{3}{5} = 0.6$

a Use short division to work out $1 \div 5$. Write down what you notice.
b Use short division to work out $3 \div 5$. Write down what you notice.
c Use short division to work out:
   i $7 \div 5$ **ii** $3 \div 4$ **iii** $5 \div 8$
   Write down the decimal equivalent of the following fractions:
   i $\frac{7}{5}$ **ii** $\frac{3}{4}$ **iii** $\frac{5}{8}$
   Write down what you notice.
d Investigate other fractions and their decimal equivalents.

This spread will show you how to:

▶▶ Calculate fractions of numbers, quantities or measurements.

▶▶ Multiply a fraction by an integer or an integer by a fraction.

▶▶ Use strategies for calculating fractions.

KEYWORDS

Fraction   Area

Integer   Divide

Equivalent

This rectangle has an area of 24 cm^2

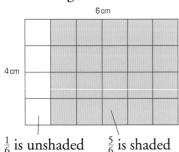

6 cm

4 cm

To find $\frac{1}{6}$ of the area you divide the area into 6 equal parts:

$\frac{1}{6}$ of the area $= \frac{1}{6}$ of 24 cm^2

$= 24$ cm$^2 \div 6$

$= 4$ cm^2

So $\frac{5}{6}$ of the area $= \frac{5}{6} \times 24$ cm^2

$= 5 \times \frac{1}{6} \times 24$ cm^2

$= 5 \times 4$ cm^2

$= 20$ cm^2

$\frac{1}{6}$ is unshaded $\frac{5}{6}$ is shaded

▶ Finding $\frac{1}{6}$ of an amount is the same as dividing the amount into 6 equal parts.

$\frac{1}{6}$ of an amount = amount ÷ 6.

▶ You can find more than one part by multiplying.

example

a   Find $\frac{7}{10}$ of £420

b   Calculate: $1\frac{1}{4}$ of 2.4 m

a $\frac{7}{10}$ is 7 lots of $\frac{1}{10}$

£420

$\frac{1}{10}$ of £420 is £42

$\frac{7}{10}$ of £420 is 7 × £42 = £294

b $1\frac{1}{4} = \frac{5}{4}$ which is 5 lots of $\frac{1}{4}$

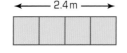

2.4 m   2.4 m

$\frac{1}{4}$ of 2.4 m is 2.4 m ÷ 4 = 0.6 m

$\frac{5}{4}$ of 2.4 m is 5 × 0.6 m = 3 m

▶ To find a fraction of an amount, multiply by the numerator and divide by the denominator.

example

Calculate:

Sometimes it is better to multiply first – it depends on the numbers.

a $12 \times \frac{5}{6}$

b 3.3×40

c $\frac{4}{7} \times 13$

a $12 \times \frac{5}{6} = \frac{5}{6} \times 12$

     $\frac{5}{6} \times 12 = 5 \times \frac{1}{6} \times 12$

         $= 5 \times 12 \div 6$

         $= 5 \times 2 = 10$

b $3.3 \times 40 = 3\frac{3}{10} \times 40$

     $3\frac{3}{10} \times 40 = \frac{33}{10} \times 40$

         $= 33 \times \frac{1}{10} \times 40$

         $= 33 \times 4 = 132$

$\frac{4}{7} \times 13 = 4 \times \frac{1}{7} \times 13$

         $= \frac{1}{7} \times 4 \times 13$

         $= \frac{1}{7} \times 52$

         $= \frac{52}{7} = 7\frac{3}{7}$

Exercise N2.5

1 A shirt normally costs £36. On sale day the price is reduced by $\frac{1}{3}$.
   a What is the reduction in the price?
   b What is the new price?

2 Calculate the fractions of the quantities given below in the units given. Use the letter next to each question to solve the puzzle code at the bottom.

W $\frac{3}{5}$ of £65	A $\frac{5}{11}$ of 638 kg
P $\frac{6}{7}$ of 133 kg	I $\frac{13}{8}$ of 144 hours
H $\frac{2}{3}$ of 18 hours	T $\frac{4}{15}$ of £345
U $\frac{7}{12}$ of 348 kg	Q $\frac{9}{20}$ of 780 hours
R $\frac{4}{9}$ of £171	D $\frac{4}{5}$ of 815 kg
C $\frac{1}{6}$ of 1026 hours	E $\frac{18}{25}$ of £225
S $\frac{3}{4}$ of 96 kg	L $\frac{3}{7}$ of 266 hours
M $\frac{11}{15}$ of £255	N $\frac{21}{13}$ of 299 kg
O $\frac{19}{21}$ of 462 hours	

351 hrs	203 kg	£162	72 kg	£92	234 hrs	418 hrs	483 kg
:		£39	12 hrs	£162	£76	£162	652 kg	418 hrs
£187	290 kg	£92	12 hrs	£162	£187	290 kg	£92
234 hrs	171 hrs	290 kg	114 hrs	72 kg	12 hrs	234 hrs	114 kg
72 kg	72 kg	290 kg	234 hrs	114 hrs	?		
290 kg	483 kg	72 kg	£39	£162	£76	:	
234 hrs	483 kg	652 kg	234 hrs	171 hrs	£162	72 kg	!

3 Calculate:
   a $\frac{9}{10}$ of 1 m   **b** $\frac{3}{4}$ of 1 km
   c $\frac{7}{20}$ of 1 kg   **d** $\frac{2}{3}$ of 1 hour

4 By changing these into fractions calculate:
   a 0.25 of 24   **b** 0.6 of £125

5 Use the number lines to help calculate:
   a $8 \times \frac{1}{4}$
   b $3 \times \frac{2}{5}$
   c $4 \times \frac{3}{7}$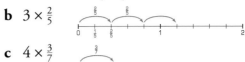

6 Draw your own number lines to help calculate:
   a $3 \times \frac{3}{4}$ **b** $5 \times \frac{2}{5}$ **c** $7 \times \frac{4}{9}$
   d $6 \times \frac{2}{3}$ **e** $12 \times \frac{7}{4}$ **f** $15 \times \frac{13}{5}$

7 Calculate:
   a $90 \times \frac{7}{9}$ **b** $\frac{3}{5} \times 35$ **c** $12 \times \frac{5}{6}$
   d $20 \times \frac{2}{5}$ **e** $8 \times \frac{3}{4}$ **f** $12 \times \frac{2}{3}$

8 a Work out the value of each calculation in this number grid.

$\frac{3}{7}$ of 14	$60 \times \frac{2}{3}$	$\frac{4}{5} \times 35$
$\frac{4}{15} \times 345$	$\frac{3}{4} \times 96$	$18 \times \frac{1}{2}$
$240 \times \frac{7}{8}$	$\frac{1}{2}$ of 18	$14 \times \frac{3}{7}$
$\frac{4}{15}$ of 345	$\frac{7}{8}$ of 240	$\frac{4}{9}$ of 189
$\frac{4}{5}$ of 35	$\frac{3}{4}$ of 96	$\frac{2}{3}$ of 60

   b Write down the pairs of calculations which give the same answer.
   c Write down what you notice.

9 Calculate:
   a $\frac{2}{3} \times 360°$ **b** $\frac{3}{4} \times 100$ m
   c $\frac{2}{3} \times 120$ min   **d** $\frac{11}{20} \times 500$ g

10 A tree is 100 cm.
Each year it increases in height by $\frac{1}{5}$ of its height at the beginning of that year.
How tall is the tree:

   a After one year?
   b After two years?
   c How many years will it take for the tree to double its height?

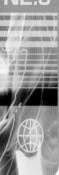

This spread will show you how to:

▶▶ Understand percentage as the number of parts in every 100, and express a percentage as an equivalent fraction or decimal.

▶▶ Recognise the equivalence of fractions, decimals and percentages.

▶▶ Calculate percentages of numbers, quantities and measurements.

KEYWORDS

Percentage   Convert
Equivalent   Cancel

Another way of describing part of a whole is using a percentage. You can use the symbol % to mean percent.

▶ A percentage is a fraction written as a number of parts per 100. For example $60\% = \frac{60}{100}$ and 32% is $\frac{32}{100}$.

You convert a percentage to a fraction by writing it out of 100 then cancelling down.

example

Write as a fraction:

a 80%

b 32%

....

a 80% means $\frac{80}{100}$
$\frac{80}{100} = \frac{8}{10} = \frac{4}{5}$

b 32% means $\frac{32}{100}$
$\frac{32}{100} = \frac{8}{25}$

▶ You can convert a fraction to a percentage by writing it as an equivalent fraction with a denominator of 100.
For example: $\frac{3}{4} = \frac{75}{100} = 75\%$

This number line is marked in fractions, decimals and percentages:

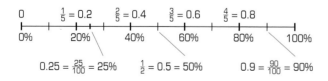

You can use fractions to calculate simple percentages of amounts mentally.

example

a Calculate 10% of £300

b What is 25% of 240 sheep?

....

a 10% of an amount is the same as $\frac{1}{10}$ of it.
10% of £300 = $\frac{1}{10}$ of £300 = £30

b 25% of an amount is the same as $\frac{1}{4}$ of it.
25% of 240 sheep = $\frac{1}{4}$ of 240 sheep = 60 sheep

Exercise N2.6

1 Match each of the fractions, decimals and percentages to the points indicated on the number line – there is more than one answer for each point.

0.2 $\frac{3}{5}$ 25% $\frac{20}{100}$

50% 10% $\frac{1}{10}$ 0.6

$\frac{1}{2}$ 0.25 0.75 $\frac{3}{4}$

2 Copy and complete this table:

Fraction		$\frac{2}{5}$		$\frac{16}{20}$	
Decimal	0.2				0.45	
Percentage			67%			15%

3 Convert these percentages to fractions in their simplest form (by cancelling down and writing as a mixed number where appropriate).

a 70%   **b** 65%   **c** 120%

d 72%   **e** 328%   **f** 360%

4 Convert these fractions to percentages.

a $\frac{3}{5}$ **b** $\frac{19}{20}$ **c** $\frac{13}{10}$

d $\frac{9}{4}$ **e** $\frac{19}{25}$ **f** $\frac{17}{40}$

5 Convert these percentages into their decimal equivalents.

a 38%   **b** 40%   **c** 4%

d 145%   **e** 400%   **f** 0.2%

6 Convert these decimals into their percentage equivalents.

a 0.83   **b** 0.3   **c** 0.03

d 1.5   **e** 3.78   **f** 1.02

7 **a** In a class of 30 pupils, $\frac{2}{5}$ live in houses, 30% live in flats and the rest live in bungalows.
What percentage of the class live in bungalows?
What fraction of the class does not live in flats?

b In a school there are 25 one-hour lessons per week. 12% of the week is spent in maths lessons, $\frac{1}{5}$ of the week is spent in science lessons and $\frac{6}{25}$ of the week is spent in humanities lessons.
What percentage of the week is not spent in maths, science or humanities?
What fraction of the week is not spent in maths?

c Investigate what fraction of the week is spent in each of your subjects at your school – do you spend more than 12% of your school week in maths lessons?

8 You can work out most of these questions mentally but you might need to make some jottings to work out the rest.

a 10% of 700 apples
b 10% of €3000
c 10% of £31
d 20% of 700 apples
e 20% of 440 buttons
f 60% of 200 cm
g 25% of 524 people
h 75% of an hour
i 150% of 38 carrots
j 15% of 670 mm
k 45% of 2520 km

9 **a** What fraction of 200 cm is 1.2 m?
b What percentage of 200 cm is 1.2 m?
c Explain how you would check your answers to see if they were correct.

N2 Summary

You should know how to …

1 Simplify fractions by cancelling all common factors and identify equivalent fractions.

2 Recognise the equivalence of percentages, fractions and decimals.

3 Extend mental methods of calculation to include decimals, fractions and percentages.

4 Break a complex calculation into simpler steps, choosing and using appropriate and efficient operations and methods.

5 Solve word problems in the context of number.

Check out

1 a Cancel these fractions to their lowest form:

   i $\frac{84}{112}$ **ii** $\frac{324}{45}$

 b Find the unknown number:

   $\frac{42}{28} = \frac{?}{16}$

2 Copy and complete this table of equivalences:

Fraction	Decimal	Percentage
$\frac{9}{20}$		
	0.32	
		140%

3 Use mental methods to answer these questions:

 a Change $\frac{6}{5}$ to a decimal

 b Calculate $\frac{3}{5} \times 17$ and express your answer as a mixed number

 c Find $\frac{3}{8}$ of £64

 d What is 15% of 600 sheep?

4 Using each of the digits 0, 1, 2, 3, 4, 5 and 6 once and only once, copy and complete this percentage calculation:

$$\square\square\% \text{ of } \square\square\square = \square\square$$

5 Make up a word problem to describe your calculation in question 4.

52

Statistics and probability

This unit will show you how to:

▶▶ Calculate statistics for small sets of discrete data.

▶▶ Interpret diagrams and graphs (including pie charts), and draw conclusions.

▶▶ Use vocabulary and ideas of probability, drawing on experience.

▶▶ Understand and use the probability scale from 0 to 1.

▶▶ Find and justify probabilities based on equally likely outcomes in simple contexts.

▶▶ Solve word problems and investigate in the contexts of handling data and probability.

We're all different – but an average is a single value that attempts to give a fair picture.

Before you start

You should know how to ...

1 Order numbers.

2 Express simple proportions as fractions.

3 Express simple fractions as percentages.

Check in

1 Write these numbers in size order, starting with the smallest:

  a 1, 7, 8, 6, 2, 3, 7

  b 1.2, 1.4, 1.3, 1.9, 0.6, 1.5, 0.8, 1.2

2 3 out of 5 people prefer to use black ink. Write this as a fraction.

3 Write these fractions as percentages:

  a $\frac{1}{2}$ **b** $\frac{1}{4}$ **c** $\frac{30}{100}$ **d** $\frac{7}{10}$

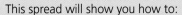
This spread will show you how to:
- ▶▶ Find the mode of a small set of discrete data.
- ▶▶ Find and use the range of a small set of discrete data.
- ▶▶ Find the median of a small set of discrete data.

KEYWORDS

Data	Frequency
Average	Median
Mode	Range
Modal	

An **average** is a single value that is typical of a set of data.
There are three different measures of average. Here are two of them:

> The mode is also called the modal value.
> There can be more than one mode or even no mode at all.

The mode

▶ The **mode** is the value in the data that occurs most frequently.

example

Find the modal amount of pocket money for each set of data:

a
Amount	Frequency
£2.50	2
£4	2
£5	6
£7	2
£7.50	3
£8	1
£10	4

b   £2.50, £5, £10, £5, £7, £7, £5
    £3, £7, £8.50, £9, £5, £7

a   The modal amount is the value that occurs most frequently.
This is the value with the highest frequency.
The modal amount is £5.

> **Be careful** – it is easy to say the modal amount is 6! 6 is the frequency, £5 is the amount.

b   £5 and £7 both occur more frequently than the other values.
There are two modes: £5 and £7.

The median

▶ The **median** is the value in the middle of the data.
The data must be arranged in order first.

example

Find the median of these sets of data:

a   Heights of students in cm:
152, 150, 145, 159, 155, 160, 149

b   Shoe sizes:
5, 6, 7, 8, 9, 8, 4, 9, 7, 5, 6, 7, 9, 8, 10, 8

a   Arrange in size order:
145, 149, 150, (152), 155, 159, 160
The middle number is 152.
The median height is 152 cm.

b   Arrange in size order:
4, 5, 5, 6, 6, 7, 7, (7, 8), 8, 8, 8, 9, 9, 9, 10
There are two middle numbers: 7 and 8.
The middle value is halfway between: 7.5.
The median shoe size is $7\frac{1}{2}$.

The range

The range is not an average – it is a measure that describes how the data is spread out.

▶ **Range** = highest value – lowest value

> The range of heights in the example above is 160 cm – 145 cm = 15 cm

Exercise D1.1

1 Work out the mode of each of these sets of data:
  a 5, 4, 5, 3, 5, 7   **b** 10 cm, 12 cm, 8 cm, 12 cm, 7 cm, 9 cm, 12 cm, 10 cm
  c 2.5, 3.4, 2.7, 3.2, 2.5, 3.1, 2.4   **d** 3, 0, 2, 0, 3, 1, 0, 3, 4, 1

2 Work out the median for each set of data in question 1.

3 Work out the range for each set of data in question 1.

4 Find the mode and range of these sets of data:

a

Shoe size	Frequency
4	3
5	4
6	5
7	2

b

Height (cm)	Frequency
156	21
157	34
158	42
159	37
160	19

c

Weight (kg)	Frequency
42	1
43	2
44	5
45	5
46	4
47	3

5 As part of a traffic survey, Maya recorded the number of people in each car that passed her observation position in a 15-minute period. 40 cars went past in that time, and the numbers of people in each one were as follows:

2	1	2	5	1	1	4	2	2	3
1	2	1	4	2	1	3	6	4	2
1	1	1	3	2	1	2	1	3	2
1	2	1	2	1	2	1	2	1	2

  a From this data, produce a frequency table, showing how many cars were recorded with each number of people.
  b Using your frequency table, write down the modal number of people in a car.

6 For each set of data:
  ► arrange the data in size order   ► find the median value   ► find the range
  A 5, 4, 5, 2, 3   **B** 4, 3, 1, 0, 2, 4, 5   **C** 2.5, 3.4, 2.7, 3.2, 2.9, 3.1, 2.4
  D 10 cm, 15 cm, 8 cm, 12 cm, 7 cm, 9 cm, 13 cm, 10 cm

7 What is the median value of these sets of data?
  a number of sweets in a packet: 9, 12, 7, 13, 11, 8, 11, 14
  b height of plants in a greenhouse: 20 cm, 24 cm, 21 cm, 25 cm, 22 cm, 19 cm, 23 cm, 22 cm, 24 cm, 21 cm
  c time taken to run 100 metres: 10.2 s, 9.8 s, 10.0 s, 10.4 s, 10.5 s, 10.3 s, 9.9 s, 10.4 s, 10.3 s
  d weight of cartons on a plane: 45 kg, 52 kg, 48 kg, 45 kg, 53 kg, 52 kg, 48 kg
  e length of TV programmes: 30 mins, 55 mins, 30 mins, 1 hour, 45 mins, 1 hour, 1 hour 15 mins, 30 mins

8 Find the range for each set of data in question 7.

This spread will show you how to:
▶▶ Calculate the mean for a small set of discrete data.

Mean   Sum
Average

There is a third average you can use – the **mean**.
It is what most people mean when they say average!

Here are three towers:

You can level out the towers so that they are all the same height:

The levelling diagram shows the mean height. The mean height is 5.

You can calculate the mean by dividing the total number of blocks (15) between the (3) towers:
15 ÷ 3 = 5

▶ The mean of a set of data is the sum of all the items divided by the number of items.

Hint
It is mean because you have to work it out!

Unlike the median and the mode, the mean uses every piece of data.
It gives you an idea of what would happen if there were equal shares.

example

Find the mean of each set of data:

a Peas in a pod: 4, 6, 7, 5, 8, 7, 11, 8   **b** Temperatures in °C: 13, 13, 11, 14, 17, 19

a   The number of items is 8.
The sum of the items is 56.
The mean = 56 ÷ 8 = 7
The mean is 7 peas in a pod.

b   The number of items is 6.
The sum of the items is 87.
The mean = 87 ÷ 6 = 14.5
The mean is 14.5°C.

Notice that the mean is not always one of the values.

Exercise D1.2

1 **a** Three tubes of sweets hold 10, 8 and 12 sweets each. What is the mean?
    b Four boxes of matches contain 46, 48, 45 and 49 matches each.
What is the mean?
    c The number of letters delivered to a house one week is 5, 2, 0, 4, 1 and 6. What is the mean?

2 In these questions, average means mean.
    a The shoe sizes of some friends are: 6, 6, 5, 4, 7, 8 and 9.
What is the average shoe size and what does it tell you?
    b A diver scores 9.2, 9.3, 9.5, 9.8 and 9.7 in her competition dives.
What was her average score?
    c The length of programmes on TV one evening were: 30 mins, 1 hour, 35 mins, 25 mins, 30 mins, 1 hour 10 mins and 1 hour 5 mins.
What was the average length of programme?
    d In the first week of March the rainfall was 2.3 cm, 3 cm, 1.2 cm, 2 cm, 0.5 cm, 0 cm and 0.2 cm.
What was the average daily rainfall?

3 The average of the numbers on these 5 balls is 4. What is the hidden number?

4 A Park Ranger records the numbers of eggs in nests of three different species of bird. Here are the results:

Species	Number of eggs
Water rail	6 8 9 6 7 9 10 11 7
Moorhen	9 7 5 5 6 10 8 11 10 6
Coot	7 6 9 9 8

Find the average number of eggs in the nest of each species of bird.

5 The manager of a basketball team needs a new player for the next match.
She has four players to choose from. Their performances in the last three matches were rated out of 20:

Player	Match 1	Match 2	Match 3
A	20	5	8
B	15	–	12
C	9	17	–
D	10	11	12

Who should she choose?
Explain the reasons for your choice.

6 The average age of some children is 15. (Assume a child is 18 years old or under.)

    a If there are 4 children, what is the total of their ages?
    b If there are 4 children and George is 17, Lana is 10 and Zoe is 16, how old is Sam?
    c If there are 3 children and Ahmet is 18 and Kemal is 13, how old is Handan?
    d If there are 5 children and Maria is 16, Rob is 18 and Amber is 14, how old are Sian and Harry?
Is your answer the only one possible?

7 The number of burials recorded in London over a 5-year period was:

Year	Burials
1663	15 356
1664	18 297
1665	97 147
1666	12 697
1667	15 841

    a Calculate the average number of burials taking place each year.
    b An average is a 'typical value'.
Comment on your answer to part **a**.

This spread will show you how to:

▶▶ Interpret diagrams, graphs and charts, and draw inferences based on the shape of graphs and simple statistics for a single distribution.

KEYWORDS

Pie chart   Statistics

Bar chart

You often find statistics presented in diagrams.
You need to be able to read and understand the diagrams.

▶ A **pie chart** uses a circle to display data.

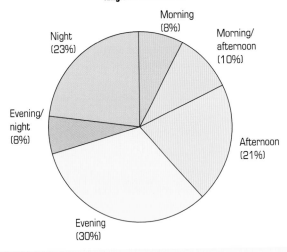

**Burglaries of domestic dwellings: by time of day, 1997
(England and Wales)**

- Morning (8%)
- Morning/afternoon (10%)
- Afternoon (21%)
- Evening (30%)
- Evening/night (8%)
- Night (23%)

▶ The pie chart shows that more burglaries were committed in the evening than at any other time of day.
▶ If there were 200 burglaries, then 60 of these were committed in the evening.
▶ If there were 24 morning burglaries, then there were 300 burglaries in total:

      8%   represents 24 burglaries
      1%   represents 3 burglaries
So   100%   is 300 burglaries.

▶ A **bar chart** uses bars to display data.

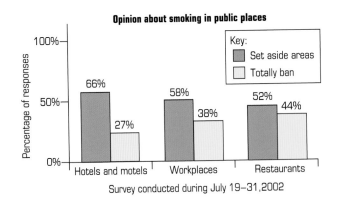

Opinion about smoking in public places

Percentage of responses

Key:
- ▨ Set aside areas
- ☐ Totally ban

- Hotels and motels: 66%, 27%
- Workplaces: 58%, 38%
- Restaurants: 52%, 44%

Survey conducted during July 19–31, 2002

▶ The bar chart shows that more people would set areas aside for smokers in public places than would ban them completely.
▶ The more enclosed the space, the more would actually ban smoking totally.
▶ None of the bars add to 100% so it is assumed that the rest of the respondents 'didn't know' or perhaps they said smoking should be allowed everywhere.
▶ There is no information about who took part in the survey, such as whether it included smokers as well as non-smokers, and so it is difficult to draw any firm conclusions.

Exercise D1.3

1 Look at the pie chart shown below.
It gives the proportion of trees in a wood.

Key:
- Elm   8%
- Chestnut 12%
- Birch   19%
- Oak   29%
- Beech   32%

a How many of each species would there be in the wood if it had 100 trees?

b How many of each species would there be in the wood if it had 600 trees?

2 The pie chart shows the results of a survey of schoolchildren to find out how they get to school.

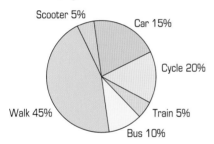

Scooter 5%   Car 15%   Cycle 20%   Walk 45%   Train 5%   Bus 10%

a If 135 children walked to school, how many children were involved in total?

b Find out the amounts of all the other categories, and draw a frequency table.

3 Farmer Grundy grows a variety of vegetables, and has drawn this pie chart to summarise his crop.

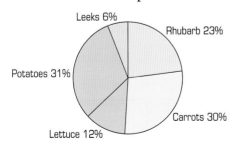

Leeks 6%   Rhubarb 23%   Potatoes 31%   Carrots 30%   Lettuce 12%

What is wrong with Farmer Grundy's chart?

4 This bar chart shows the number of children per family in a survey.

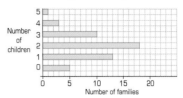

a How many families were involved in the survey?

b What is the modal number of children per family?

c Calculate how many children were involved in the survey.

5 This bar chart shows the number of people using a cross-Channel ferry service during one particular week.

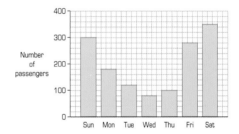

a Which day had least passengers?

b Which day had most passengers?

c Describe how the number of people using the service varies during the week.

6 This bar chart appeared in an advertisement for the new Hilbert V8 sports car.

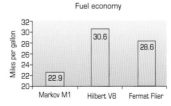

Fuel economy

a Do you think it gives a fair impression of the real difference in fuel economy between the different cars?

b Redraw the bar chart to give a fairer picture of the figures.

This spread will show you how to:
▶▶ Use vocabulary and ideas of probability, drawing on experience.
▶▶ Understand and use the probability scale from 0 to 1.

The chance of an event happening is somewhere between certain and impossible:

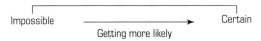

Impossible ⟶ Certain
Getting more likely

▶ **Probability** is a measure of the chance of an event happening.
It describes how likely something is to happen.

The probability of pigs flying is 0

The probability of the Sun rising tomorrow is 1

0
It is impossible!

1
It is certain!

The probability of an event can change in time.
It is **certain** to be Friday tomorrow if it is Thursday today – otherwise it is impossible!

▶ All probabilities are measured on a scale from 0 to 1.

example

Six pupils enter a lucky draw at the school fete.

Jude   Jack   Fred   Sheila   Kamal   Dave

Their names are written on a blank dice and then the dice is rolled.
The name at the top shows the winner of a prize.
Who is most likely to win a prize – a girl, or Fred?

Fred has a 1 in 6 chance of winning the first prize.
The probability of Fred winning the first prize is $\frac{1}{6}$.

There are 2 girls, so there is a 2 in 6 chance of a girl winning the first prize.
The probability of a girl winning the first prize is $\frac{2}{6}$.

You can say that a girl is more likely to win a prize than Fred.

Exercise D1.4

1 a Write down the names of four sports.
Label them A, B, C and D.
Which do you think you are more likely to get hurt playing?

> Some popular sports are: soccer, rugby, hockey, canoeing, cricket, skiing ...

b Put the sports in the order you think are the most dangerous.

Least dangerous ⟶ Most dangerous

Compare your list with others in your class.

2 When these events occur they can cause traffic accidents:

A: skidding on ice
C: going round a bend too fast

B: being dazzled by the sun
D: driving on unlit roads at night

Imagine any of the events can occur.

a Is A or B more likely to cause an accident?
b Compare the other events in pairs. Write: *I think A is more likely than...*
c Put the events in order, least likely to most likely.

3 A box contains 10 number cards, marked with the numbers 1 to 10. If a card is chosen at random, find the probability that the number chosen is:

a 7
c a number greater than 8
e less than 12

b an even number
d 13

Put the events in order, least likely to most likely, and mark them on a probability scale.

4 Use the information in the example to answer these questions:

a What is the probability of Jude winning?
b Order these events on a probability line:

A: Jude wins
C: either Jack or Sheila wins
E: Jude does not win

B: a boy wins
D: no-one wins

5 Bill and Jane are playing the Ladder Game. They take it in turns to roll a dice.

▶ Jane is evens. If she throws:
   ▶ an even number she moves up that number of spaces on the ladder
   ▶ an odd number she moves down that number of spaces.

▶ Bill is odds. If he throws:
   ▶ an odd number he moves up that number of spaces
   ▶ an even number he moves down that number of spaces.

a Who is more likely to win the game?
b Explain your answer to part **a**.

This spread will show you how to:
▶▶ Find and justify probabilities based on equally likely outcomes.
▶▶ Identify all the possible outcomes of a single event.

▶ Probabilities can be written as fractions, decimals or percentages.

This box contains the numbers 3, 5, 1, 6 and 4 on pieces of card.

If a card is picked out of the box there are 5 possible outcomes.
Each of the outcomes 3, 5, 1, 6 and 4 is **equally likely**.
They each have a probability of $\frac{1}{5}$ of being picked.

There is a 1 in 5 chance of picking the 3.
The probability of picking a 3 is $\frac{1}{5}$, or 0.2 or 20%.

There is a 2 in 5 chance of picking an even number.
The probability of picking an even number is $\frac{2}{5}$ or 0.4 or 40%.

3

4   6

As a fraction:
▶ Probability of an event happening $= \dfrac{\text{number of ways the event can happen}}{\text{total number of possible outcomes}}$

example

Here is a spinner marked from 1 to 10.
Place the probabilities of these events on a probability scale:
    A: the spinner lands on a 6
    B: the spinner lands on an odd number
    C: the spinner lands on a number greater than 4 but less than 8
    D: the spinner lands on 0
    E: the spinner lands on a number less than 10

There are 10 possible outcomes. The probability of each outcome is $\frac{1}{10}$.

You could use any of these probability scales:

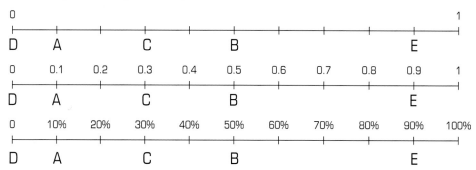

Exercise D1.5

1 All eight letters in the word NOVEMBER are placed in a bag.
What is the probability of picking out:

a a V   **b** an R

c an E   **d** a vowel

e a consonant?

Give your answers using fractions.

2 The numbers 2, 5, 6, 1, 4 and 8 are put into a box.
A number is drawn at random (without looking).
What is the probability that:

a a 6 is drawn   **b** an even number is drawn?

A 5 is drawn from the box. It is not replaced.
What is the probability that:

c a 6 is drawn   **d** an even number is drawn?

Show your answers to parts **a–d** on a probability scale.

3 A game uses a bag that contains 26 letter tiles, one for each letter of the alphabet. Players take a tile from the bag, and score a point if they choose a letter that is in their first name.
What is the probability that each of the following players will score a point?
Give your answer using fractions.

a Samantha   **b** Tom

c Sabina   **d** Christopher

Which of these players has the best chance of scoring a point?

4 The diagram shows information about 50 families living in a street.

		Number of children				
		0	**1**	**2**	**3**	**4**
Number of cars	**0**	4	2	1	0	0
	1	6	7	8	3	1
	2	4	3	8	1	0
	3	0	1	0	1	0

There are 8 families with 1 car and 2 children.

If a family is chosen at random, what is the probability that they will have:

a 2 children   **b** no car

c 3 cars and 1 child   **d** more cars than children

e more that one car and less than 3 children?

Mark these probabilities on a copy of each of these probability scales:

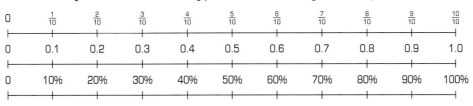

This spread will show you how to:
▶▶ Collect data from a simple experiment and record in a frequency table.
▶▶ Estimate probabilities based on experimental data.

KEYWORDS
Likely   Experiment
Outcome   Frequency
Estimate   Fair

To **calculate** the probability of an event you need to know the number of ways the event can happen, and the total number of possible outcomes:

▶ Probability of an event happening = $\dfrac{\text{number of ways the event can happen}}{\text{total number of possible outcomes}}$

You can also **estimate** probabilities using experimental data.

example

Sheena and Ray want to know whether a dice is biased.
To check, they throw the dice 120 times and record the outcome.
Here are their results:

Dice score	Tally	Frequency
1	JHT JHT JHT I	16
2	JHT JHT JHT JHT II	22
3	JHT JHT JHT JHT I	21
4	JHT JHT JHT JHT IIII	24
5	JHT JHT JHT JHT JHT JHT I	31
6	JHT I	6

a   Which is the most likely score on Sheena and Ray's dice?
b   What is the least likely score?
c   What would you expect the frequency of each score to be for an ordinary dice?
d   Do you think the dice is fair?
e   What could you do to check further?

a   From the table of results it seems that the score 5 is the most likely outcome.
b   The least likely outcome is a 6.
c   For an ordinary dice each score would be equally likely to occur. As there are 6 possible outcomes each would have a probability of $\frac{1}{6}$ so you would expect each to occur about 20 times.
d   It looks like the dice may be unfair as you are more than 5 times as likely to get a 5 than to get a 6, which is a big difference.
e   You could perform the experiment again.
    The more times you try the more reliable the data will be.

Exercise D1.6

1 **Experiment 1** – you will need four different-coloured cubes.
  ▸ Put the four cubes in a bag, then shake it.
  ▸ Predict what colour the first cube you draw out will be.
  ▸ Pick a cube from the bag at random (without looking).
    Look at the colour.
  ▸ Copy this table:

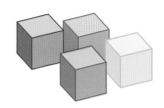

> **Remember:**
> Predict before you choose the cube!

	Guesses			
	First	Second	Third	Fourth
1				
2				
3				
4				
5				
6				
7				
8				
9				
10				

  ▸ If your prediction was correct, put a tick in the first box.
    If not, put a cross. **Do not** put the cube back in the bag.
  ▸ Repeat until you have taken out all four cubes.
  ▸ Repeat the experiment nine more times to fill the table.

  a Draw a probability scale from 0 to 1.
       Use the results in the table to mark on it the
       probability of guessing the first cube correctly.

  > Write the probability as a fraction.

  b Now mark the probability of guessing the second cube correctly.
  c Mark the probability of guessing the third cube and the last cube correctly.

2 **Experiment 2: Test a coin**
  ▸ Take any coin. Stick a small amount of plasticine to the tails side to weight the coin.
  ▸ Spin it 100 times and note whether it lands on heads or tails.
  ▸ Record your results in a copy of this table:

Outcome	Tally	Frequency
Head		
Tail		

Use your table to answer these questions:
  a What is the probability of getting a head with your coin?
  b What is the probability of getting a tail with your coin?
  c What should the frequency of each score be for a fair coin?
  d Do you think your coin is biased? Give a reason for your answer.

You should know how to ...

1 Calculate statistics for small sets of discrete data:
- ▶ Find the mode, median and range and the modal class for grouped data;
- ▶ Calculate the mean, including from a simple frequency table, using a calculator for a larger number of items.

2 Understand and use the probability scale from 0 to 1; find and justify probabilities based on equally likely outcomes in simple contexts.

3 Solve word problems and investigate in the contexts of handling data and probability.

Check out

1 Here is a set of test marks obtained by a group of 20 children:

| 18 | 10 | 9 | 12 | 24 | 3 | 8 | 10 | 8 | 8 |
| 12 | 6 | 8 | 7 | 12 | 11 | 8 | 17 | 16 | 9 |

  a Find the median of the marks.
  b Find the mode of the marks.
  c Find the mean of the marks.
  d Find the range of the marks.
  e Put the data into classes: 0–5 marks, then 6–10, 11–15, 16–20 and 21–25. Show this information in a table, and find the *modal class* (this is the class that contains the mode).

2 A bingo 'Prize Ball' can be any number from 1 to 100; all the numbers are equally likely to be chosen. What is the probability that the Prize Ball will be:

  a a multiple of 10
  b an even number
  c the number 24
  d less than 105
  e more than 20
  f the number 101?

Give your answers as decimals, and mark them on a probability scale. Explain what each of the probabilities means by explaining in words how likely each of the six outcomes is.

3 These three discs are drawn from a bag:

  a What is the mean of the numbers shown on the discs?
  b A fourth disc is drawn. The mean is now 19. What number is shown on the fourth disc?
  c If you close your eyes and pick one of the four discs at random, what is the probability of picking an even number?

Expressions and formulae

This unit will show you how to:

▶▶ Use letter symbols to represent unknown numbers or variables.

▶▶ Know the meaning of the words term and expression.

▶▶ Understand that algebraic operations follow the same conventions and order as arithmetic operations.

▶▶ Simplify expressions by collecting like terms.

▶▶ Use simple formulae.

▶▶ Substitute positive integers into simple linear expressions and, in simple cases, derive a formula.

▶▶ Solve word problems and investigate in the context of algebra.

▶▶ Identify the necessary information to solve a problem.

▶▶ Represent problems mathematically, making correct use of symbols.

If only they'd use the same language, it'd be so much easier to compare.

Mobile Phones

Before you start

You should know how to ...

1 Use letter symbols to stand for numbers.

2 Use function machines.

Check in

1 Answer these questions using algebra:

a Joe can play *t* songs on the guitar. He learns 9 more.
How many can he play now?

b Geoff has *m* minutes on his phone card.
He talks for 6 minutes.
How many minutes does he have left?

c Moggie has *n* cats. They each have a kitten.
How many cats does she have now?

2 Find the output for each machine when the input is 7.

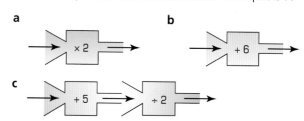

a
→ ×2 →

b
→ +6 →

c
→ +5 → ÷2 →

This spread will show you how to:
- ▶▶ Know that letters are used to stand for numbers.
- ▶▶ Recognise algebraic conventions.
- ▶▶ Use letter symbols.

KEYWORDS

Algebra   Perimeter

Expression   Unknown

This is a 100 square. It is organised in rows of 10.

1	2	3	4	5	6	7	8	9	10
11	12	13	14	15	16	17	18	19	20
21	22	23	24	25	26	27	28	29	30
31	32	33	34	35	36	37	38	39	40
41	42	43	44	45	46	47	48	49	50
51	52	53	54	55	56	57	58	59	60
61	62	63	64	65	66	67	68	69	70
71	72	73	74	75	76	77	78	79	80
81	82	83	84	85	86	87	88	89	90
91	92	93	94	95	96	97	98	99	100

Start at: 26
If you add 1 you get $26 + 1 = 27$
If you add 10 you get $26 + 10 = 36$
If you take 2 you get $26 - 2 = 24$
If you take 11 you get $26 - 11 = 15$

Start at: 67
If you add 1 you get $67 + 1 = 68$
If you add 10 you get $67 + 10 = 77$
If you take 2 you get $67 - 2 = 65$
If you take 11 you get $67 - 11 = 56$

This is part of a 100 square. No one knows exactly which part it is.
You can still describe what happens when you add or subtract.
You use a letter to stand for the unknown starting place.

The letter n stands for a number in the 100 square but it is not a specific number like 26 or 67.

Start at the general place: n
If you add 1 you get: $n + 1$
If you add 10 you get: $n + 10$
If you take 2 you get: $n - 2$
If you take 11 you get: $n - 11$

Using a letter to stand for an unknown number is called **algebra**.
$n + 1$, $n + 10$, $n - 2$ and $n - 11$ are ways of expressing a place using the starting place n.
They are called algebraic expressions.

Using a letter to stand for an unknown number is very common in maths.
For example, this equilateral triangle has an unknown side:

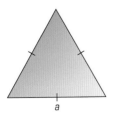

The length of the unknown side is a cm.
All the sides are equal in length, so each side is a cm long.
Perimeter is a cm + a cm + a cm
which is 3 lots of a cm.

▶ $a + a + a$ is 3 lots of a or $3 \times a$ or $a \times 3$. You write this as $3a$.

Exercise A2.1

These grids are taken from a 100 square.
In questions 1 to 3, copy each grid onto squared paper and write in the numbers given.

1 **a**
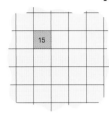

Write in:
17, 45, 24, 6, 36

b

Write in:
57, 54, 78, 46, 85

c
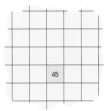

Write in:
47, 27, 44, 14, 56, 33

2 **a**
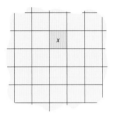

Write in:
$(x+1)$, $(x-2)$, $(x-10)$,
$(x+30)$, $(x+21)$, $(x+19)$

b
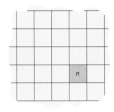

Write in:
$(n+1)$, $(n+11)$, $(n-2)$,
$(n-12)$, $(n-30)$, $(n+9)$

c
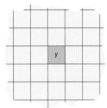

Write in:
$(y+2)$, $(y+12)$, $(y+20)$,
$(y+18)$, $(y-10)$, $(y-12)$

3 **a**

Write in:
$(m+22)$, $(m+11)$,
$(m+2)$, $(m-1)$

b

Write in:
$(p+10)$, $(p+1)$,
$(p+41)$, $(p+23)$

c

Write in:
$(a-13)$, a, $(a+10)$,
$(a+7)$, $(a-21)$

4 Write in the algebraic terms that fit into the squares marked A to F.

a

			F	
D				E
	C	x		
	B		A	

b

			F	
C		x+3	B	
		E		
	D	A		

5 On a copy of a 5 × 5 grid mark a square $y+2$.
Now write in $(y+1)$, $(y+12)$, $(y-8)$, $(y+14)$

6 **a** You are at a square with value y in a 100 square.
You go down 2 squares and back (left) 3 squares.
What is the value of the new square you are at?
   b You are at a square with value p in a 100 square.
Explain how you would move to a square with value $p-19$.

This spread will show you how to:
▶▶ Recognise algebraic conventions.
▶▶ Use letter symbols.
▶▶ Know that algebraic operations follow the same conventions and order as arithmetic operations.

KEYWORDS

Algebra   Term
Expression x-axis
Unknown

In algebra you use letters to stand for unknown numbers or values.
The letters follow the same rules as numbers.

▶ You can add numbers together in any order:
  You can add letters together in any order:

$1 + 2 + 3 = 2 + 3 + 1 = 3 + 2 + 1$
$a + b + c = b + c + a = c + b + a$

▶ You can multiply numbers together in any order:
  You can multiply letters together in any order:

$2 \times 3 \times 4 = 4 \times 3 \times 2 = 3 \times 2 \times 4$
$x \times y \times z = z \times y \times x = y \times x \times z$

You often use the letter x in algebra.

▶ It is easy to confuse the letter x with the multiplication sign $\times$, so you usually leave out the sign.

  For example, $3 \times q$ is $3q$ and $x \times y \times z$ is xyz

▶ You write algebraic terms in alphabetical order, and with numbers before letters.

In graphs you use x and y to label the axes.

example

Add together xyz, zxy and yxz.

$xyz = zxy = yxz$ because you can multiply in any order.
So $xyz + zxy + yxz = xyz + xyz + xyz$
= 3 lots of xyz
= $3xyz$

$xyz + xyz + xyz =$

3 lots of xyz = $3xyz$

example

Match these terms into equivalent pairs, and find the odd one out.
xy zxy yz xz xzy zy yx

xy is the same as yx.
zxy is the same as xyz.
yz is the same as zy.

The pairs of terms are equivalent.

xz is the odd one out.

Exercise A2.2

1 Here are 11 algebraic expressions.
- ▶ Match 5 pairs of expressions that have the same meaning.
- ▶ For the odd one out, write a matching expression.

$a \times b \times a$	$3a$	$b \times a$	$a^2 b$	$b \times b$

$ab + ba$	$5b - 3b$	$a + a + a$	b^2	ab	$2b$

2 Rewrite these expressions using correct algebraic conventions.
a $a \times 3$ **b** $b \times c$ **c** $2b \times c$ **d** $a \times 3b$ **e** $2b \times 3c$
f $a \times a$ **g** $b \times 5 \times a$ **h** $4 \times a \times 3 \times b$ **i** $b \times 2 \times c \times 5$ **j** $a \times 5 \times b \times 3 \times c$

3 Equivalences:
Copy these diagrams.

a Add three different ways of writing $3ab$

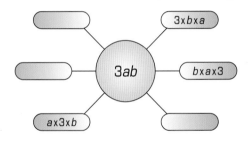

b Add different ways of representing $12pq$

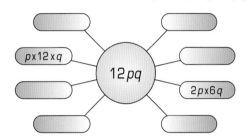

4 Simplify each of these expressions.
You should write each expression using one term.
a $ab + ba$
b $n + n + n + n$
c $xyz + yxz + zxy$
d $3 \times q \times 2 \times p$
e $s \times t + t \times s$
f $3 \times m + 2 \times m + m$
g $rs + r \times s + s \times r + sr$
h $abc + bac + cab + cba - bca - acb$
i $8a - 5a$
j $4p \times 3q \times 5r$

5 Sean got his algebra homework wrong.
Copy the questions and write the correct answers.
a $xy + yx = x^2 + y^2$ ✗
b $4a - 3a = 1$ ✗
c $6x + 6x = 12x^2$ ✗
d $p \times q \times p = 2pq$ ✗
e $n \times n \times n = 3n$ ✗

A2.3 Simplifying expressions

This spread will show you how to:
- ▶▶ Recognise algebraic conventions.
- ▶▶ Use letter symbols.
- ▶▶ Simplify linear expressions by collecting like terms.

KEYWORDS

Consecutive   Expression
Symbol   Terms
Simplify   Unknown

This is part of a 100 square. No one knows which part it is.

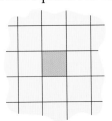

> Remember that a 100 square is organised in rows of 10.

You can fix a place using a symbol to stand for the unknown number.
Once you fix one place in the 100 square you can fix them all.

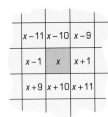

$x-11$	$x-10$	$x-9$
$x-1$	x	$x+1$
$x+9$	$x+10$	$x+11$

> In a normal 100 square you can add consecutive numbers together: 17 + 18 = 35.
> In this 100 square you can do the same using letter symbols:
> $x + x + 1$

Remember:

   ▶ $a + a + a$ is 3 lots of a or $3 \times a$ or $a \times 3$. You write this as $3a$.

You can use this convention to **simplify expressions** such as $x + x + 1$.
Each part of the expression is called a **term**.
In $x + x + 1$ there are three terms: x, x and 1.

When terms are the same they can be collected together:
They are called **like terms**.

$$x + x + 1$$
$$= 2x + 1$$

> ▶ To simplify expressions you collect like terms together.
> Terms are like when they use the same combination of symbols.

---

example

For each of these expressions, identify which terms are like and simplify where possible.

a $a + a + 2$ **b** $p + q + q + r$ **c** $x + y + z + 2y + x$

a and a are like terms
$a + a + 2$
$= 2a + 2$

q and q are like terms.
$p + q + q + r$
$= p + 2q + r$

y and $2y$ are like terms.
x and x are like terms.
$x + y + z + 2y + x$
$= 2x + 3y + z$

Exercise A2.3

The grids in questions 1 to 3 are taken from a 100 square.

1 a The two shaded squares total 47.
What is the value of each square?

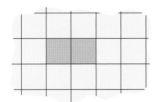

b The two shaded squares total 80.
What is the value for each square?

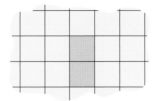

c In this grid $a + b = 32$.
What numbers do a and b represent?

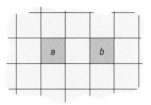

2 Find the total for the two given squares.

a

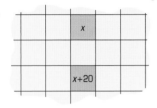

b

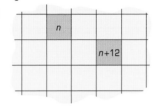

c

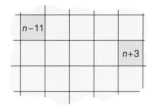

3 a The given square (p) is added to another and the total is $2p + 3$.
What is the value of the other square?

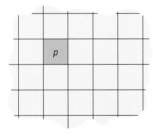

b The given square ($n + 1$) is added to another and the total is $2n + 12$.
What is the value of the other square?

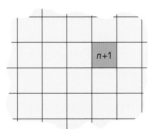

c Given the square $x + 1$, find the value of the squares marked A and B.
What is the total of the three squares?

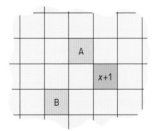

4 Simplify these algebraic expressions.

   a $b + b + b + a$ **b** $2x + 2y + 3x$ **c** $5x - 2x$ **d** $3y + 2r - y$

   e $a + a + b + b + b$ **f** $2r + 3s - 2s$ **g** $3m - 2n + 5n + m$ **h** $4p + 2q - 2p + q$

   i $2a + 3a + 4a$ **j** $3c + 4d - 2d$ **k** $3l + 4l - 5m$ **l** $6r + 3s - 2r - s$

5 You can add three terms together to get the answer $5a$.
One possible solution is $a + a + 3a$.
Find as many different solutions as you can.

6 Two expressions are added together to make the expression $5a + 3b$.
Give three possible solutions.

Substitution

This spread will show you how to:
- ⏵⏵ Recognise algebraic conventions.
- ⏵⏵ Use simple expressions with brackets.
- ⏵⏵ Substitute positive integers into simple linear expressions.

KEYWORDS

Variable	Symbol
Substitute	Evaluate
Expression	Squared

You are going to use the rules of algebra in a game.
The game involves **substituting** a value for the letter in an algebraic expression.

▶ To **evaluate** an expression you substitute a value for a symbol and work out the answer.

Before you can play the game you need to know the rules of algebra.
You already know that:

▶ $a + a + a$ is 3 lots of a or $3 \times a$ or $a \times 3$. You write this as $3a$.

You also need to know that:

▶ You never use the division sign: write $\frac{x}{10}$ not $x \div 10$

▶ $2(d + 3)$ means do $(d + 3)$ first then multiply the answer by 2.

▶ d^2 means $d \times d$ so $4^2 = 4 \times 4 = 16$.
You say 'd squared'.

For example: when $d = 4$, $d + 3 = 7$
so $2(d + 3) = 2 \times 7 = 14$.

The Dice Run
This is a game for two players.
Both players start in the top left corner:

START $3d + 4$	$2d + 1$	
$10 - 2d$	$d^2 - 5$	

Rules of the game
- ▶ Throw the dice.
- ▶ You can only move one square, either vertically or horizontally.
- ▶ Move to the square that gives the largest total when you substitute your dice score into the expression.
- ▶ Each player takes turns throwing the dice and moving.
- ▶ Keep playing until all the players reach the bottom right-hand corner.
- ▶ Count up all your totals. The player with the largest overall total wins the game.

example

Harry throws a 3. He could move to $2d + 1$ or $10 - 2d$.

....

$2d + 1$ will score $2 \times 3 + 1 = 7$
$10 - 2d$ will score $10 - 2 \times 3 = 4$
He should move to $2d + 1$.

START $3d + 4$	$2d + 1$	
$10 - 2d$	$d^2 - 5$	

Exercise A2.4

The Dice Run

- ▶ This is a game for two players.
- ▶ You need a dice and counters.
- ▶ Throw the dice to see which player starts – the highest score on the dice starts.

The rules are given on page 74.

START $3d + 4$	$2d + 1$	$\dfrac{2d + 8}{2}$	$2(d - 1)$	$8d$
$10 - 2d$	$d^2 - 5$	$4 - d$	$3d + 1$	$d^2 + 10$
$\frac{1}{2}(2d + 4)$	$3(d - 2)$	$2d + 5$	$d - 3$	$2 - d^2$
$3 - d$	$16 - 2d$	$2d - 10$	$d^2 + 2$	$3(4 - d)$
$(d + 1)^2$	$2 - 4d$	$3(2 - d)$	$(d - 1)^2$	$8 - 3d$ FINISH

Play the game twice then answer these questions:

1 If you throw a 1 with a dice, which expression gives the highest score, and what is the score?

2 If you throw a 3 with a dice, which two expressions give a value of 10?

3 Find five expressions that will always give a positive result.

4 Which expression will always give a negative result?

5 Do you agree with this statement?
$(d - 1)^2$ is larger than $d^2 - 6$ for all throws of the dice.
Give reasons for your answer.

6 If the dice can show any number from 1 to 6, which expressions can you make exactly equal to 8?
Set out your work like this:
$3d - 4 = 8$ when $d = 4$.

7 Explain why $2d + 1$ will never equal 8.

8 Play the game again using one of these alternative rules:

- ▶ Start in the top right corner and finish in the bottom left.
- ▶ The lowest total wins.
- ▶ Use a different dice.

This spread will show you how to:

▶▶ Explain the meaning of and substitute integers into formulae expressed in words.

▶▶ Derive simple algebraic expressions and formulae.

KEYWORDS

Variable   Equals (=)

Input   Output

Your brain is your very own personal computer:

Input | Process | Output
Take in information → Process information → Feed out answers

▶ You can often process information by using a **formula**.

> A formula links two or more variables together with an equals (=) sign.

To find the formula for changing £s into 10ps, you can ask:

How many 10ps are there in £1?   There are ten 10ps in £1.
How many 10ps are there in £2?   There are 2 × ten 10ps in £2.
How many 10ps are there in £x?   There are x × ten 10ps in £x.

> n and x are **variables**. The key explains what they stand for.

The formula is: number of 10ps = number of £s × 10

Using algebra: n = $x \times 10 = 10x$

where n = number of 10ps and x = number of £s

Now you can find the number of 10ps in £7.60:

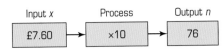

Input x | Process | Output n
£7.60 → ×10 → 76

There are 76 ten pences in £7.60

a Look at the flowchart. What does the formula do?

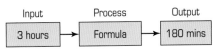

Input | Process | Output
3 hours → Formula → 180 mins

b Write the formula using algebra.

....

a The formula changes hours to minutes.

b The question to ask is:

How many minutes are there in n hours?

There are 60 mins in each hour so

the formula is   number of minutes = number of hours × 60

Using algebra: n = $x \times 60 = 60x$

where n = number of minutes and x = number of hours

> When you invent a formula you should always explain what your letters stand for.

Exercise A2.5

1 Explain in words what these formulae mean.
   a Age = $x \div 12$ ($x \longrightarrow$ number of months old)
   b Length = $1000n$ ($n \longrightarrow$ length in kilometres)
   c Pints = $8x$ ($x \longrightarrow$ number of gallons)

2 For each formula:
   ▶ explain what the formula does
   ▶ write the formula using algebra

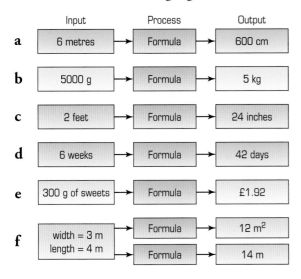

	Input	Process	Output
a	6 metres	Formula	600 cm
b	5000 g	Formula	5 kg
c	2 feet	Formula	24 inches
d	6 weeks	Formula	42 days
e	300 g of sweets	Formula	£1.92
f	width = 3 m / length = 4 m	Formula / Formula	12 m² / 14 m

3 Convert these word formulae into algebraic rules.
   a Number of days = number of hours ÷ 24
      (let n = number of days and x = number of hours)
   b Number of pounds = number of pence ÷ 100
      (let n = number of pounds and y = number of pence)
   c Number of mm = 10 times number of cm
      (let x = number of cm and n = number of mm)

4 Medium-sized goldfish (5–8 cm) need at least 5 litres of water each.
   a Write this as an algebraic formula
      (let x = amount of water required (in litres) and n = number of goldfish)
   b If I have 10 medium-sized goldfish how much water should be in the tank?
   c If my tank holds 34 litres of water, what is the greatest number of goldfish I can have?

5 Write a formula to convert £ sterling to € euros. (In 2002, £1 = €1.6)
   Explain what your letters stand for.

You should know how to ...

1 Use letter symbols to represent unknown numbers or variables.

2 Understand that algebraic operations follow the same conventions and order as arithmetic operations.

3 Simplify linear expressions by collecting like terms.

4 Substitute positive integers into simple linear expressions.

5 Solve word problems in the context of algebra.

Check out

1 Write these sentences using letters.
  a June has some sweets. She eats five of them. How many does she have now?
  b Colette has some football stickers. She buys a packet of 6. How many does she have now?
  c Kerim has some chips. He shares them with his friend. How many do they each have?

2 Simplify each of these expressions:
  a $3w + 2w + w$
  b $p \times 2 \times q$
  c $ab + 2ba + 3ab$
  d $3 \times v \times w + w \times v \times 2$
  e $6pq - q \times 4 \times p$

3 Simplify these expressions by collecting like terms:
  a $2p + 3 + 3p - 2$
  b $3x + 3y + 2x - 2y$
  c $d - 2e + 3d + 2e$
  d $4t + 3s - t$
  e $15y + 15x - 7y$
  f $a + 2b - 3 + 4a - 5b + 6$

4 A 2 is thrown with a dice. What is the value of each of these expressions if $d = 2$:
  a $3d - 5$
  b $2(d + 1)$
  c $16 - d$
  d $22 - 4d$?

5 Make up sentences for these expressions:
  a $n + 7$
  b $2n$
  c $2n - 5$

Angles and shapes

This unit will show you how to:

▶▶ Use correctly the vocabulary, notation and labelling conventions for lines, angles and shapes.

▶▶ Identify parallel and perpendicular lines.

▶▶ Begin to identify and use angle, side and symmetry properties of triangles and quadrilaterals.

▶▶ Know the sum of angles at a point, on a straight line and in a triangle and recognise vertically opposite angles.

▶▶ Use conventions and notation for 2-D coordinates in all four quadrants.

▶▶ Find coordinates of points determined by geometric information.

▶▶ Use angle measure; distinguish between and estimate the size of acute, obtuse and reflex angles.

▶▶ Solve word problems and investigate in the context of shape and space.

▶▶ Explain and justify methods and conclusions.

Simple geometrical shapes occur commonly in architecture.

Before you start

You should know how to ...

1 Recognise special quadrilaterals.

2 Plot points on a coordinate grid.

Check in

1 Name these quadrilaterals.
   Choose from: *kite, trapezium, square, parallelogram, rectangle*

   a   **b**

2 a Plot these points on a grid marked from 0 to 5 on both axes:
   (1, 5)   (2, 5)   (4, 3)   (2, 1)   (1, 1)

   b Join the points together in order.
   What shape have you drawn?

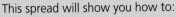
Measuring angles

This spread will show you how to:
- ▶ Use accurately the notation and labelling conventions for lines, angles and shapes.
- ▶ Estimate the size of acute, obtuse and reflex angles.

KEYWORDS

Angle	Measure
Degree (°)	Side
Protractor	Draw
Vertex	

An angle is a measure of turn. You can measure it in degrees, °.

 There are 360° in a full turn.

There are 180° in a half turn.

 There are 90° in a quarter turn.

A full turn takes you back to the start. A half turn makes a straight line. A quarter turn makes a right angle.

You measure and draw angles in degrees using a protractor:

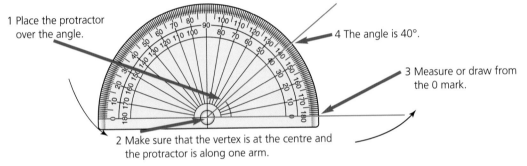

1 Place the protractor over the angle.

4 The angle is 40°.

3 Measure or draw from the 0 mark.

2 Make sure that the vertex is at the centre and the protractor is along one arm.

You can use a protractor in a clockwise or anticlockwise direction.
To make sure you use the right scale you should estimate the size of the angle first.

An angle smaller than 90° is an acute angle.

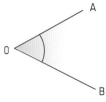

An angle between 90° and 180° is an obtuse angle.

An angle between 180° and 360° is a reflex angle.

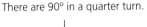

You can use this notation for an angle:

Angle AOB is 55° ∠A is 154° ∠DEF is 220°

Estimate then measure the reflex angle EDC:

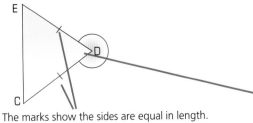

The marks show the sides are equal in length.

The angle is reflex so it is more than 180°.
It is more than $\frac{3}{4}$ turn so it is between 270° and 360°.
It is about 300°.

Measure the acute angle: it is 70°.
So the reflex angle is 360° − 70° = 290°.

Exercise S2.1

1 Copy and complete the table for the angles shown.

Shape	Angle	Type of angle	Estimate	Measurement
a	∠BAD			
b	∠ABC			
c	∠BCD			
d	∠CDE			

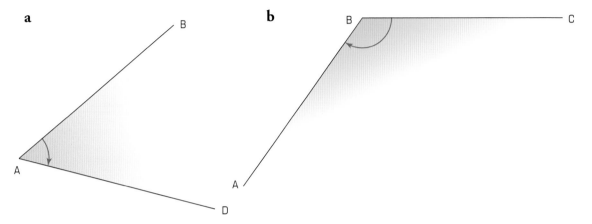

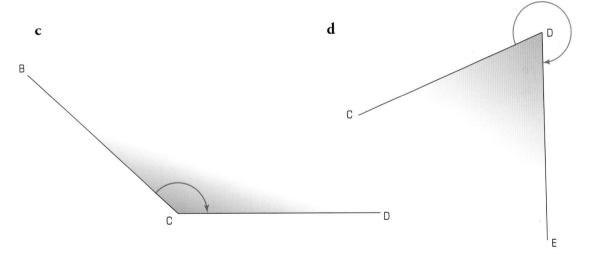

2 Draw these angles and label them.
Write down whether the angle is right, straight, acute, obtuse or reflex.
  a ABC = 90°   **b** ∠ABC = 24°   **c** ∠B = 180°   **d** AOB = 123°   **e** ∠F = 254°

3 Draw angles of your own choice and label them.
See if a partner can estimate the size of your angles.
Use different orientations to make it more difficult.

This spread will show you how to:
- ⏩ Identify parallel and perpendicular lines.
- ⏩ Know the sum of angles at a point, on a straight line and in a triangle.
- ⏩ Recognise vertically opposite angles.

You know that there are:

... 360° at a point

... 180° on a straight line

... 90° on a corner

You can use these facts to help solve angle problems.

example

Find the missing angles in these diagrams:

a

55° x

b

20° b 30°

c

c 120° c c

a $x + 55° = 180°$
$125° + 55° = 180°$
so $x = 125°$

b $30° + 20° + b = 90°$
$50° + b = 90°$
$50° + 40° = 90°$
so $b = 40°$

c $120° + c + c + c = 360°$
$120° + 3c = 360°$
$120° + 240° = 360°$
so $3c = 240°$ and $c = 80°$

These are also useful angle facts:
- ▶ Parallel lines // are always the same distance apart.
- ▶ Perpendicular lines ∟ meet at right angles or 90°.
- ▶ All other lines meet at an angle other than 90°.

b a c d

The cross forms two different angles:
a and b make a straight line.
The vertically opposite angles are equal:
$a = c$ and $b = d$.

The arrows show // sides.

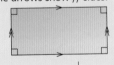

The squares show ∟ sides.

Activity

Draw any triangle.

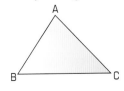

A
B   C

Cut out the corners.

A
B   C

Put them together.

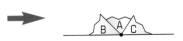

B A C

- ▶ The angles in a triangle add to 180°. They make a straight line.

Exercise S2.2

Find the value of the letters in questions 1 to 8.

Find the unknown angles in questions 9 to 13.

1
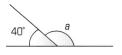
40° a

2
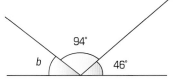
94° b 46°

3
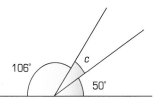
106° c 50°

4
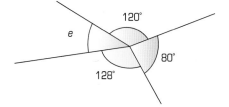
140° d

5
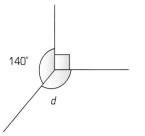
120° e 80° 128°

6
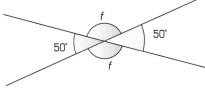
f 50° 50° f

7

156° g g

8 h = 4i
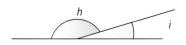
h i

9
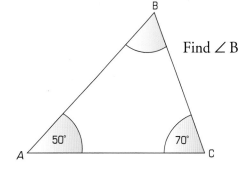
B
Find ∠ B
50° 70°
A C

10
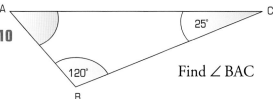
A C
25°
120°
B
Find ∠ BAC

11
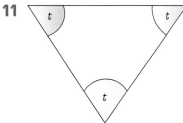
t t
t

12
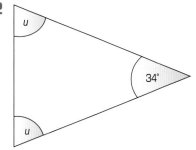
u 34°
u

13
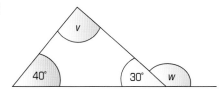
v
40° 30° w

83

Coordinates and shapes

This spread will show you how to:
▶▶ Read and plot points using coordinates in all four quadrants.
▶▶ Plot points determined by geometric information.
▶▶ Identify parallel and perpendicular lines.

KEYWORDS
Quadrilateral   Intersection
x-axis   Origin
y-axis   Quadrant
Direction   Grid
x, y, coordinates

You can plot points on a grid.

▶ A grid has two axes that are perpendicular to each other: the *x*-axis and the *y*-axis.
   The axes split the grid into four quadrants.

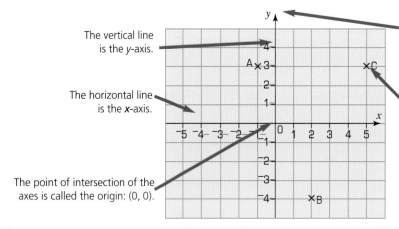

The vertical line is the *y*-axis.

The horizontal line is the *x*-axis.

The point of intersection of the axes is called the origin: (0, 0).

The arrows on the axes show the positive direction.

A coordinate is a pair of numbers: (*x*, *y*) that fixes a point on a grid.

(5, 3) means 5 along the *x*-axis and 3 up the *y*-axis.

▶ Negative numbers in coordinates mean you go backwards or downwards.

($^-$1, 3) means
1 backwards along the *x*-axis and 3 up the *y*-axis.
This is point A on the grid.

(2, $^-$4) means
2 along the *x*-axis and 4 down the *y*-axis.
This is point B on the grid.

You can draw shapes on a grid.

example

The diagram shows three vertices of a quadrilateral:
P, Q, R.
What coordinates could the fourth vertex have if the quadrilateral is:

a a kite   **b** a parallelogram   **c** an arrowhead?

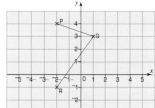

....

a A ($^-$5, 3) makes a kite
b B ($^-$5, 0) makes a parallelogram
c You can't draw an arrowhead because the points are not symmetrical.

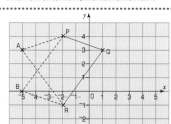

Exercise S2.3

1 Draw a grid with both axes labelled ⁻10 to +10. On your grid plot the point A(1, 2).
  a Find four sets of coordinates B, C, and D that will complete the rectangle ABCD so that the dimensions of the rectangle are 3 units by 5 units.
  b Write down four sets of coordinates that make squares with sides 5 units.
  c Check that adjacent sides are perpendicular and opposite sides are parallel.

2 Copy this grid and plot the points shown.

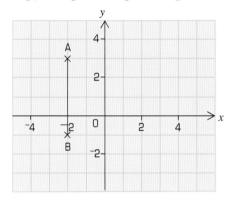

Write down all the possible pairs of points that will make:
  a rectangles with dimensions 3 units by 4 units
  b squares with dimensions 4 units

3 You will need four grids with both axes labelled 0 to 12.
Plot these sets of vertices on separate grids. Find the coordinates of the vertex that will complete the shape:
  a square: (2, 9) (5, 8) (3, 12)
  b parallelogram: (9, 10) (10, 12) (12, 9)
  c rectangle: (2, 5) (7, 5) (2, 7)
  d trapezium: (7, 2) (9, 4) (11, 2)
Identify any parallel and perpendicular lines on your shapes.

4 Copy this grid and plot the points shown.

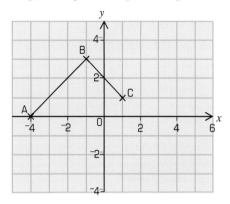

Write down, if possible, the extra point that will make:
  a a rectangle
  b a parallelogram
  c a rhombus
  d an arrowhead
  e a square
Explain your choice.

5 Copy this grid and plot the points shown.

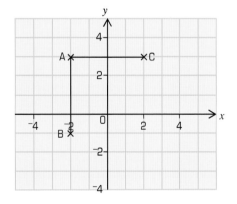

Write down, if possible, the extra point that will make:
  a a rectangle
  b a parallelogram
  c a rhombus
  d an arrowhead
  e a kite
Explain your choice.

You should know how to ...

1 Identify parallel and perpendicular lines.

Check out

1 Copy these shapes and mark all the parallel and perpendicular lines.

2 Know the sum of angles:
- ► round a point = 360°
- ► on a straight line = 180°
- ► in a triangle = 180°

2 Calculate the missing angles.

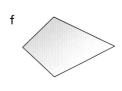

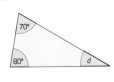

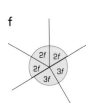

3 Explain and justify methods and conclusion.

3 Explain why it is impossible to draw a triangle which has a pair of parallel lines.

This unit will show you how to:

▶▶ Given a problem that can be addressed by statistical methods suggest possible answers.

▶▶ Decide which data would be relevant to an enquiry and possible sources.

▶▶ Plan how to collect and organise small sets of data; design a data collection sheet or questionnaire to use in a simple survey.

▶▶ Collect small sets of data from surveys and experiments, as planned.

▶▶ Construct diagrams to represent data.

▶▶ Construct frequency tables for discrete data.

▶▶ Interpret diagrams and graphs (including pie charts), and draw simple conclusions.

▶▶ Solve word problems and investigate in the context of handling data.

▶▶ Present and interpret solutions in the context of the original problem.

▶▶ Suggest extensions to problems by asking 'What if ...'.

Some questions can only be answered by collecting data.

Before you start

You should know how to ...

1 Order numbers.

2 Round decimals to the nearest whole number.

Check in

1 Write these numbers in size order, starting with the smallest:

a 23, 43, 24, 19, 34, 41, 24, 29, 82

b 1.6, 7, 0.3, 3.2, 4.0, 4.11, 5

2 Write these numbers to the nearest whole number:

2.6, 3.5, 4.8, 19.15, 4.45, 108.78, 3.545

This spread will show you how to:
▶▶ Given a problem that can be addressed by statistical methods, suggest possible answers.
▶▶ Decide which data would be relevant to the inquiry and possible sources.

KEYWORDS
Data
Survey
Experiment

The governors of Maypole High School are concerned about students' safety at the beginning and end of the school day because of the parked cars.

They hold a meeting to decide what action to take.
They all have different ideas ...

It's got worse since they reduced the bus service.

They should cycle – it's quicker.

There's a perfectly good zebra crossing down the road.

They decide the most important issues to explore are:

▶ When do most students arrive at school?
▶ How do students travel to school?
▶ How long does it take students to travel to school?

The colour of the car is irrelevant – but the size isn't.

Once you know what questions to ask you must think about where to find the answers!

▶ Data you collect yourself is **primary data.**
You can collect primary data using a survey or experiment.

▶ Data already collected is **secondary data.**
You can find secondary data in books or on the internet.

Exercise D2.1

1 The Governors of Maypole High School ask Year 7 to identify the issues affecting the traffic at the beginning and the end of the day.
Here are their suggestions:

A lot of us live too far away to walk.

There aren't enough proper parking spaces.

There should be more buses.

We should find out which parent does the driving.

I won't walk home in the winter because it gets too dark.

A lot of the parked cars aren't to do with the school.

Which suggestions do you think are relevant to the problem? Why?
Which suggestions, if any, are irrelevant? Why?

2 Imagine you need to identify the issues affecting the traffic outside school.
Make a list of all the questions you would ask.

3 At Maypole High School, class 7W decide to find out if:
- most students travel to school by bus
- students who walk to school have less distance to travel
- most cars bring only one student to school
- students living furthest away take the longest time to travel to school
- do students travel to school the same way each day?
  - if not, what affects their choice?
- do students consider it safe to cycle to school?
- what do people think about the school's cycle parking facilities?
- what do drivers think about parking facilities/restrictions in the school area?
- what do local residents think about congestion in the area?

Compare these questions to your own.
Decide whether to alter your own questions.

4 Look at your list of questions.
How could you collect primary data on them for your school?
Describe any questions that may be difficult to collect data on, and say why.

5 Describe how you could use secondary data to compare the results for your school with schools generally in the UK.

This spread will show you how to:

▶▶ Decide how to collect and organise the data needed.

▶▶ Design a data collection sheet or questionnaire to use in a simple survey.

KEYWORDS

Data collection sheet

Survey   Range

Questionnaire   Frequency

To decide whether traffic outside school can be reduced, the Maypole High Governors want to ask drivers:

▶ *How far is it to school?*
▶ *Do you drive in every day?*
▶ *Why do you drive your children to school?*
▶ *How long does your car journey take?*

▶ *How many people do you bring to school?*
▶ *Do any other students live near you?*
▶ *What do you think about the traffic outside school?*
▶ *What buses go from near your house?*

Some of the questions have yes or no answers:

▶ *Do you drive in every day?*
▶ *Do any other students live near you?*

Others have numerical answers:

▶ *How far is it to school?*
▶ *How long does your car journey take?*
▶ *How many people do you bring to school?*

These have many different answers:

▶ *Why do you drive your children to school?*
▶ *What buses go from near your house?*
▶ *What is your opinion on the traffic outside school?*

These are **closed** questions. They have particular answers. You could use tick boxes to collect this data.

These are **open** questions. They can include answers you haven't thought of.

The Governors develop a questionnaire for their questions:

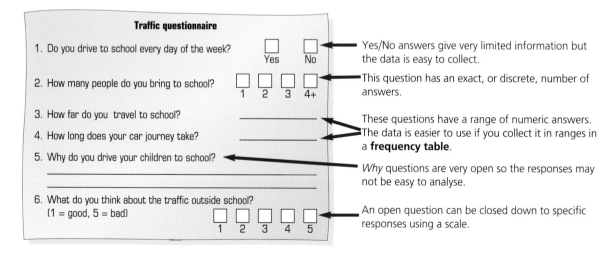

Yes/No answers give very limited information but the data is easy to collect.

This question has an exact, or discrete, number of answers.

These questions have a range of numeric answers. The data is easier to use if you collect it in ranges in a **frequency table**.

Why questions are very open so the responses may not be easy to analyse.

An open question can be closed down to specific responses using a scale.

▶ You can use a questionnaire to conduct a survey.
  Open questions invite any response.
  Closed questions invite choice.

  You can close down an open question using a scale.

Remember:
Data you collect yourself is **primary** data.

Exercise D2.2

1 Gina and Bhavna decide to explore who uses a car to come to school and why.
They develop a questionnaire, which starts with these three questions.

Ways to school questionnaire

1. How do you travel to school?
   Walk   Bus   Car   Train   Bicycle   Tram   Scooter   Motorbike

2. How far do you live from school?
   (A, B or C)

3. How long does it take you to get to school? ....

a For each of the questions decide:
   ▸ Is it easy to ask/understand?
   ▸ Will it encourage useful responses?
   ▸ Should it be improved?

b Improve the questionnaire if possible.

2 Gina and Bhavna want to collect data on the students at Maypole High, but the school contains about a thousand students.
They decide to collect information on 60 students, chosen throughout the school.
Suggest a way in which they could do this fairly.

3 Draw up a **data collection sheet** about the traffic outside your school,
based on questions you have thought of.
You can use your answer to question 2 from exercise D2.1 if it will help.

Here is an example of a data collection sheet:

Name	Class	Form of travel	Distance from home	Depart time	Arrival time	Length of journey
Connie Jones	7W	Walk	half a mile	8.35	8.50	15 minutes

Note: A data collection sheet is simply a table. You can use it instead of a questionnaire to collect data.

This spread will show you how to:
▶▶ Construct frequency tables for sets of data, grouped where appropriate in equal class intervals.
▶▶ Collect and record small sets of data as planned from surveys and experiments or secondary sources.

KEYWORDS

Range   Class interval
Frequency   Tally
Table

Numeric data can be **discrete** or **continuous**.

▶ Discrete data can take a limited number of specific values.
▶ Continuous data can take any value in a range.
  It is usually a measure such as length or time.

Remember:
The **range** is the difference between the highest and the lowest values.

This question has a limited number of specific responses:
How many people do you bring to school?

1   2   3   4
☐   ☐   ☐   ☐

You can collect this data in a tally chart.

Number of people	Tally	Frequency
1	⊥⊥⊥⊥ l	6
2	⊥⊥⊥⊥ ⊥⊥⊥⊥ l	11

If you survey your classmates you could just count them!

This sort of data is called discrete data – it can take a discrete number of values.

Other questions can have a range of responses:

This sort of data is called continuous data. It can take any value in a given range.
Organising the data in a **frequency table** makes it easier to handle.

Journey time (minutes)	0–10	10–20	20–30	30–40	40–50	50–60
Number of pupils	5	12	9	4	2	1

Each section is called a **class**.

Using equal class intervals makes it easier to compare the class frequencies.

▶ You can use a tally chart or frequency table to organise data.
▶ To make a frequency table first consider the range, then choose appropriate intervals.
  There should be between 4 and 10 intervals and they should be equal in size.

Exercise D2.3

1 Gina and Bhavna ask their class: '*How long did it take you to get to school this morning?*'
Here are the responses (time in minutes):

| 6 | 4 | 6 | 9 | 1 | 22 | 24 | 7 | 17 | 25 | 22 | 15 |
| 5 | 28 | 26 | 13 | 18 | 1 | 1 | 11 | 8 | 12 | 14 | 19 |

Better if it was 0 to 5 minutes, 6 to 10 minutes, 11 to 15 …

Our class intervals could be 0 to 1 hour, 1 to 2 hours and so on.

Complete this frequency table for the data, using Bhavna's class intervals.

Journey time (minutes)	0–5	6–10	11–15	16–20	21–25	26–30
Number of students						

2 Draw up a frequency table for each of these data sets.
Choose the most appropriate class intervals.
  a The heights of members of your class to the nearest cm.
  b The weights of members of your class to the nearest kg.
  c The numbers of brothers or sisters of members of your class.
  d The length of surname of members of your class.

You do not need to collect the data.

3 For each of these sets of data, decide whether they are numeric or not.
For the numeric sets, decide whether they are discrete or continuous.
  a The hair colour of members of your class.
  b The age of teachers in your school.
  c The time taken to run 100 metres by members of your class.
  d The main course menu in your school canteen, monitored each day for a month.
  e The number of students using the school canteen, monitored each day for a month.

4 Data collection activity
  a Collect the data you need for your data collection sheet in question 3 of exercise D2.2.
     You could survey members of your class.
  b Draw frequency tables for appropriate data.
  For each frequency table you draw, state the highest and lowest possible values and give reasons for your choice of class intervals.

For example, you might draw up a frequency table on length of journey, like the one above.

This spread will show you how to:

▶▶ Construct graphs and diagrams to represent data and identify key features.

KEYWORDS

Interval   Pie chart
Label   Bar chart
Frequency diagram
Bar-line graph

The Governors of Maypole High want to discuss the traffic problem with the people who drive to school.

To illustrate the problem they want to use diagrams to show the data.

They must choose the most appropriate diagram to get the point across.

These diagrams are useful for displaying non-numerical and discrete data:

▶ A pie chart uses a circle to show data.
  Each class or category has a slice of the circle.

▶ A bar chart uses bars to show data.
  Each bar represents a category or class.

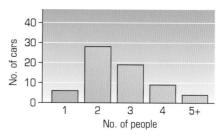

The size of the sectors represents the proportion in each category.
It is useful when you want to compare the size of a category with the whole.

The height of the bars represents the frequency of each category.
It shows the actual values and is useful when you want to compare the size of a category with other categories.

You display continuous data using a scale.
You can use a **frequency diagram** when the intervals are equal in size.

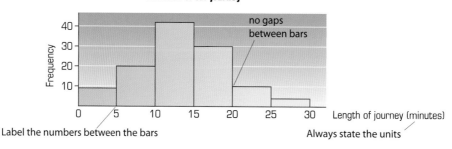

Duration of car journey

no gaps between bars

Label the numbers between the bars

Always state the units

▶ You can use frequency diagrams for showing continuous data which is organised into groups or classes.

Exercise D2.4

1 For each set of data, choose the most appropriate diagram to use. Choose from:

pie chart   *bar chart*   *bar-line graph*   *frequency diagram*

Give a reason for your choice.
  a number of goals scored by a football team:
     2, 3, 0, 0, 1, 5, 2, 0, 1, 1, 6, 2, 1
  b number of hours of sunshine monitored over a number of days:
     7, 2, 0, 1, 8, 9, 5, 4, 6, 0, 0, 0, 0, 1, 4, 2, 7
  c favourite colour of a group of students:
     green, purple, pink, black, pink, red, black, green, black, blue, orange, white, yellow
  d speed of cars on a motorway (in mph):
     56, 68, 51, 70, 66, 60, 58, 52, 73, 64, 49, 59, 60

2 A bar-line graph uses lines instead of bars to display
  discrete data.
  Draw a bar-line graph to display this data:

  Number of people in car:

3	2	4	1	5
4	5	2	2	3
2	3	4	1	5
6	4	3	1	3
4	2	2	3	2

  It will help to make a tally of the data first.

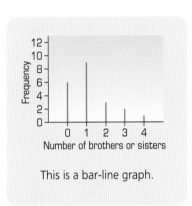

This is a bar-line graph.

3 For the data in question 1 of exercise D2.3, choose which is the most appropriate diagram
  to use, giving a reason for your choice. Choose from:

  pie chart   *bar chart*   *bar-line graph*   *frequency diagram*

  Draw the diagram.

4 Sammy counted the number of letters of the first 100 words of two books.
  The chart shows her results:

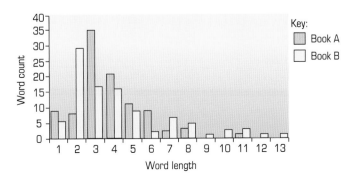

Key:
  Book A
  Book B

One of the books is a novel, *Pride and Prejudice.* The other one is a book for young children. Use the information in the table to decide which is which.
Explain how you decided.

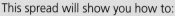

D2.5 Interpreting your diagrams

This spread will show you how to:
- ▶▶ Interpret diagrams, graphs and charts, and draw inferences based on the shape of the graphs.
- ▶▶ Relate the inferences to the initial problem.

KEYWORDS

Bar chart   Pie chart
Interpret
Frequency diagram

Different people may find different conclusions from the same diagram ...

The most common number of visits to the doctor is two.

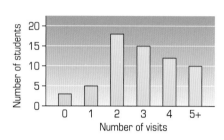

Most students have actually been to the doctor **more** than twice.

▶ Once you have drawn a diagram you should interpret it.
The interpretation should relate to the original aims of the survey.

The Maypole High Governors interpret the diagrams for the drivers.

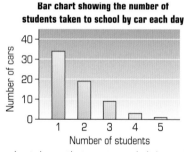

Bar chart showing the number of students taken to school by car each day

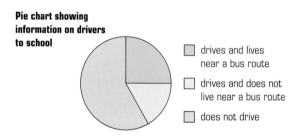

Pie chart showing information on drivers to school

- drives and lives near a bus route
- drives and does not live near a bus route
- does not drive

The bar chart shows that most people bring only one student to school.

The pie chart shows that more than half the people who drive live near a bus route.

The data raises further issues: what puts people off using the bus – even when they live near a bus route?
The Governors need to do more research – they must start the cycle again:

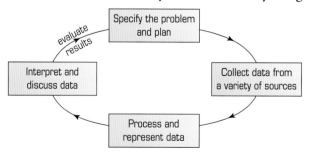

Exercise D2.5

1 Foxley Comprehensive, close to Maypole High, also conducted a traffic survey. They split their findings up into boys and girls, as shown in this composite bar chart:

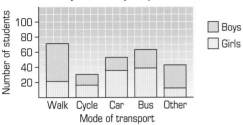

Composite bar chart showing modes of transport at Foxley Comprehensive

a How many students travel by bus?
b How many girls cycle to school?
c How many boys travel by car?
d Summarise the differences in the way that boys and girls travel to Foxley Comprehensive.

2 The pie chart shows some information about the number of people using different facilities in a leisure centre.

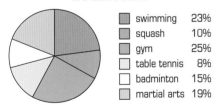

Pie chart showing use of facilities in a leisure centre

swimming	23%	
squash	10%	
gym	25%	
table tennis	8%	
badminton	15%	
martial arts	19%	

a Which of these statements are true?
A: *Less than a quarter of the people used the swimming pool.*
B: *More than half of the people were either playing badminton or squash.*
C: *The gym was over three times as popular as table tennis.*
b The manager of the leisure centre wants to expand two of the existing facilities. Which two would you suggest she might expand? Give a reason for your answer.

3 The frequency diagram shows the age of people visiting the Teeth 'R' Us dental surgery one day.

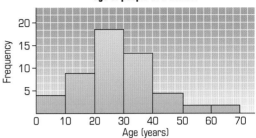

Frequency diagram showing age of people at a dentist

a How many people were aged between 10 and 20?
b How many people were aged between 30 and 50?
c How many people were aged over 40?
d Which is the modal age group?
e Can you use this graph to find out how many people were aged between 32 and 45? If not, why not?
f If you were conducting a survey on attendance at the Teeth 'R' Us surgery, what other information (apart from age) would you want to collect?

4 These pie charts show the types of bird monitored on two nearby lakes during a particular day.

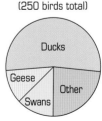

Lake Bigwater (1000 birds total)

Lake Smalldrop (250 birds total)

a Roughly what percentage of birds on Lake Bigwater are geese?
b Lisa says: '*The charts show that there are more ducks on smalldrop than on Bigwater.*' Lisa is wrong. Explain why the charts do not show this.

You should know how to ...

Solve word problems and investigate in a range of contexts.

Check out

1 The chart shows the number of goals scored by a football team in their last 20 home and away matches.

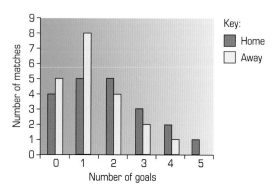

David says, 'You can tell from the chart that the team won more games at home than they did away.' Explain why David is *wrong*, and explain what conclusions you *can* draw from this chart.

2 Lauren asks 40 people which month their birthday is in.
The pie chart shows her results.

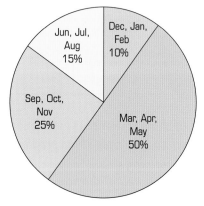

Lauren says, 'The chart shows that half of all babies are born between March and May.' Explain why she could be wrong. What should Lauren do to check her statement?

This unit will show you how to:

- ▶▶ Understand multiplication and division as they apply to whole numbers and decimals.
- ▶▶ Read and interpret scales on a range of measuring instruments.
- ▶▶ Convert one metric unit to another.
- ▶▶ Know and use the order of operations, including brackets.
- ▶▶ Know how to use the laws of arithmetic and inverse operations.
- ▶▶ Consolidate and extend mental methods of calculation.
- ▶▶ Multiply and divide three-digit by two-digit whole numbers.

- ▶▶ Extend to multiplying and dividing decimals with one or two places by single-digit whole numbers.
- ▶▶ Round positive whole numbers to the nearest 10, 100 or 1000 and decimals to the nearest whole number or one decimal place.
- ▶▶ Check a result by considering whether it is of the right order of magnitude.
- ▶▶ Break a complex calculation into simpler steps, choosing and using appropriate and efficient operations, methods and resources.

You might save money if you can multiply in your head.

Before you start

You should know how to ...

1 Recall multiplication facts up to 10 × 10 and derive associated division facts.

2 Understand place value.

3 Find multiples of a number.

Check in

1 Write down the answers to:

   a 8 × 7   **b** 9 × 6   **c** 5 × 8   **d** 7 × 6

   e 9 ÷ 3   **f** 12 ÷ 2   **g** 72 ÷ 8   **h** 24 ÷ 3

2 Write these numbers using words:
4.32 and 13.07

3 Find the first four multiples of 6.

This spread will show you how to:

▶▶ Understand and use decimal notation and place value.
▶▶ Multiply and divide numbers by 10, 100 and 1000.
▶▶ Convert between one metric unit and another.
▶▶ Read and interpret scales on a range of instruments.

KEYWORDS

Place value | Convert
Thousandth | Divide
Zero | Multiply

The decimal system uses powers of 10 to show place value.
This makes it easy to multiply by 10, 100 and 1000:

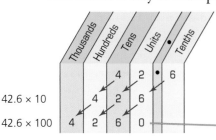

42.6 × 10

42.6 × 100

▶ When you multiply by 10, each digit moves 1 place to the left.

▶ When you multiply by 100, each digit moves 2 places to the left.

The zero is important as it holds the place value – otherwise you might read it as 426!

You can divide by 10, 100 and 1000 in a similar way.

▶ When you divide, positive numbers get smaller so the digits move to the right:

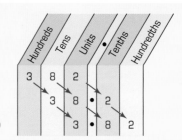

382 ÷ 10

382 ÷ 100

Metric measures are based on the decimal system.
Remember these metric lengths:

▶ 1 km = 1000 m   1 m = 100 cm   1 cm = 10 mm
▶ To convert from:

large to small means **more** so **multiply**
km ⟹ m

small to large means **less** so **divide**
mm ⟹ cm

Convert:

a 3 m to cm   **b** 6800 m to km   **c** 283 mm to cm

a More cm than m –
more means multiply
1 m = 100 cm
3 m = (3 × 100) cm
= 300 cm

b Less km than m –
less means divide
1000 m = 1 km
6800 m =
(6800 ÷ 1000) km
= 6.8 km

c Less cm than mm –
less means divide
10 mm = 1 cm
283 mm = (283 ÷ 10) cm
= 28.3 cm

Exercise N3.1

1 Write down the missing numbers.
  a $27 \times 100 = \Box$
  b $6400 \div 100 = \Box$
  c $17 \times \Box = 170$
  d $48\,000 \div \Box = 480$
  e $2.5 \times 1000 = \Box$
  f $87\,000 \div \Box = 87$

2 How many times larger is 8300 than 83?

3 Convert these measurements into the units indicated.
  a $4 \text{ km} = \Box\text{m}$
  b $30 \text{ mm} = \Box\text{centimetres}$
  c $450 \text{ cm} = \Box\text{metres}$
  d $3.5 \text{ m} = \Box\text{millimetres}$
  e $7.5 \text{ cm} = \Box\text{millimetres}$

4 Complete these statements.
  a $38 \div 10 = \Box$
  b $2.3 \times \Box = 23$
  c $17 \div \Box = 0.17$
  d $\Box \times 100 = 7.2$
  e $0.63 \times 1000 = \Box$
  f $2.8 \div 100 = \Box$
  g $32.3 \times 100 = \Box$
  h $7480 \div 100 = \Box$

5 Copy and complete this bill.

100 rulers @ £0.42 each =	$\Box$
10 pencil sharpeners @ £2.32 each =	$\Box$
1000 rubbers @ £0.06 each =	$\Box$
10 biros @ £0.15 each =	$\Box$
10 calculators @ £8.97 each =	$\Box$
10 protractors @ £3.49 each =	$\Box$
Postage and packing =	£3.25
Total =	$\Box$

6 Write the lengths of each of these objects:

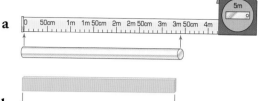

  a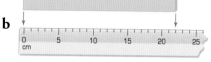

  b

7 **a** A climber travelled the following distances: 4.6 km, 1.95 km, 830 m, and 946 m.
    Find, in kilometres, the total distance travelled.
  b A plank of wood is 4.2 m long. It has the following lengths cut from it: 48 cm, 576 mm, 77 cm, 325 mm and 1.23 m.
    What length in millimetres remains?
  c Calculate the mass of 100 boxes, each weighing 47.5 kg.
    Give your answer in tonnes.
    (1 tonne = 1000kg)

8 **a** Convert these measurements into the units indicated.
    i $62 \text{ mm} = \Box\text{m}$
    ii $0.34 \text{ km} = \Box\text{mm}$
    iii $0.074 \text{ m} = \Box\text{cm}$
    iv $8780 \text{ mm} = \Box\text{km}$
  b Investigate how to convert from mm to km using just one calculation.

9 Calculate:
  a $\frac{3}{5}$ of 4 metres (giving your answer in m and cm)
  b $\frac{7}{10}$ of 12 cm (giving your answer in cm and mm)
  c $\frac{2}{3}$ of 372 mm (giving your answer in cm and mm)

This spread will show you how to:
- ▶▶ Know, or derive quickly, squares of numbers.
- ▶▶ Know and use the order of operations, including brackets.
- ▶▶ Relate fractions to division.

KEYWORDS

Brackets
Square
Order of operations

The decimal system is based on **powers** of 10:

$$10 = 10^1$$
$$100 = 10 \times 10 = 10^2 \quad \text{You can call this '10 squared'.}$$
$$1000 = 10 \times 10 \times 10 = 10^3 \quad \text{You can call this '10 cubed'.}$$

You can apply the same rules to other numbers:
2^3 means $2 \times 2 \times 2$, which equals 8.

Index is another word for power.

Note: 2^3 is **not** the same as $2 \times 3 = 6$.

A power or index is an **operator**. It tells you what to do to the number.
Other operators are $+$, $-$, $\times$ and $\div$.

When there are a lot of different operations you must do them in this order:

Work out $\qquad 3^2 + 4 \times (7 - 2)$

Brackets $\qquad = 3^2 + 4 \times 5$

Powers or indices $\qquad = 9 + 4 \times 5$

Multiplication or division $\quad = 9 + 20$

Addition or subtraction $\quad = 29$

All scientific calculators use this order of operations.
It is a mathematical convention.

You should perform a string of multiplications and divisions (or additions and subtractions) from left to right.

For example:
$$12 \div 6 \div 2 \qquad \text{and} \qquad 13 - 7 - 4$$
$$= 2 \div 2 = 1 \qquad\qquad\qquad\qquad = 6 - 4 = 2$$

You would not get the same answer if you did the $7 - 4$ first. Try it and see.

- ▶ You can write a division as a fraction: $\qquad 3 \div 4 = \frac{3}{4}$
- ▶ You do not always need to include brackets when writing a division in fractional form.

For example: $\qquad \dfrac{17 + 3}{2}$ is really $(17 + 3) \div 2$

Brackets $\qquad = 20 \div 2$

Division $\qquad = 10$

Both the 3 **and** the 17 are divided by 2.

Exercise N3.2

1 Calculate:

  a $2 + 3 \times 7$ **b** $(2 + 3) \times 7$

  c $4 \times 3 + 2 \times 5$ **d** $83 - 13 \times 4$

  e $7 + 16 \div 4$

2 Start with the box marked **Start**:

Start 27 $2 + 2 \times 4$	**T** 10 $8 - 3 \times 2$	**T** 8 $5 \times 7 + 6 \times 9$	**O** 12 $5 \times 2 + 7$
R 7 $37 - 4 \times 8$	**D** 26 $(5 - 2) \times 5$	**E** 18 $6 \times (9 - 7)$	**R** 60 $7 \times 8 - 9$
H 2 $2 \times (4 + 5)$	**T** 6 $64 \div (5 + 3)$	**S** 47 $9 \times (5 - 2)$	**M** 5 $(4 + 5) \times 8$
A 72 $48 \div (6 + 2)$	**E** 89 $4 \times (3 + 2) \times 3$	**R** 17 $3 \times 4 + 2 \times 7$	**E** 15 $11 \times 3 - 2 \times 13$

  ▶ Work out the answer to the question in the box.

  ▶ Find the box that has this answer.

  ▶ Write down the letter in this box.

  ▶ Work out the answer to the question in this box.

  ▶ Find the box that has this answer …

  Continue until you return to the Start box.

  ▶ What is the secret message?

3 **Puzzle**

Use the numbers 2, 5, 7 and 8 to make all the numbers from 1 to 30.

For example: $8 \div 2 \times 7 = 28$

  ▶ You may use each number only once in each calculation.

  ▶ Make sure you write all calculations in the correct order of operations.

4 Solve each of these calculations. You will need to decide whether to use a mental, written or calculator method.

  a $(47.3 + 52.7) \times 3$ **b** $13 \times 7 - 18 \times 9$

  c $3 \times 0.6 + 10 \times 0.4$ **d** $(3 + 4)^2 - 15 \times 9$

  e $47 - 10 \times 2.4$ **f** $(32 - 12) \times (47 - 5)$

  g $32 \div 8 \times 2$ **h** $\dfrac{6^2 + 8}{2^3 + 3}$

  i $3 \times 4^2 \div (3^2 \times 2 + 6) + 2$

5 Calculate the following, expressing your answers as mixed numbers where appropriate.

  a $\dfrac{6 \times 9}{4 \times 3}$

  b $\dfrac{4 + 3 \times 7}{18 - 5 \times 2}$

  c $\dfrac{5^2 - 6}{2^2 - 1}$

  d $\dfrac{5^2}{(37 - 13) \times 4 + 7 \times 3 + 8}$

6 **Puzzle**

The expression $4 \times 5 + 8 - 3 \times 7 + 1$ equals 8.

> **Check** this is true.

Find as many different answers as possible by putting brackets into the expression.

For example: $4 \times (5 + 8) - 3 \times 7 + 1 = 32$

7 Here are six numbers.

  30   6   5   12   50   3

Use these numbers to make a calculation that results in the target number.

For example: You can use three of the numbers to give a target number of 33.

$6 \times 5 + 3 = 33$

> You may only use each number once in each calculation.

  a Use three of the numbers to make a target number of 247.

  b Use four of the numbers to make a target number of 126.

  c Use five of the numbers to make a target number of 181.

  d Use all six numbers to make a target number of 18.

8 If $x = 2$, $y = 3$ and $t = 5$, calculate:

  a $3x$ **b** y^2 **c** xy **d** $3x + t$

This spread will show you how to:
- ▶▶ Understand addition, subtraction, multiplication and division as they apply to whole numbers and decimals.
- ▶▶ Consolidate and extend mental methods of calculation.

You can work out most multiplications in your head. Here are two useful strategies:

Partitioning

Multiplication is shorthand for repeated addition: $7 \times 5 = \underbrace{7 + 7}_{} + \underbrace{7 + 7 + 7}_{}$

You can use this idea to partition multiplications: $7 \times 5 = 7 \times 2 + 7 \times 3$

example

Use partitioning to work out mentally:

a 3.7×20 　　　　　　　 **b** 1.2×17

To find 3.7 × 20, split the 20 into 10 and 10 so it becomes 3.7 × 10 + 3.7 × 10.
This is just 37 + 37, which equals 74.

To find 1.2 × 17, split the 17 into 10 and 7 so it becomes 1.2 × 10 + 1.2 × 7.
This is just 12 + 8.4, which equals 20.4.

Doubling and halving

Some calculations are easier to do if you first double one of the numbers.
You later compensate by halving the answer.

example

Work out mentally:

a 2.7×50 　　　　　　　 **b** 5.5×8

a It is easier to × by 100: 2.7 × 100 = 270
Now halve the answer: 270 ÷ 2 = 135

b It is easier to × by 11: 　　11 × 8 = 88
Then halve the answer: 　　88 ÷ 2 = 44

Most people find divisions harder to do mentally. Here are two strategies that can help:

Inverse multiplication

Division is the inverse of multiplication:

$7 \times 5 = 35$ 　　　　 35 ÷ 5 = 7 and
35 ÷ 7 = 5

You can use this relationship to divide if you know the multiplication:

To find 8.4 ÷ 2.8. If you know 28 × 3 = 84
then you know 2.8 × 3 = 8.4
so 8.4 ÷ 2.8 = 3

Repeated subtraction

A division is a repeated subtraction: to find $143 \div 13$, subtract 13 until you reach zero.
143 – 130 – 13 = 0
143 – 10 × 13 – 1 × 13 = 0
143 – 11 × 13 = 0 so 143 ÷ 13 = 11

You only need to keep count of how many 13s you've taken away.

Exercise N3.3

1 Connect 4 Game

This is a game for two players.

▸ The First Player picks a Target Number from the board. Then they select a number from Group A and a number from Group B, which they estimate will make the Target Number when the two numbers are multipled together.

▸ Both players work out the multiplication.

▸ If the answer is the same as the Target Number, then the First Player can cover that number on the grid with a counter.

▸ Now it is the turn of the Second Player to select a Target Number, a number from Group A and a number from Group B.

The first player to get four counters in a line is the winner.

104	78	252	95	200	91
52	180	190	154	144	84
120	99	128	70	140	475
56	96	65	110	32	75
33	36	60	55	80	88
126	256	147	72	198	40

Group A	
1	2
3	4
5	6
7	8
9	10

Group B			
10	11	13	14
15	16	17	18
20	21	22	24
25	26	28	32
	95		

2 Calculate the following mentally. You may need to do some rough workings out.

a 7.4×11
b 16.5×9
c 3.7×19
d 1.64×50
e $308 \div 28$
f $153 \div 9$
g $126 \div 7$
h $352 \div 16$

3 Find the missing number in each of these calculations.

a $12 \times \square = 312$
b $1.1 \times \square = 30.8$
c $1.8 \times 7 = \square$
d $308 \div \square = 28$
e $357 \div 17 = \square$

4 a Copy and complete this diagram.

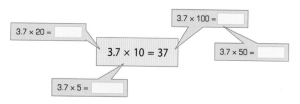

b Make up some more statements of your own and add them to the diagram.

5 Puzzle

Use the numbers in boxes A, B and C to make six different multiplications. You must use one number from Box A multiplied by one number from Box B to make an answer that is in Box C.

Box A   ×   Box B   =   Box C

Box A	Box B	Box C
3.4 2.2	3.6 2.7	39.6 37.4
11	12 17	35.2
5.1		40.8 45.9
16	11 9	43.2
3.2		

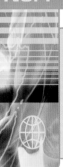

This spread will show you how to:

▶▶ Understand multiplication as it applies to whole numbers.

▶▶ Refine written methods of multiplication of whole numbers to ensure efficiency.

▶▶ Use rounding to approximate and judge whether an answer is of the right order of magnitude.

KEYWORDS

Approximate   Product
Round   Consecutive
Partition
Approximately equal to (≈)

When numbers are too difficult to multiply in your head you need to use a written method. Here are two written methods for multiplying numbers together.

Partitioning and the grid method
You can split up difficult multiplications by partitioning:

example

Work out 48×12

First approximate: $48 \times 12 \approx 50 \times 12 = 600$.
So the answer is just under 600.
48×12 can be split into $48 \times 10 +$ 48×2

You can split these further: $40 \times 10 + 8 \times 10 + 40 \times 2 + 8 \times 2$
Now work it out: $400 + 80 + 80 + 16 = 576$

Using a grid can help:

	40	8
10	40×10 = 400	8×10 = 80
2	40×2 = 80	8×2 = 16

$400 + 80 + 80 + 16$
$= 480 + 96 = 576$
This is called the grid method.

Standard method
Partitioning takes up a lot of space. Instead you could use the standard method:

You write 48×12 in columns:

```
              48
            × 12
Do 48 × 10:  480
Do 48 × 2:  + 96
Then add:    576
```

You should always approximate first so you know your answer is correct.

example

Work out 615×87 using the grid method and the standard method.

First approximate: $615 \times 87 \approx 600 \times 90 = 54\ 000$

Grid method:

	80	7
600	$600 \times 80 = 48\ 000$	$600 \times 7 = 4200$
10	$10 \times 80 = 800$	$10 \times 7 = 70$
5	$5 \times 80 = 400$	$5 \times 7 = 35$

$48\ 000 + 800 + 400 + 4200 + 70 + 35$
$= 49\ 200 + 4305$
$= 53\ 505$

Standard method:

```
                615
              ×  87
(× 80)        49 200
(× 7)        + 4 305
              53 505
```

Exercise N3.4

1 You may be able to do some of these questions mentally.
For others you will probably need to use a written method.
Calculate:

a 11×15 **b** 17×17
c 25×9 **d** 18×16
e 48×57 **f** 67×275

2 Copy and complete this diagram.

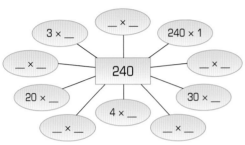

3 In each of these multiplication trails you must choose numbers, one from each row, which multiply together to give the target number.
For example:

3	6	8
9	7	2
13	11	18

| 231 |

In this trail, $3 \times 7 = 21$
$21 \times 11 = 231$

a

7	11	6
8	4	3
25	21	23

| 552 |

b

14	13	12
7	3	5
29	24	27

| 1134 |

c

5	8	4
12	9	6
34	32	28

| 1536 |

4 Find two consecutive numbers with a product of 756.

> **Remember:** Product means multiplication.

5 a Many products can be made with the digits 1, 2, 3 and 4.
For example: $23 \times 41 = 943$
$241 \times 3 = 723$
  i Find as many products as you can.
  ii Find the largest and the smallest product you can make with all four digits.
b Investigate all the products you can make with the digits 1, 2, 3, 4 and 5. Find the largest and the smallest product you can make.

6 a Sylvia orders 48 packets of crisps. Each packet costs 27p.
What is the total cost of the crisps?
b At Verybad Football Club the tickets cost £24 each. Last Saturday 378 people and two cats attended the match. If the cats got in for free, what was the total gate receipt?

7 In an arithmagon, the number in the squares is the product of the numbers in the circles on either side.
For example:

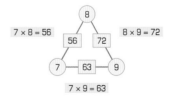

Find the missing numbers in these arithmagons.

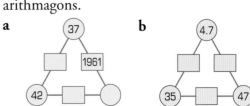

This spread will show you how to:

▶▶ Refine written methods of multiplication of whole numbers to ensure efficiency, and extend to decimals.

▶▶ Use rounding to approximate and judge whether the answer is of the right order of magnitude.

KEYWORDS
Decimal place
Approximately equal to ($\approx$)
Round   Approximate

You can multiply decimals on paper in the same way as whole numbers.

▶To multiply decimals you can either use the **grid method** or the **standard method**.

It is important to find an approximate answer first so you can check your answer.

example

Work out:

a 5.37×6
using the grid method and the standard method.

b 326.4×5

a Approximate: $5.37 \times 6 \approx 5 \times 6 = 30$

Grid method

$6 \times 5 =$	$6 \times 0.3 =$	$6 \times 0.07 =$
30	1.8	0.42

5.37×6
$= 5 \times 6 + 0.3 \times 6 + 0.07 \times 6$
$= 30 + 1.8 + 0.42$
$= 32.22$

Standard method

$$\begin{array}{r} 5.37 \\ \times\ 6 \\ \hline \end{array}$$

$\begin{array}{ll} 0.07 \times 6 & 0.42 \\ 0.3 \times 6 & 1.8 \\ 5 \times 6 & +30.0 \\ \hline & 32.22 \end{array}$

$5.37 \times 6 = 32.22$

b Approximate: $326.4 \times 5 \approx 300 \times 5 = 1500$

Grid method

$5 \times 300 =$	$5 \times 20 =$	$5 \times 6 =$	$5 \times 0.4 =$
1500	100	30	2

326.4×5
$= 300 \times 5 + 20 \times 5 + 6 \times 5 + 0.4 \times 5$
$= 1500 + 100 + 30 + 2$
$= 1632$

Standard method

$$\begin{array}{r} 326.4 \\ \times\ 5 \\ \hline \end{array}$$

$\begin{array}{ll} 0.4 \times 5 & 2.0 \\ 6 \times 5 & 30.0 \\ 20 \times 5 & 100.0 \\ 300 \times 5 & +1500.0 \\ \hline & 1632 \end{array}$

$326.4 \times 5 = 1632$

Exercise N3.5

1 Calculate the following. You may be able to do some of these questions mentally. For others you will probably need to use a written method.
   a 17×11 **b** 0.6×9 **c** 0.7×15
   d 1.4×7 **e** 2.3×12 **f** 3.7×15

2 **a** Copy and complete this × grid.

×	0.1	0.7	1.7	2.5
9				
17				
32				
170				
0.6				

   b Explain how you multiply by 1.7.

3 In each multiplication trail you must identify the numbers that multiply to give the target number.
   For example: $12 \times 0.7 \times 3 = 25.2$:

9	12	14
0.7	0.4	0.6
3	5	2

25.2

a

0.4	0.5	0.8
11	7	9
13	15	17

95.2

b

1.3	1.1	1.2
10	9	8
7	6	5

58.5

4 **a** Find two numbers, one of which is a whole number, whose sum is 30.3 and whose product is 167.9.
   b Explain your strategy for solving this problem.

5 Calculate the following.
   a 4.27×5 **b** 3.82×7 **c** 9.64×8
   d 28.6×19 **e** 183.7×8 **f** 247.8×7

6 **a** A new steel radial tyre for a Golf Gti costs £46.35. What is the cost of replacing all four tyres?
   b The distance around a racing track is 1.84 km. What is the total distance travelled for 23 laps of this track?
   c Calculate the cost of eight gallons of petrol at £3.64 per gallon.

7 At Rent-a-Car, a car can be hired in two ways:
   Method A – a fixed charge of £49.50 per day for unlimited mileage.
   Method B – £19.50 per day plus £0.48 per mile.
   a At which mileage does it become cheaper to pay using Method A?
   b Explain your strategy for solving this problem.

8 Calculate the missing number in each of these equations.
   a $7.28 \times \square = 174.72$
   b $423.6 \times \square = 16\ 096.8$

9 **Investigation: Splitting 11**
   a Find a set of numbers that adds up to make 11.
   b Multiply these numbers together to find their product.
   For example:
   $7 + 4 = 11$ $7 \times 4 = 28$
   $10.5 + 0.5 = 11$ $10.5 \times 0.5 = 5.25$
   c Find the set of numbers with a sum of 11 that have the largest product.
   d Investigate the largest product for other starting numbers.

This spread will show you how to:
- ▸▸ Understand division as it applies to whole numbers.
- ▸▸ Refine written methods of division of whole numbers to ensure efficiency.
- ▸▸ Use rounding to approximate and judge whether the answer is of the right order of magnitude.

KEYWORDS

Divide	Multiple
Subtraction	Remainder
Approximate	Quotient
Divisor	

This is a division:

$$20 \div 4 = 5$$

These are the names for each part of the division: dividend   divisor   quotient

You use division when you share something.

Peter wants to share his chocolate between his 4 friends.
He divides it into equal pieces.
$32 \div 4 = 8$
They get 8 pieces each.

You can also think of division as grouping.

There are 32 people in the class.
They get into groups of 4.
$32 \div 4 = 8$
There are 8 groups altogether.

Grouping can help you work out quite difficult divisions on paper.

Repeated subtraction method
In this method you subtract multiples of the divisor until you can't subtract any more.

example

Work out:

a $216 \div 9$ **b** $884 \div 26$

First approximate: $\approx 220 \div 10 = 22$ $\approx 900 \div 30 = 30$

Then calculate:

$$
\begin{array}{r}
9\overline{)216} \\
-180 \\
\hline
36 \\
-36 \\
\hline
0
\end{array}
$$
  9×20

  9×4

$9 \times 24 = 216$
so $216 \div 9 = 24$

$$
\begin{array}{r}
26\overline{)884} \\
-780 \\
\hline
104 \\
-104 \\
\hline
0
\end{array}
$$
  26×30

  26×4

$26 \times 34 = 884$
so $884 \div 26 = 34$

Exercise N3.6

1 Calculate the following. You may be able to do some of these questions mentally.

    a $24 \div 8$ **b** $72 \div 9$ **c** $55 \div 11$

    d $84 \div 7$ **e** $102 \div 6$ **f** $184 \div 8$

2 Investigation

Example

   ▶ Start with the number 432.

   ▶ Form all the 2-digit numbers you can:

      43   42   34   32   23   24

   ▶ Add together all the 2-digit numbers:

      $43 + 42 + 34 + 32 + 23 + 24 = 198$

   ▶ Divide the total by the sum of the **three** digits: $4 + 3 + 2 = 9$

      $198 \div 9 = \square$

   ▶ Write down the answer.

Activity

Repeat for different 3-digit numbers. Write down what you notice.

3 Identify which of these 10 numbers are multiples of:

    a 17   **b** 28   **c** 31.

442	2325
589	961
1054	2604
644	1785
2576	7378

The multiples of 17 are:
17×1, 17×2, 17×3, 17×4 …

4 Calculate the following.

    a $598 \div 23$ **b** $589 \div 32$

    c $1134 \div 27$ **d** $1330 \div 51$

    e $2350 \div 76$ **f** $1654 \div 61$

5 a Shagufta is packing oranges into boxes. Each box holds exactly the same number of oranges. She has 2800 oranges, and she packs 62 boxes. How many oranges are left over?

    b Tintin the turtle has been alive for 8132 weeks. How old is Tintin in years?

6 Game: Remainder Max (2 players)

The object of the game is to have the largest remainder.

   ▶ Each player takes it in turns to choose one number from Box A and one number from Box B. (Numbers can only be chosen once.)

Box A	Box B
2400	36
1650	32
2200	73
2150	89
1750	86
1700	41

   ▶ The number in Box A must be divided by the number in Box B.

   ▶ The player scores the value of the remainder.

   ▶ After three turns each the player with the highest total remainder is the winner.

7 What number am I?

Clue 1: *I lie between 1 and 400.*

Clue 2: *When I am divided by 61, the remainder is 24.*

Clue 3: *When I am divided by 2, the remainder is zero.*

Clue 4: *When I am divided by 15, the remainder is 13.*

8 Calculate the value of a single item in each case.

    a Seven golf balls at £19.60 total.

    b A 1015 ml bottle just fills 7 glasses.

    c Twelve coins weigh 924 g.

    d Nine salad rolls cost £10.71.

    e A 360 g packet of chocolate is divided into 24 pieces.

N3.7 Dividing with remainders

This spread will show you how to:
- ▶▶ Refine written methods of division of whole numbers to ensure efficiency, and extend to decimals.
- ▶▶ Round decimals to the nearest whole number or to one decimal place.
- ▶▶ Relate fractions to division.

KEYWORDS

Decimal place
Fraction   Approximate
Remainder   Divide

When you divide a number there is sometimes a remainder left over.
You can write remainders as whole numbers, fractions or decimals.

---

example

Work out $117 \div 5$ as:

a whole number   **b** a fraction   **c** a decimal

a First approximate:
$\approx 120 \div 5 = 24$
Then calculate:
$$5\overline{)117}$$
$$\begin{array}{r} -100 \quad 5 \times 20 \\ \hline 17 \\ -15 \quad 5 \times 3 \\ \hline 2 \end{array}$$

$5 \times 23 = 115$
so $117 \div 5 = 23$ remainder 2

b From **a**, $117 \div 5 = 23$ rem 2
You are grouping in 5s so 2 out of 5, or $\frac{2}{5}$, is left over.
So $117 \div 5 = \frac{117}{5} = 23\frac{2}{5}$

c $117 \div 5$:
$$5\overline{)117}$$
$$\begin{array}{r} -100 \quad 5 \times 20 \\ \hline 17 \\ -15 \quad 5 \times 3 \\ \hline 2 \\ -2 \quad 5 \times 0.4 \\ \hline 0 \end{array}$$

So $117 \div 5 = 23.4$

You can use repeated subtraction to divide decimals.

---

example

Calculate $140.4 \div 9$

First approximate: $\approx 140 \div 10 = 14$
Then calculate:
$$9\overline{)140.4}$$
$$\begin{array}{r} -90 \quad\quad 9 \times 10 \\ \hline 50.4 \\ -45.0 \quad\quad 9 \times 5 \\ \hline 5.4 \\ -5.4 \quad\quad 9 \times 0.6 \\ \hline 0.0 \end{array}$$

$9 \times 15.6 = 140.4$

so $140.4 \div 9 = 15.6$

Remember to always approximate the answer first as it is easy to make mistakes!

Think of the 9 times table:
$9 \times 6 = 54$
so $9 \times 0.6 = 5.4$

Exercise N3.7

1 Calculate the following. You may be able to do some of these questions mentally. You should use a written method for the others.

   a $12.6 \div 2$ **b** $7.4 \div 2$
   c $17.2 \div 10$ **d** $22.1 \div 5$
   e $11.2 \div 4$ **f** $7.6 \div 5$
   g $5.4 \div 9$ **h** $7.2 \div 8$

2 In this number tree the answer to the divisions is always 4.8.

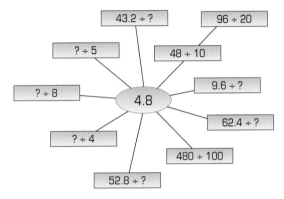

   a Complete the tree by finding the missing numbers.
   b Design your own division diagram for 13.7.

3 Work out all these divisions, and then rearrange them in order from lowest to highest to discover a famous character.

   P: $73.5 \div 5$ R: $160.2 \div 6$
   M: $891 \div 27$ A: $756 \div 21$
   E: $138.4 \div 8$ U: $624 \div 48$
   N: $292.6 \div 7$ S: $34.2 \div 9$

4 Calculate the following, leaving the remainder as shown in brackets.

   a $115.2 \div 9$ (decimal)
   b $294 \div 35$ (fraction)
   c $300 \div 23$ (whole number)
   d $123.2 \div 7$ (decimal)

5 In these calculations, you will need to decide how to leave the remainder.

   a Alan has 138 CDs. He stacks them in groups of 15. How many groups of CDs can he make?
   b Billie-Jo buys 15 CDs at the same price. The total cost is £138. What is the cost of each CD?
   c Chanelle has 138 cakes which she shares equally between 15 guests at her party. How many cakes does each person receive?
   d Davina has completed 138 laps of her race. Each 15 laps takes her one hour to complete. For how long has she been competing in the race?

6 Edwina is buying conifers at the garden centre. She sees this notice:

Pack of 6 conifers £45.60
Pack of 25 conifers £185

   Which is better value for money? Explain your answer.

7 Calculate the following.

   a $1012 \div 40$
   b $\frac{738}{80}$ expressed as a mixed number
   c $30 \times \square = 2439$
   d The amount won by each person in a syndicate of 28 people sharing a prize of £34 566.
   e The number of journeys a ski lift will take to transport 2870 people, if the maximum load per journey is 52 people.
      i How many people will ride up in the last journey?
     ii How many people will already be at the top of the mountain, before the last lift journey arrives?

This spread will show you how to:

▶▶ Carry out more complicated calculations using the facilities on a calculator.

▶▶ Interpret the display on a calculator in different contexts.

KEYWORDS

Display   Memory

Brackets   Interpret

You can use a calculator to do difficult calculations – always approximate first.

Use these examples to check you know how your calculator works.
You should ensure that your calculator uses the correct order of operations.

The examples use a Casio *fx* 82 scientific calculator.

---

example

Calculate $496 \div (12 + 8.4)$

a   using brackets

b   using the memory keys

---

a   First approximate:
$\approx 500 \div 20 = 25$

Input: $496 \div (12 + 8.4) =$
The output should be: 24.31

b   Input: $12 + 8.4 =$ ⎯⎯⎯⎯⎯ | Calculate the brackets |
The answer should be: 20.4
Input: M+ ⎯⎯⎯ | This puts your answer in the memory |
Input: C ⎯⎯⎯ | This clears the screen |
Input: $496 \div$ MR
The output should be: 24.31

In the example, the output is the answer. This is not always the case.

▶ **When you use your calculator you must interpret the output to find the answer.**

---

example

a 1314 m of cable is cut into 15 pieces.
How long is each piece?

b A jackpot of £1314 is shared between 15 winners. How much does each winner receive?

c William sleeps 1314 hours in 15 weeks. How much does he sleep each week?

Each question uses the same calculation.   Input: $1314 \div 15 =$ Output: 87.6
You need to interpret the output in each case:

a 87.6 m means
87 m and 0.6 m.
1 m = 100 cm
0.6 m = (0.6 × 100) cm
= 60 cm
So 87.6 m is
87 m and 60 cm.

b £87.6 means
£87 and £0.6.
£1 = 100p
£0.6 = (0.6 × 100)p
= 60p
So £87.6 is £87 and 60p.

c 87.6 hours means
87 hours and 0.6 hours.
1 hour = 60 mins
0.6 hour = (0.6 × 60) mins
= 36 mins
So 87.6 hours is
87 hours and 36 mins.

Exercise N3.8

1 For each question, show clearly whether you used a mental, written, or calculator method.
Calculate:
  a $(7.3 + 2.7) \times 4.3$ **b** $12 \times 9 - 13 \times 7$
  c $38.4 \div (2.9 + 3.5)$
  d $(2.7 + 8.5)^2 - 12.93$
  e $\dfrac{4.2 + 6.4 \times 8}{18 - 7 \times 2}$
  f $243.86 \div (4.8 + 2.6 + 1.5)$
  g $140.4 \div (3.7 + 2.7 + 2.6)$
  h $\dfrac{6.64 \times 3.7}{37}$ **i** $\dfrac{3.8^2 + 6}{5^2}$
  j $4003.7 - 2998.7$
  k $4^2 + 5^2 \div (3 + 6)$

2 Solve each of the following.
You may need to use a calculator.
  a 12 jars of coffee cost £21.60.
    How much does each jar cost?
  b i In the triple-jump competition, Michael jumped 14.23 m, 14.78 m, 14.43 m, 14.37 m, 14.62 m and 13.97 m.
    What was his mean jump?
  ii How many centimetres below 15 m was his mean jump?

3 a Simon paid £5.45 for printing his book, including its cover.
    The cover cost £1.10.
    Each page cost 3p.
    How many pages were in the book?
  b An apple weighs 240 g.
    Apples cost £1.50 per kg.
    How much does one apple cost?

4 Convert these times into hours and minutes.
  a 16.6 hours
  b 8.45 hours
  c $3\frac{2}{5}$ hours

5 Here are six numbers:
27 5 50 1.2 11.8 22.5
Use these numbers to make a calculation which gives the target number as its answer.
For example: target number = 251.2
Calculation = $5 \times 50 + 1.2$
  a Use two of the numbers to make a target number of 13.
  b Use three of the numbers to make a target number of 12.
  c Use four of the numbers to make a target number of 10.
  d Use five of the numbers to make a target number of 355.

6 **Investigation**
$25 \div 7 = 3$ remainder 4
However, when I do this on my calculator the answer is 3.571428571.
Investigate.

7 **Puzzle**
This activity works best in pairs.
  a Pass the calculator to your friend.
    Ask them to:

  ▸ Key in their age   *for example 13*
  ▸ Multiply it by 25   *325*
  ▸ Add 36   *361*
  ▸ Multiply by 4   *1444*
  ▸ Add the number of the month of their birth (Jan = 1, Feb = 2 ...)
    if March then 3 + 1444 =   1447

Take back the calculator.
Subtract 144   *1303*

The first two digits give their age

The second two digits give their month of birth

  b Investigate this puzzle.

You should know how to ...

1 Know and use the order of operations including brackets.

2 Extend mental methods of calculation; multiply and divide 3-digit by 2-digit whole numbers; extend to multiplying and dividing decimals with one or two places.

3 Check a result by considering whether it is the correct order of magnitude.

4 Convert one metric unit to another; read and interpret scales on a range of measuring instruments.

5 Break a complex calculation into simpler steps, choosing and using appropriate and efficient operations, methods and resources.

Check out

1 Identify which of these statements are true and which are false:
  a $7 + 2 \times 3 = 27$
  b $3 \times 8 - 2 \times 7 = 10$
  c $14 \div 2 + 5 \times 6 = 12$
  For each of the false statements, use brackets to make the statement true.

2 For each question, clearly show whether you use a mental or written method.
  Calculate:
  a 7.3×20 b 17.2×7
  c 3.64×8 d 128×29
  e $1374 \div 29$ f $16.4 \div 10$
  g $8.1 \div 9$ h $120.6 \div 9$

3 Use an approximation to check each of your answers in question 2.

4 a Convert these measurements:
      i   48 mm to cm
      ii 0.6 m to mm
      iii 42 840 mm to km
  b Read these measurements:
      i
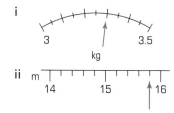
      ii

5 Work out the missing operation in each of these questions:
  a $1725 \boxed{?} 25 = 69$
  b $69 \boxed{?} 250 = 319$
  c $319 \boxed{?} 46 = 273$
  d $273 \boxed{?} 21 = 13$

This unit will show you how to:

▶▶ Recognise and use multiples, factors, common factors and primes.

▶▶ Recognise the first few triangular numbers, squares of numbers to at least 12 × 12, and the corresponding roots.

▶▶ Generate sequences from practical contexts and describe the general term in simple cases.

▶▶ Express simple functions in words, then using symbols.

▶▶ Represent functions in mappings.

▶▶ Generate coordinate pairs that satisfy a simple linear rule.

▶▶ Plot the graphs of simple linear functions, where y is given explicitly in terms of x.

▶▶ Solve word problems and investigate in the context of algebra,

▶▶ Represent problems mathematically, making correct use of symbols, words, tables and graphs.

I predict that by 2020 we will have doubled in size. Any comments?

Expel all the boys!

No, all the girls!

Move to another building!

Graphs provide an effective way of showing information.

Before you start

You should know how to ...

1 Plot points on a coordinate grid.

2 Use function machines to generate sequences.

Check in

1 Draw a grid from ⁻5 to 5 in both directions. Plot these points on your grid and join them up. What did you notice? Explain any pattern.

(3, 1) (3, 4) (3, ⁻1) (3, ⁻4) (3, 2)

2 Input the numbers 1 to 5 into this function machine.

Write the output values in a sequence:

—, —, —, —, —

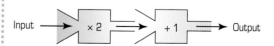

Input ⟶ × 2 ⟶ + 1 ⟶ Output

Factors and multiples

This spread will show you how to:
- ▶▶ Explore links between factors, primes and multiples.
- ▶▶ Find the factors of a number.

KEYWORDS

Product   Prime

Multiple   Square

Factor   Area

You multiply two or more numbers together to find their **product**.
The product of 2 and 7 is 14: $2 \times 7 = 14$ and $7 \times 2 = 14$

14 is a **multiple** of 2 and is also a multiple of 7.

▶ A multiple of a number n is $n \times$ any whole number.

> **example**
>
> Write down three multiples of 4.
>
> $4 \times 1 = 4$ $4 \times 2 = 8$ $4 \times 3 = 12$
> So 4, 8 and 12 are all multiples of 4.   12 is a multiple of 4 and 3. 4 and 3 are **factors** of 12.

▶ Any whole number can be written as the product of two **factors**.

There is often more than one way of writing a number as a product of factors.
For example: $18 = 6 \times 3$ and $18 = 9 \times 2$ and $18 = 18 \times 1$

▶ **You can list all the factor pairs of a number ...**
The factor pairs of 15 are:
$1 \times 15, 3 \times 5, 5 \times 3, 15 \times 1$

... or you can write the factors in a list:
15 has four factors: 1, 3, 5 and 15.

You can think of factor pairs as rectangles:

```
       5
   ┌────────┐
 3 │        │
   └────────┘
```

The area is the product.

▶ If there are only two factors, the number is a **prime** number.
$5 = 5 \times 1$ and $5 = 1 \times 5$ so 5 is a prime number.

▶ A **square** number has an odd number of factors.
9 is a square number – it has three factors: 1, 3 and 9.

> **example**
>
> Which of these numbers is:
> **a** prime **b** square **c** a multiple of 3?
> **1**   **6**   **11**   **16**   **21**
> **d** List the factors for each number.
>
> You can draw a square number as a square.
>
> ```
>        4
>    ┌──────┐
>  4 │      │
>    └──────┘
> ```
> Area =
> $4^2 = 4 \times 4$
> $= 16$
>
> **a** 11 is prime as it has two factors.
> **b** 1 and 16 are square as they have an odd number of factors.
> **c** 6 and 21 are multiples of 3 as they have 3 as a factor.
> **d** 1: 1   6: 1, 2, 3, 6   11: 1, 11   16: 1, 2, 4, 8, 16   21: 1, 3, 7, 21

Exercise A3.1

Questions 1 to 6 are about factor-pillars.

Factor-pillars are like caterpillars except they have numbers on their segments and factors on their legs.

Here is the factor-pillar for 18:

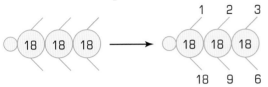

18 has three segments on the factor-pillar.
18 has three factor pairs: 1 × 18, 2 × 9, 3 × 6

In questions 1 to 3:
▶ complete the factor-pillars
▶ list the factor pairs

1

2

3
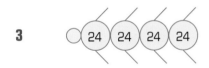

4 Draw factor-pillars for:
   a 30   **b** 21   **c** 36

5 a Make a different factor-pillar that is four segments long.
   b Make a factor-pillar with five segments.

6 Can you make a factor-pillar with only one segment?
What is the special name for this type of number?

Questions 7 to 11 are about factor-spiders. Here is an example:

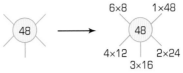

48 makes a five-legged spider with factors 1, 48, 2, 24, 3, 16, 4, 12, 6, 8.

Complete the factor-spiders in questions 7 to 9.

10 Find a number that will make a one-legged factor-spider. What type of number is this?

11 Find a number that will make a four-legged factor-spider.

12 Find the factors for each of these numbers:
   a i 12   **ii** 7   **iii** 9   **iv** 4
   v 13   **vi** 25   **vii** 23   **viii** 27
   b Which of the numbers are prime?
   c List all of the prime numbers less than 30.
   d There are three square numbers, how many factors have each of these?
   e List the multiples of 3.

13 List all the square numbers up to 12 × 12. How many different factors does each one have?

14 By finding the factor pairs for each number, find the value of each letter.
   a 42 = 1 × a; b × 21; 3 × c; 6 × d
   b 60 = 1 × g; 2 × h; i × j; 4 × k;
          5 × l; m × 10
   c 35 = 1 × n; p × q

This spread will show you how to:
▶▶ Recognise squares and corresponding roots.
▶▶ Recognise triangular numbers.
▶▶ Generate and describe simple integer sequences.

KEYWORDS

Square   Factor
Square root   Sequence
Triangular number

The number 36 has lots of factors:
1, 2, 3, 4, 6, 9, 12, 18, 36

You can describe 36 in many different ways.
These drawings show you three ways:

Challenge
360 has a lot of factors – that's why the circle is split into 360 degrees.
You know 36 has 9 factors. Does that mean 360 has 90 factors?

Square number

Rectangular number

Triangular number

The **square root** of 36 is the length of a side: 6.

Every number can be drawn as a rectangle.

36 is the 8th triangular number.

▶ A square number can be drawn as a square.
  The square root is the length of one side.

Here are the first four square numbers:

1st   2nd   3rd   4th

1   4   9   16

You can use the √ key on your calculator:
$\sqrt{81} = 9$
So 81 is the 9th square number.

▶ A triangular number can be drawn as an isosceles right-angled triangle.

Here are the first four triangular numbers:

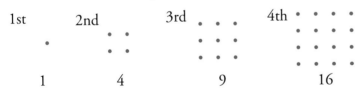

1st   2nd   3rd   4th

1   3   6   10

The patterns make isosceles right-angled triangles:
two equal sides and a 90° angle.

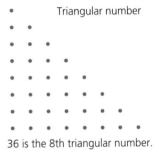

▶ The square numbers and the triangular numbers form sequences.
  You can write the sequences using patterns or numbers.

Exercise A3.2

1 a Using dots draw the next four square numbers.

     1   4   9

b Copy and complete this table for square numbers:

Position	1	2	3	4	5	6	7	8
Square number		4						

c Look at the difference between consecutive square numbers.
Explain the pattern of differences.

d Use this rule to predict the values for 9^2 and 10^2.

e $15^2 = 15 \times 15 = 225$. Does this agree with your pattern?

2 a Here are dot diagrams for the first four triangular numbers.

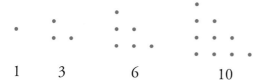

  1   3   6   10

Using dots, draw the next three triangular numbers.

b i Copy and complete this table for triangular numbers:

Position	1st	2nd	3rd	4th	5th	6th	7th	8th	9th
Triangular number									

  ii Explain how the size of each triangular number is increasing.

  iii Work out what the value is for the 10th triangular number.

  iv Use this pattern to see if 100 is a triangular number.

3 Here is a function machine to find triangular numbers.

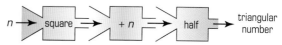

An input of 8 gives an output of 36:

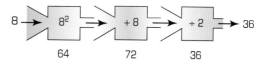

The 8th triangular number is 36.

Use the function machine to find:
a the 5th triangular number ($n = 5$)
b the 9th triangular number ($n = 9$)
c the 12th triangular number ($n = 12$)
d the xth triangular number ($n = x$)

4 Complete this function machine to change 49 to 7 (you must not use any of the four operations $+ - \times \div$).

5 You can use a calculator to find square roots.
To find $\sqrt{49}$ press 49 $\boxed{\sqrt{}}$ $\boxed{=}$
*The display should show 7.
a Using a calculator, find the square root of each of these numbers:
  i 92.16 **ii** 33.9889 **iii** 412.09
  iv 4.5796 **v** 62.41
b Look at your answers. Which answer is nearest to:
  i the number in a pair
  ii the number of mm in 1 cm
  iii the number of ounces in $\frac{1}{2}$ pound
  iv the number of halves in 3
  v a score?
*(Your calculator may work differently to this.)

The general term

This spread will show you how to:

▶▶ Generate a sequence given a rule for finding each term from its position in a sequence.

▶▶ Begin to find a rule for the *n*th term of some simple sequences.

Here is a sequence of dot patterns:

Pattern number →	1	2	3	4
Number of dots →	3	5	7	9

To **predict** the number of dots needed for the 123rd pattern you could:

▶ Draw 123 diagrams.
▶ Find a way of linking the pattern number with the number of dots.

Linking the pattern number to the actual value is called a **position-to-term rule**.

You can see that the sequence grows by 2 each time.
Another sequence that grows by 2 each time is the sequence of multiples of 2.
Compare the sequences:

Multiples of 2:　 2,　 4,　 6,　 8 ⎱
Number of dots:　 3,　 5,　 7,　 9 ⎰　 add 1

This table shows you how the pattern number and number of dots are linked:

Pattern or term number	1	2	3	4
Number of dots	3	5	7	9
Multiples of 2	2	4	6	8
Multiples of 2 + 1	2 + 1 = 3	4 + 1 = 5	6 + 1 = 7	8 + 1 = 9
Link	1 × 2 + 1	2 × 2 + 1	3 × 2 + 1	4 × 2 + 1

The general rule is: number of dots = pattern number × 2 + 1.

For the 5th pattern or term you would need 5 × 2 + 1 = 11 dots.
Check by drawing a diagram:

For the 123rd term you would need 123 × 2 + 1 = 246 + 1 = 247 dots.

For the *n*th term you would need $n \times 2 + 1$ dots.
You write this expression as $2n + 1$.

$2n + 1$ represents the 2 needed for each extra pattern plus the 1 from the first pattern.

This one was there from the first pattern, giving the +1.

Exercise A3.3

1 For each sequence:

A

B

  a Draw the next two patterns.
  b Complete the table and predict the results for the next pattern.

Pattern number	1	2	3	4	5	6
Number of counters						

  c Explain in words how the pattern is developing.
  d Predict the number of counters in the 10th pattern and in the nth pattern.

2 Draw the next four patterns and the table of results for patterns 1 to 5 for each sequence. You are given the first pattern and the rule for the nth pattern.

  A   1st pattern

Counters in nth pattern $= 5n$

  B   1st pattern

Counters in nth pattern $= 2n - 1$

3 In this question you are given the table of results and the first pattern for two sequences. For each sequence:
  a Draw the next three patterns.
  b Explain in words how the pattern is developing.
  c Explain how to find the number of counters for the nth pattern.

Sequence A

Pattern number	1	2	3	4	5	...	n
Number of counters	3	6	9	12	15	...	

1st pattern

Sequence B

Pattern number	1	2	3	4	5	...	n
Number of counters	5	7	9	11	13	...	

1st pattern

4 **Challenge**
  ▶ Here are the rules and the first pattern for six sequences.
  ▶ Match the rule with the first pattern and draw the next two patterns in each sequence.

$3n - 1$
$6n - 2$
$3n$
$2n + 5$
$2n + 3$
$n + 5$

This spread will show you how to:
▶▶ Express simple functions at first in words then using symbols.
▶▶ Draw simple mapping diagrams.
▶▶ Begin to find a simple rule for the *n*th term.

KEYWORDS

Function   Equation
Mapping   Equals (=)
                    *n*th term

Here is a function machine.
When you input the counting numbers: 1, 2, 3 ...   the output numbers form a sequence.

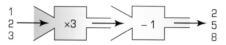

You can put the information in a table: or use a mapping diagram:

Input	1	2	3
Output	2	5	8

1 ──────▶ 2
2 ──────▶ 5
3 ──────▶ 8

The *n*th term of a sequence describes the general rule for the sequence.

You find the *n*th term when you input *n*:

n ─▶ ×3 ─▶ $3n$ ─ 1 ─▶ $3n-1$

$n \times 3 - 1$ is $3n - 1$

You can write the general rule for a sequence in different ways:

Using words: input × 3 − 1 = output
Using algebra: as a **mapping**, the general rule is $n \rightarrow 3n - 1$, where *n* is the input
                        as an **equation**, $y = 3x - 1$,   where *x* is the input and *y* is the output

▶ An equation links two or more expressions using an equals (=) sign.

example

Find the missing function and express the general rule as a mapping and as an equation.

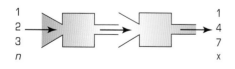

The outputs go up in 3s so the rule will include × 3
The first term is × 3 then −2
Check with the other terms: 2 × 3 − 2 and 3 × 3 − 2
The functions are × 3 and −2
The mapping is $n \rightarrow 3n - 2$
The equation is $y = 3x - 2$

Exercise A3.4

1 In these questions work out:

▶ the function machine rule and
▶ an equation for *y* in terms of *x*.

The first question has been done for you.

a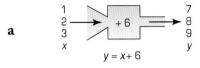

$$y = x + 6$$

b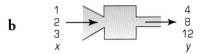

c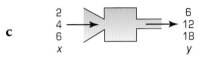

d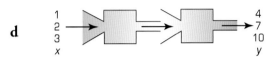

e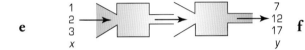

f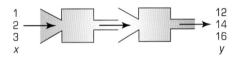

2 In these questions use the function machines to work out the output and then transfer your results into a table. The first question has been started for you.

a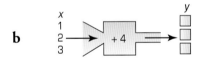

x	1	2	3
y = 6*x*		12	

b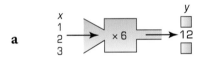

x	1	2	3
y =			

c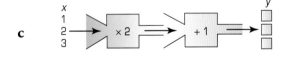

x	1	2	3
y = 2*x* + 1			

d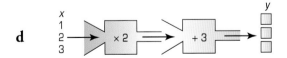

x	1	2	3
y =			

e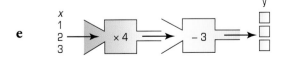

x	1	2	3
y =			

This spread will show you how to:
- ▶▶ Generate and plot pairs of coordinates that satisfy a simple linear relationship.
- ▶▶ Begin to consider the features of graphs of simple linear functions.

KEYWORDS
Coordinates   Relationship
Value   Equation
Coordinate pair

The input and output values of a function machine form a pair of values:

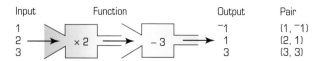

Input	Function	Output	Pair
1		¯1	(1, ¯1)
2	× 2 – 3	1	(2, 1)
3		3	(3, 3)

You can plot these pairs of values on a coordinate grid.
The input is the *x* value and the output is the *y* value.

The points lie in a straight line so the relationship is **linear**.

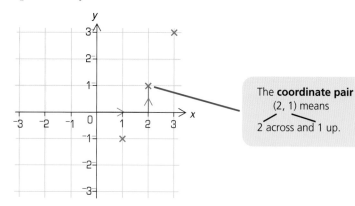

The **coordinate pair** (2, 1) means

2 across and 1 up.

▶ A linear function forms a straight line on a coordinate grid.

You can continue the line to predict an output for any given input value.
When the input or *x* value is 5, the output or *y* value is 7: (5, 7) is a point on the line.

▶ You can express a linear relationship using algebra.

The relationship or equation of the line above is $y = 2x - 3$.

The input is *x* and the output is *y*.

Plot the points (¯1, 2) (0, 3) (1, 4) (2, 5) (4, 7)
Write down the equation of the line they form.

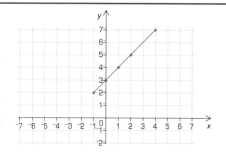

The points form a line.
y is 3 more than *x* for each coordinate pair.
The equation is $y = x + 3$

Exercise A3.5

1 You need a large coordinate grid and counters.

You can copy this grid on squared paper:

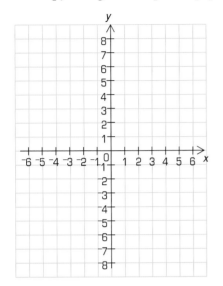

a i On your grid, place five counters where the *y* coordinate is one greater than the *x* coordinate.

ii Sketch the result and write down the five coordinate pairs.

iii Write this as an equation where *y* is one more than *x*.

Repeat part **a** for these questions:

b Where the *y* coordinate is double the *x* coordinate.

c Where the *y* coordinate is 2 less than the *x* coordinate.

d Where the *y* coordinate is one more than double the *x* coordinate.

e Where the *y* coordinate is 3 times the *x* coordinate.

2 Here are four coordinate grids with counters marked on each.

▶ Write down the coordinate pairs and explain how the *y* coordinate is related to the *x* coordinate in each question.

▶ Write this as an equation.

a 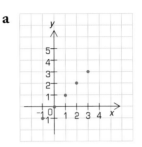 **b**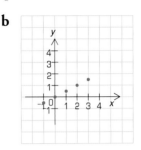

c 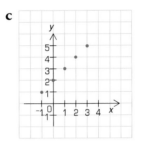 **d**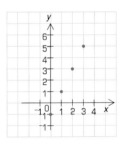

3 a Copy and complete this table of results for the equation $y = x + 4$:

x	⁻1	0	1	2	3
y = x + 4	3		5		

b Write down the coordinate pairs from the table:

($^-$1, 3); (0,); (1); (2,); (3,)

c Plot these points on a coordinate grid. (All of the points lie on the line $y = x + 4$.)

This spread will show you how to:
▶▶ Begin to consider the features of graphs of simple linear functions.
▶▶ Recognise that equations of the form $y = mx$ correspond to straight-line graphs through the origin.

KEYWORDS

Coordinates   Value
Equation   Graph
Straight-line graph

Here are six different straight-line graphs and six equations.

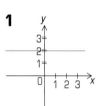 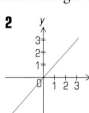 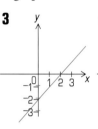  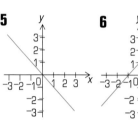

1 **2** **3** **4** **5** **6**

a $y = x$ b $y = {}^-x$ c $y = x + 1$ d $y = x - 2$ e $y = 2$ f $x = 1$

You can match up the graph with its equation.
Using a table of values will help you find the right graph.
In a table of values:

Sometimes you need to use y values – see $x = 1$ below.

▶ Use $x = 1$, $x = 2$ and $x = 3$ and find the corresponding y values.
▶ The resulting pairs are coordinates on the graph.

For $y = x$

x	1	2	3
y	1	2	3
Coordinates	(1, 1)	(2, 2)	(3, 3)

For $y = x - 2$

x	1	2	3
y	$^-1$	0	1
Coordinates	(1, $^-1$)	(2, 0)	(3, 1)

For $y = {}^-x$

x	1	2	3
y	$^-1$	$^-2$	$^-3$
Coordinates	(1, $^-1$)	(2, $^-2$)	(3, $^-3$)

For $y = 2$ (y is always 2)

x	1	2	3
y	2	2	2
Coordinates	(1, 2)	(2, 2)	(3, 2)

For $y = x + 1$

x	1	2	3
y	2	3	4
Coordinates	(1, 2)	(2, 3)	(3, 4)

For $x = 1$ (x is always 1)

x	1	1	1
y	1	2	3
Coordinates	(1, 1)	(1, 2)	(1, 3)

You have to change the y value!

These are the correct pairings:
1e   **2a**   **3d**   **4f**   **5b**   **6c**

Exercise A3.6

1 **a** Complete this table of values that satisfy the rule $y = x + 2$:

x	⁻3	⁻2	⁻1	0	1	2	3
$y = x + 2$		0		2			

b Draw a coordinate grid as shown and plot the points from your table. Join up the points to draw the graph $y = x + 2$.

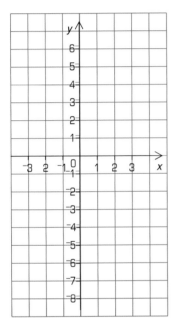

c Complete the table of values for $y = 2x - 1$.

x	⁻3	⁻2	⁻1	0	1	2	3
$y = 2x - 1$			⁻3				

d Using the same coordinate grid, draw in the line $y = 2x - 1$.

e Write down the coordinates where the two graphs **intersect**.

'Intersect' means 'cross'.

2 On another coordinate grid:
a Complete the table for $y = 3 - x$ and plot the graph of $y = 3 - x$.

x	⁻3	⁻2	⁻1	0	1	2	3
$y = 3 - x$			4				

b Complete the table for $y = 2x$ and draw the graph on the same coordinate grid.

x	⁻3	⁻2	⁻1	0	1	2	3
$y = 2x$							

c Write down the coordinates where the two graphs intersect.

3 These two lines intersect at (1, 2):

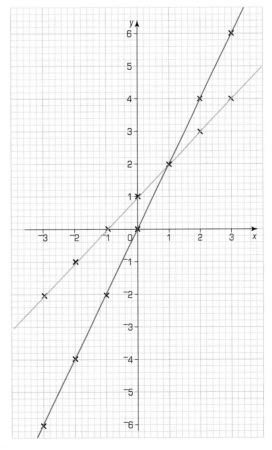

Find the equation of each line.
It may help to complete a table of values.

You should know how to ...

1 Generate coordinate pairs that satisfy a simple linear rule.

Check out

1 a Input the counting numbers 1, 2, 3, 4 to this function machine to generate the first four terms of a sequence.

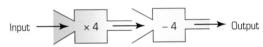

Input → × 4 → − 4 → Output

b Input n to find the nth term of the sequence.

c Generate pairs of coordinates using the input and output values.

d Plot the coordinate pairs on a copy of this grid and join them up:

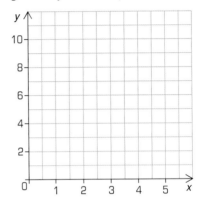

e What is the equation of the line?

2 Plot the graphs of simple linear functions.

2 a Copy and complete this table of values that satisfy the rule $y = x - 1$

x	0	1	2	3	4
y	⁻1		1		

b Plot the points from the table on the grid in question 1.
Join them up to make a straight-line graph.

c Write down the coordinates of the point where the graphs in questions 1 and 2 intersect.

3 Solve word problems and investigate in the context of algebra.

3 Decide whether the point (52, 53) lies on the line $y = x - 1$.
Justify your answer.

Triangles and quadrilaterals

This unit will show you how to:

▶▶ Use correctly the vocabulary, notation and labelling conventions for lines, angles and shapes.

▶▶ Begin to identify and use angle, side and symmetry properties of triangles and quadrilaterals and use them to solve problems.

▶▶ Use 2-D representations, including plans and elevations, to visualise 3-D shapes and deduce some of their properties.

▶▶ Use a ruler and protractor to:
 – measure and draw lines and angles
 – construct a triangle.

▶▶ Solve word problems and investigate in the context of shape and space.

▶▶ Explain and justify methods and conclusions.

▶▶ Begin to generalise and to understand the significance of a counter-example.

The base is made from 128 isosceles triangles. These two pieces are the same …

BLACKPOOL TOWER.

Buildings use properties of shapes.

Before you start

You should know how to ...

1 Recognise these special quadrilaterals:

 ▶ kite
 ▶ rhombus
 ▶ parallelogram
 ▶ square
 ▶ rectangle
 ▶ trapezium

2 Estimate angles in degrees.

3 Collect like terms:

$a + a + a = 3a$

Check in

1 What are each of these quadrilaterals?

a  **b**

2 **Estimate** the size of these angles.

a   **b**

3 Simplify these expressions:

a $a + a + 2a$ **b** $b + 2b + 3b$

c $3 + c - c$ **d** $d + 2d + 3e - e$

Finding angles

This spread will show you how to:
- ▶▶ Know the sum of angles at a point and on a straight line.
- ▶▶ Use a protractor to measure and draw angles, including reflex angles, to the nearest degree.

KEYWORDS

Angle	Vertex
Protractor	Measure
Angles at a point	
Angles on a straight line	

Remember:

An angle smaller than 90°
is an acute angle.

An angle between 90° and 180°
is an obtuse angle.

An angle between 180° and 360°
is a reflex angle.

You measure and draw angles in degrees using a protractor:

1 Place the protractor over the angle.

4 The angle is 40°

3 Measure or draw from the 0 mark.

2 Make sure that the vertex is at the centre and the protractor is along one arm.

Note: There are two scales – to make sure you use the right one you should estimate the size of the angle first.

---

example

Measure this angle in degrees:

Hint: To draw a reflex angle, first subtract the angle from 360° then draw the associated smaller angle.

- ▶ Estimate the size of the angle: it is more than $\frac{3}{4}$ of a turn which is 270° – it is roughly 300°.
- ▶ Then measure the acute angle:
- ▶ Then subtract this from 360°:

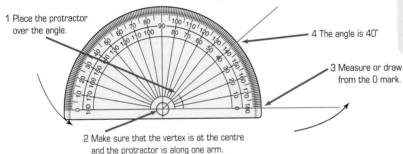

360° − 48° = 312°

You should know these angle facts:

There are 90° on a corner.

$a + b = 90°$

There are 180° on a straight line.

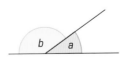

$a + b = 180°$

There are 360° on a full turn.

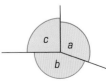

$a + b + c = 360°$

Exercise S3.1

1 Find the missing angles in these diagrams by calculating.

a

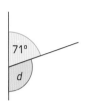

32°

b

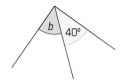

b 40°

c

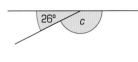

26° c

d

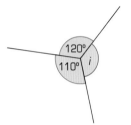

71°

d

e

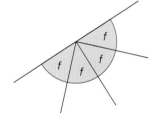

e e

e

f

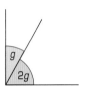

121° 180°

h

g

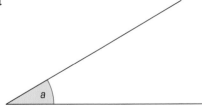

120°

110° i

h

f

f f

i

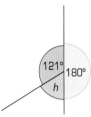

g

2g

2 Measure these angles:

a

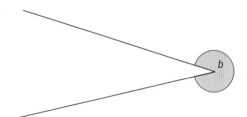

a

b

b

3 Draw an angle ABC = 55°.
What is the associated reflex angle?

4 Draw an angle of 300°.

5 Draw a line AB = 5 cm.
Draw an angle ABC = 50° on the same diagram.
Draw an angle BAC = 70° on the same diagram.
Mark the point C where the lines meet.
Measure the angle BCA.

6 ▶ Sketch a quadrilateral. Use a ruler to make sure the sides are straight.
▶ Cut the quadrilateral out.
▶ Tear off the corners. Put them together carefully.
▶ What do you notice?

This spread will show you how to:

▶▶ Know the sum of angles in a triangle.

▶▶ Recognise angles on a straight line.

▶▶ Visualise and sketch 2-D shapes.

KEYWORDS

Quadrilateral   Diagonal

Concave   Shape

Convex   2-D

Triangle

▶ The angles inside a shape are called **interior** angles.

> *example*
>
> Measure the interior angles of this quadrilateral:
>
> Interior angles are inside the shape.
>
> Using a protractor the angles are:
> A = 210°, B = 25°, C = 90° and D = 35°

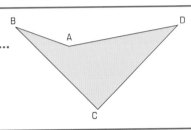

If you ...

... draw any triangle   ... cut out the corners and   ... put them together

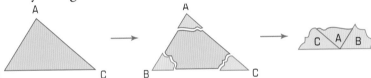

the angles should always make a straight line, so long as you cut them out carefully.

▶ The angles in a triangle add to 180°. They make a straight line.

You can use this fact to find the angle sum for other shapes.

Quadrilaterals

Draw any quadrilateral:

concave      or   convex

Split it into triangles by drawing a diagonal:

Cut out the angles and fit them together to make a full turn, 360°.

Any quadrilateral can be split into two triangles.
A quadrilateral has 2 × the angle sum of a triangle.

▶ The interior angles of a quadrilateral add up to 360°.

Exercise S3.2

1 Find the missing angles in these triangles

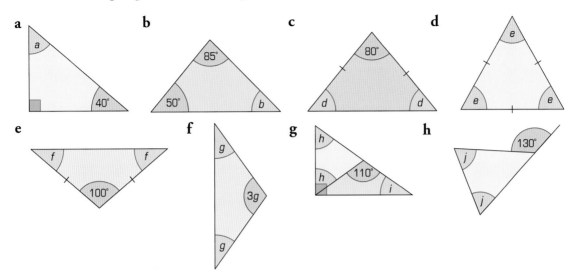

a

b

c

d

e

f

g

h

2 State whether these triangles are possible or impossible:
   a a triangle with an obtuse angle
   b a triangle with an reflex angle
   c a triangle with two obtuse angles

3 Is this statement sometimes true, always true or never true?
   Half a reflex angle is an obtuse angle.

4 Calculate the missing angles. Explain each of your answers.

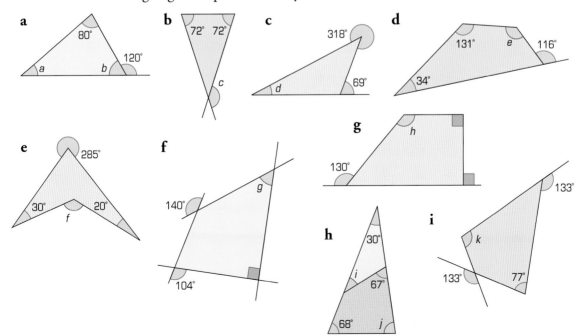

a

b

c

d

e

f

g

h

i

This spread will show you how to:
- ▶▶ Identify parallel and perpendicular lines.
- ▶▶ Visualise and sketch 2-D shapes.
- ▶▶ Identify and use the geometric properties of triangles and quadrilaterals to solve problems.

KEYWORDS

Parallel	Triangle
Perpendicular	Quadrilateral
Adjacent	Equal
Opposite	

You can describe a shape by its angles and sides.
Some common shapes have special names and properties that you need to know.

Triangles

Any triangle with exactly two equal angles is **isosceles**.

Two equal angles means two equal sides.

If a triangle has all three angles equal it is **equilateral**.

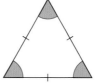

Three equal angles means three equal sides.

If all the angles are different the triangle is **scalene**.

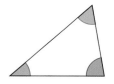

No equal angles means no equal sides.

example

Describe this triangle. Be as specific as possible.

The triangle has two equal angles so it has two equal sides – it is isosceles.
It also has a right angle so you can say it is a **right-angled isosceles** triangle.

Quadrilaterals

All angles equal	**Square** all sides equal	**Rectangle** opposite sides equal	
Two pairs of angles equal	**Rhombus** all sides equal	**Parallelogram** opposite sides equal	**Isosceles trapezium** one pair of opposite sides equal
One pair of angles equal	**Kite** adjacent sides equal	**Right trapezium** may have sides equal	This trapezium has no sides or angles equal:

Exercise S3.3

You will need some 7-dot isometric grids.

1 This is a 7-dot isometric grid:

On 7-dot isometric grids, draw different triangles and quadrilaterals.
Name each of the shapes you draw.
For example:

right-angled triangle

Shapes that are the same but in different orientations only count once.
For example, these are drawings of the same shape:

They are both equilateral triangles.

2 Describe the shapes you drew in question 1.
Use these terms as appropriate:
▶ opposite sides
▶ adjacent sides
▶ symmetrical
▶ acute
▶ reflex
▶ parallel
▶ perpendicular
▶ regular
▶ obtuse
▶ right angle

3 Name any triangles or quadrilaterals that you cannot draw on the isometric grid.
Try to explain why they cannot be drawn.

4 Sort the shapes you drew in question 1 into this two-way table:

> You put a rectangle here because it has two pairs of parallel sides and two pairs of perpendicular sides.

	At least one pair of parallel sides	No parallel sides
At least one pair of perpendicular sides	Rectangle	
No perpendicular sides		

Are there any empty spaces in your table? Give reasons.

5 On an isometric grid the lines intersect to form equilateral triangles:

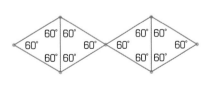

Use this fact to work out the size of the interior angles for each of the shapes drawn in question 1.

This spread will show you how to:
▶▶ Use accurately the labelling conventions for lines, angles and shapes.
▶▶ Use a ruler and a protractor to measure and draw lines to the nearest millimetre and angles to the nearest degree and construct triangles.

KEYWORDS

Construct   Protractor
Sketch   Measure
Ruler

There are lots of shorthand ways of writing 'angle'. These are the most common:

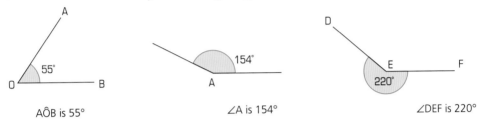

AÔB is 55°   ∠A is 154°   ∠DEF is 220°

You can **construct** a triangle using a protractor and a ruler.

> Construct means draw accurately. The examples are drawn to scale, 1 cm : 4 cm.

example

Draw triangle ABC where AB = 6 cm, B = 50° and A = 46°

First sketch the triangle.   Draw the base – label it.   Draw angle A at point A.   Draw angle B at point B.

The joined up triangle is ABC.

You can check your drawing is correct – just measure angle C.
A + B = 96° so C should be 180° − 96° = 84°

example

Draw triangle PQR where PQ = 5.5 cm, PR = 7 cm and P = 52°

First sketch the triangle.   Make the longest side the base – label it.   Draw angle P at point P.   Mark Q 5.5 cm from P.

Draw in the last side by joining PR.

You can construct a triangle when you know:

▶ two angles and one side (ASA)
▶ two sides and the included angle (SAS).

> You need to know these facts to ensure your triangle is **unique** – there are no other possible triangles that you can draw.

Exercise S3.4

1 Construct these triangles:

a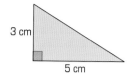
3 cm
5 cm

b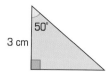
50°
3 cm

c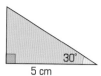
30°
5 cm

d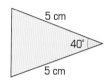
5 cm
40°
5 cm

e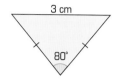
3 cm
80°

f
4 cm

2 Construct these triangles.
Remember to make a sketch of your triangle first.
a ABC, where AC = 7 cm, BC = 6 cm, C = 72°
b PQR, where PR = 7.3 cm, P = 52°, R = 43°
c LMN, where LM = 8.5 cm, L = 31°, M = 127°
d GHI, where HI = 6.8 cm, GI = 4.8 cm, I = 134°
e ABC, where A = 64°, B = 40°, BC = 6.3 cm
f ABC, where AB = 5.6 cm, B = 24°, C = 53°

Hint: Do you have all the information you need?

3 Construct these triangles:

a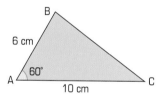
B
6 cm
60°
A
10 cm
C

b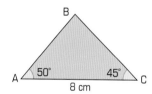
B
50°
45°
A
8 cm
C

c Write down all the information you were given for your shapes.
d Measure and write down any other information you can.

4 Construct these shapes.

a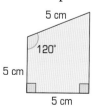
5 cm
120°
5 cm
5 cm

b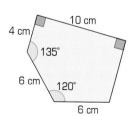
10 cm
4 cm
135°
6 cm
120°
6 cm

This spread will show you how to:
▶▶ Use 2-D representations and oral descriptions to visualise 3-D shapes and deduce some of their properties.

KEYWORDS

3-D   Vertices
Faces   Base
Edges

You should be able to name different 3-D shapes.

▶ **Prisms** have a constant cross-section.

▶ **Pyramids** taper to a point.

Triangular prism

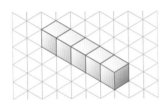

Circular prism or cylinder

equilateral triangles

Triangular-based pyramid – when all the faces are equilateral triangles it is a tetrahedron

Circular-based pyramid or cone

3-D shapes are all around us, but the paper you draw them on is flat!
Isometric paper makes it easier to draw 3-D shapes.

The uprights should be upright!

It is not easy to describe a 3-D shape to someone so they can draw or make it.
Here are some terms you may find useful:

Faces, edges and vertices

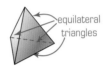

The shape is a **triangular prism** because the triangular face is constant along the whole length.

This prism has: 5 faces, 9 edges and 6 vertices.

Views
This shape is made up of five multilink cubes.
It has: 8 faces, 18 edges and 12 vertices.

The **front** looks like an L shape.

The **side** looks like a rectangle.

From **above** you see a rectangle.

If your information is specific, it is more likely someone else can draw your shape!
It can help if you try to sketch the shape on paper first.

Exercise S3.5

1 Match each solid with its name:
Choose from:
- cylinder
- cone
- square-based pyramid
- cube
- cuboid
- tetrahedron
- triangular-based pyramid
- triangular prism.

a   **b**

c   **d**

e   **f**

g   **h**

2 For each object, name the solid that closely matches its shape:
- pound coin
- cornflake packet
- can of beans
- dice.

3 Name three other objects that are in the shape of:
a a cube   **b** a cone
c a cuboid   **d** a cylinder

4 Platonic solids have all their faces identical and regular.
Which solids in question 1 are Platonic?

5 Copy and complete the table for solids c to h in question 1.

Name of solid	No. of faces	No. of vertices	No. of edges

Try to find a formula to link:
- the number of faces f
- the number of edges e
- the number of vertices v

6 Use four multilink cubes.
Make as many different shapes as you can.
For example:

For each different shape you make:
a Draw what it looks like from above, the front and the side.
b Draw the shape on isometric paper.
c Describe the shape in words for someone else to construct.

You should know how to ...

1 Know the sum of angles at a point, on a straight line and in a triangle.

2 Identify parallel and perpendicular lines.

3 Construct lines, angles and shapes using a ruler and a protractor.

4 Explain and justify methods and conclusions.

5 Solve word problems and investigate in the context of shape and space.

Check out

1 Find the missing angles:

a

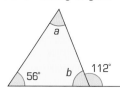

b

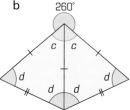

2 Copy and mark all the parallel and perpendicular sides on these shapes:

a    b

3 a Construct the triangle ABC where
AB = 6.8 cm, AC = 6.2 cm, BAC = 70°
  b Construct the triangle where
AB = 8 cm, BAC = 50°, ABC = 45°

4 Is it possible to have a triangle with interior angles 41°, 62° and 80°?
Explain your answer.

5 This is the net of a closed cube.

Copy the net onto squared paper.
Mark the pairs of edges that fit together to make the cube.

Percentages, ratio and proportion

This unit will show you how to:

- ▶▶ Recognise the equivalence of percentages, fractions and decimals.
- ▶▶ Calculate simple percentages and use percentages to compare simple proportions.
- ▶▶ Understand the relationship between ratio and proportion.
- ▶▶ Use direct proportion in simple contexts.

- ▶▶ Use ratio notation, reduce a ratio to its simplest form and divide a quantity into two parts in a given ratio.
- ▶▶ Solve simple problems about ratio and proportion using informal strategies.
- ▶▶ Check a result by considering whether it is the right order of magnitude.
- ▶▶ Solve word problems and investigate in the context of number.

Hmmm, 4oz of fat to 8oz of flour. That's half fat to flour. I've got 6 eggs so I can use 6oz fat – that means 12oz flour. Oh, but I can only measure in grams. There are 25 grams to an ounce …

When you cook you need to use the right proportions.

Before you start

You should know how to …

1 Find equivalent fractions, decimals and percentages.

Check in

1 Copy and complete the table:

Fraction	Decimal	Percentage
		75%
	0.6	
$\frac{1}{5}$		

2 Simplify a fraction by cancelling common factors.

2 Write in their lowest terms:
   a $\frac{60}{180}$ **b** $\frac{9}{24}$ **c** $\frac{16}{72}$

3 Calculate simple fractions of an amount.

3 Calculate:
   a $\frac{1}{10}$ of £340
   b $\frac{3}{5}$ of £740
   c $\frac{3}{4}$ of £250

This spread will show you how to:
▶▶ Understand percentage as the number of parts in every 100, and express a percentage as an equivalent fraction or decimal.
▶▶ Recognise the equivalence of fractions, decimals and percentages.

KEYWORDS

Fraction	Equivalent
Percentage	Convert
Decimal	Cancel

All these amounts show part of a whole: $\frac{3}{4}$, 0.25 and 70%.

▶ A percentage is a fraction written as a number of parts per 100.
For example $60\% = \frac{60}{100}$ and 132% is $\frac{132}{100}$.

You should be able to convert between fractions, decimals and percentages ...

▶ Using place value: $63\% = \frac{63}{100} = 0.63$ $1.43 = \frac{143}{100} = 143\%$

▶ Cancelling factors: $70\% = \frac{70}{100} = \frac{7}{10}$ (÷10)

▶ Finding an equivalent fraction: $\frac{1}{4} = \frac{25}{100} = 25\%$ (×25)

▶ By dividing the numerator by the denominator of a fraction.
For example: $\frac{3}{4} = 3 \div 4 = 0.75$

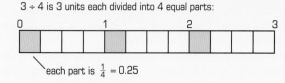

3 ÷ 4 is 3 units each divided into 4 equal parts:

each part is $\frac{1}{4}$ = 0.25

Put the parts together:

$\frac{3}{4}$ = 0.75

Once you change a fraction to a decimal you can easily convert it to a percentage.
You just multiply the decimal by 100.

example

Write these fractions as decimals and then as percentages.

a $\frac{3}{8}$ **b** $\frac{8}{5}$ **c** $\frac{5}{16}$ **d** $\frac{1}{3}$

a $\frac{3}{8} = 3 \div 8$
= 0.375
= 37.5%

b $\frac{8}{5} = 8 \div 5$
= 1.6
= 160%

c $\frac{5}{16} = 5 \div 16$
= 0.3125
= 31.25%
= $31\frac{1}{4}\%$

d $\frac{1}{3} = 1 \div 3$
= 0.333 ...
= 33.3 ... %
= $33\frac{1}{3}\%$

This number line will help you to learn the equivalences:

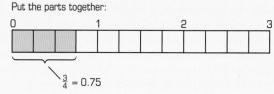

$\frac{5}{16} = 0.3125$ $\frac{3}{4} = 0.75$ $\frac{8}{5} = 1.6$

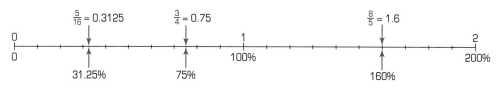

31.25%   75%   100%   160%   200%

Exercise N4.1

1 Match each of the fractions, decimals and percentages to the points indicated on the number line – there is more than one answer for each point.

0.4 $\frac{3}{8}$ 72% $\frac{40}{100}$ 66.6%

50%   14% $\frac{7}{50}$ 0.375 $\frac{2}{3}$

$\frac{1}{2}$ 0.72

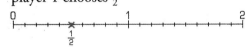

2 Copy and complete this table.

Fraction (in its simplest form)		$\frac{7}{16}$		$\frac{3}{11}$	
Decimal (up to 3 dp)	0.7			0.45	
Percentage (to 1 dp)		65%			32.5%

3 Convert the following percentages to fractions in their simplest form.
a 72%   **b** 6%   **c** 165%
d 12.5%   **e** 372%   **f** 0.5%

4 Convert the following fractions to percentages (to 1 dp where appropriate).
a $\frac{7}{8}$ **b** $\frac{21}{16}$ **c** $\frac{3}{11}$ **d** $\frac{9}{5}$ **e** $\frac{19}{23}$

5 Convert these percentages into their decimal equivalents.
a 31%   **b** 2%   **c** 45.7%
d 187%   **e** 33.3%   **f** 40%

6 Convert these decimals into their percentage equivalents.
a 0.87   **b** 0.3   **c** 0.535
d 1.54   **e** 3.265   **f** 0.015

7 For each pair of numbers work out which one is greater.
a $\frac{7}{8}$ or $\frac{4}{5}$ **b** $\frac{34}{16}$ or 2.2   **c** 1.3 or $\frac{19}{16}$
d $\frac{25}{18}$ or $\frac{37}{26}$ **e** $\frac{2}{3}$ or 0.6   **f** $\frac{3}{7}$ or 0.4

8 These are the marks which Rufus scored in each of his exams:
French $\frac{38}{50}$ German $\frac{17}{20}$
History $\frac{31}{45}$ Maths 77%
English $\frac{41}{57}$ Geography 72%
a In which subject did he do the best? Explain your answer.
b Put the marks for each subject in order, starting with the lowest.
c Convert all the marks to percentages.

9 Convert these fractions and decimals to percentages (expressed to 1 dp as appropriate).
a $\frac{5}{9}$ **b** 0.564   **c** $\frac{3}{11}$ **d** $\frac{7}{23}$ **e** $\frac{2}{3}$

10 Fraction game
Take turns in choosing a fraction and then marking it on a number line from 0 to 2 marked in tenths. The winner is the first person to mark three fractions adjacent to each other on the number line.

For example:
▸ player 1 chooses $\frac{1}{2}$

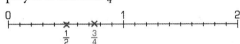

▸ player 2 chooses $\frac{3}{4}$

▸ player 1 chooses $\frac{1}{4}$

▸ player 2 chooses $\frac{3}{5}$

▸ player 1 chooses $\frac{1}{3}$ ... and wins the game (the three fractions are next to each other).

Finding simple percentages

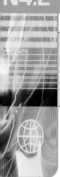

This spread will show you how to:

▶▶ Calculate percentages of numbers, quantities and measurements using mental methods and informal written methods.

KEYWORDS

Fraction   Equivalent

Percentage   Amount

Shops use percentages to express reductions in a sale:

It helps if you can calculate a percentage of an amount in your head.
Using fractions makes this easier.

▶ Finding 10% of an amount is the same as finding $\frac{1}{10}$ th of the amount.

---

example

Find 10% of £300

10% of £300 $= \frac{1}{10}$ th of £300
           $= £30$

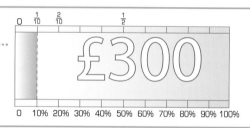

You can use this fact to calculate other percentages:

5% of £300 $= \frac{1}{2}$ of (10% of £300) 20% of £300 $= 2 \times (10\%$ of £300)
             $= \frac{1}{2}$ of £30 $= 2 \times £30$
             $= £15$ $= £60$

You can calculate any percentage ending in 5 or 0 quite easily on paper.

---

example

a   Calculate 15% of £1900   **b**   Find 60% of £2740

a 10% of £1900 $= \frac{1}{10}$ of £1900 $= £190$
     5% of £1900 $= \frac{1}{2}$ of ($\frac{1}{10}$ of £1900) $= £95$
    15% of £1900 $= 5\%$ of £1900 $+ 10\%$ of £1900
                      $= £190 + £95 = £285$

b 50% of £2740 $= \frac{1}{2}$ of £2740 $= £1370$
     10% of £2740 $= \frac{1}{10}$ of £2740 $= £274$
    60% of £2740 $= 50\%$ of £2740 $+ 10\%$ of £2740
                      $= £1370 + £274 = £1644$

▶ To find a percentage of an amount, start from a percentage that you know.
    For example: $15\% = 10\% + 5\%$ and $60\% = 50\% + 10\%$

Exercise N4.2

1 Calculate the following:

  a 10% of £750   **b** 10% of £32.50

  c 20% of 45 apples

  d 5% of 80 sheep **e** 25% of 424 pencils

  f 90% of 800   **g** 30% of 560 people

  h 15% of 40 litres

2 **a** Copy and complete this diagram.

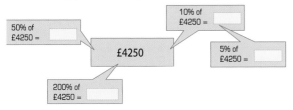

  b Make up some more statements of your own and add them to the diagram.

3 **Puzzle**

Match the percentages, the amounts and the final answers to give six correct statements.

Percentages	Amounts	Answers
15%	600 g	90 g
11%	500 g	40 g
10%	1125 g	75 g
8%	800 g	82.5 g
12%	750 g	60 g
5%	550 g	66 g

4 **Game**

Box A	12½%	15%	17½%	20%	25%
Box B	£300	£350	£400	£450	£500

▶ The first player selects a percentage from Box A and an amount from Box B.

▶ The player calculates the percentage of the amount they have chosen, e.g. 15% of £400 = £60.

▶ The players take it in turns to select a percentage and an amount. Each player has four turns. The winner is the player whose four answers make the total amount of money closest to £250.

5 Calculate the following. You can work out some of the questions mentally but you might need to make some jottings to work out the rest.

  a 40% of 700 apples

  b 35% of $3000

  c 11% of £31

  d 22% of 700 apples

  e 70% of 440 buttons

  f 60% of 240 cm

  g 45% of £520

  h 35% of an hour

  i 115% of 40 carrots

  j 65% of 670 cm

  k 85% of 2520 km

6 A mathematics textbook has 420 pages. 35% of the pages are on number, 30% are on algebra and the remainder are on shape.

How many pages are there on shape?

7 Which is more:

45% of 640 or 35% of 840?

Explain your answer.

8 Make up five different percentage questions to which the answer is $3.20.

9 Calculate the following.

  a 72% of 6400   **b** 37% of 380

  c 83% of 590   **d** 123% of 82 400

  e 242% of 430

10 Put these amounts in order from smallest to largest: 60% of 60 mm; 18% of 16 700 mm; 14% of 2000 cm; 4% of 90 m; 150% of 20.4 m; 45% of 80 cm; 90% of 340 cm

Comparing amounts

This spread will show you how to:

▶▶ Calculate percentages of numbers, quantities and measurements.

▶▶ Use the equivalence of fractions, decimals and percentages to compare two or more simple proportions.

KEYWORDS

Fraction   Equivalent

Percentage   Proportion

Compare

Some percentage calculations are difficult to do in your head.
You can use a pen and paper or a calculator.
Often it helps to convert the percentage to a fraction or a decimal first.

example

Calculate:

a   12% of £37

b   17% of 356 euros

a   12% of £37 $= \frac{12}{100} \times £37$
$$= 12 \times \frac{1}{100} \times £37$$
$$= 12 \times £0.37$$
$$= £4.44$$

b   17% of 356 euros $= \frac{17}{100} \times 356$ euros
$$= 0.17 \times 356 \text{ euros}$$
$$= 60.52 \text{ euros}$$

A fraction shows a **proportion**:

$\frac{2}{5}$ of the boys have black hair.

$\frac{2}{20}$ of the girls wear glasses.

You will learn more about proportion in N4.4.

It is easier to compare fractions or proportions if you use the equivalent percentages.

Abacus School has 350 students.
Abacus School has 210 boys.

Calculator School has 1540 students.
Calculator School has 847 boys.

The proportion of boys is:
Abacus School: $\frac{210}{350}$
$$= \frac{3}{5}$$
$$= \frac{60}{100}$$
$$= 60\%$$

Calculator School: $\frac{847}{1540}$
$$= 0.55$$
$$= 55\%$$

Abacus School has a higher proportion of boys than Calculator School.

▶ You use percentages to compare proportions.

Exercise N4.3

1   Calculate the following:
  a 10% of 434 m
  b 20% of £12.30
  c 15% of 60 cups
  d 11% of 340 cm
  e 35% of 480 km
  f 65% of 8400 people
  g 95% of 660 donkeys
  h 60% of 48 kg

2   **a** What fraction of 1000 g is 400 g?
  b What percentage of 1000 g is 400 g?

3   Calculate the following (giving your answer to 2 dp where appropriate). You can work out some of the questions mentally, some using written methods and for others you may need to use a calculator.
  a 45% of £725
  b 38% of 650 rabbits
  c 13% of 37 m
  d 29% of 865 kg
  e 68% of 5420 litres
  f 14% of 64
  g 12% of £148
  h 95% of a minute
  i 135% of £3450
  j 80% of 45 cm
  k 184% of 1550 km

4   What percentage of:
  a 200p is 84p
  b 50 apples is 12 apples
  c 2 hours is 15 minutes
  d £2.50 is 30p
  e 8 kg is 1400 g?

5   Find:
  a 14% of 376 hectares
  b 12% of £7000
  c 118% of £1 430 000
  d 107% of 0.72 m^2

6   Here are the results of a survey to find the favourite types of holiday of the inhabitants of two towns – Diggle and Eble.

Type of holiday	Diggle	Eble
Skiing	36	54
Sunbathing	60	72
Exploring	48	51
Activity	96	123
Total	240	300

  a What percentage of the people in Diggle like exploring holidays?
  b In which town was skiing the more popular type of holiday? Explain your answer.
  c For which town was:
    i   sunbathing
    ii exploring
    iii activity
    the preferred type of holiday?

7   **Investigation**
The price of a pair of trainers is decreased by 15% in a sale. A month later the price is increased by 15%. The final price is not the same as the original price. Investigate.

8   Bernard invests £3000 in a savings account. Each year the total value of the money in the account increases by 6%.
  a How much money is there in the account at the end of the first year?
  b How much money is there in the account after 2 years?
  c How many years will it take for the money to double in value?

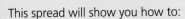

Proportion

This spread will show you how to:
- ▶▶ Understand proportion.
- ▶▶ Use direct proportion in simple contexts.

KEYWORDS

Increase   Proportion

Decrease

▶ A proportion compares the size of the part (or portion) to the size of the whole.

In a class of 30, 18 are girls and 12 are boys.
The proportion of girls is 18 out of 30.
The proportion of boys is 12 out of 30.

▶ You can express a proportion as a fraction, a decimal or a percentage.

example

In a bag of 20 marbles, 14 are green and the rest are blue.
What proportion are green?

$\frac{14}{20} = \frac{7}{10}$ marbles are green.

You can also write the proportion of green marbles as 0.7 or 70%.
The proportion of blue marbles is:
$\frac{6}{20} = \frac{3}{10} = 0.3 = 30\%$

The word proportion can be used to describe how two or more quantities are linked.

The more powerful your computer, the faster it responds.

▶ When an increase in one quantity means another quantity increases in the same proportion, the quantities are in **direct** proportion.

example

a Three packets of crisps cost 90p.
What is the cost of six packets of crisps?

b £4 is worth $5.60.
What is the value of £1?

a
3 packs of crisps cost 90p
×2   ×2
6 packs cost   180p
or £1.80

b
£4 is worth $5.60
÷4 or ×¼   ÷4 or ×¼
£1 is worth $1.40

Exercise N4.4

1 Calculate the proportion of black cats in each of the following cat families. Express each proportion in its simplest form.
  a 3 white; 2 black; 5 tortoiseshell
  b 6 white; 4 black; 4 tabbies
  c 4 white; 7 black; 3 tortoiseshell
  d 11 white; 3 black; 6 tabbies

2 Work out the following using mental or written methods.
  a Four apples cost 92 pence.
     How much would 12 apples cost?
  b 24 eggs cost £3.36.
     How much would three eggs cost?
  c 7 kg of sugar costs £4.
     How much would 56 kg of sugar cost?
  d 51 calculators cost £229.50.
     How much would three calculators cost?

3 Rufus and Tim collect postage stamps from different places. Here is a table showing the different stamps they own.

Country	Rufus	Tim
Great Britain	60	91
Europe	96	133
Africa	168	259
Rest of the world	156	217
Total	480	700

  a Who has the greater proportion of stamps from Great Britain?
  b Who has the greater proportion of stamps from:
     i Europe   ii Africa?

4 a In Anytown school the proportion of boys is 48%.
     The school has 1600 pupils.
     How many girls attend the school?
  b Asif has to pay $\frac{2}{5}$ of his salary in tax.
     He earns £38 400 a year.
     How much money does he pay in tax?

5 Copy and complete this diagram.

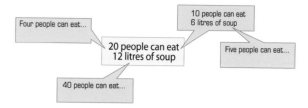

  a Make up some more statements of your own and add them to the diagram.
  b Use your diagram to work out how many litres of soup would be eaten by 37 people.

6 **Puzzle**
Joanne, Amanda and Karen have divided their marbles into three sets. Each set is in a precise proportion. There are different numbers of marbles in each set. They have a total of 20 red, 42 blue, 21 green and 37 black marbles.
Work out the number of marbles there will be of each colour in each set.

Set	Red	Blue	Green	Black
Amanda	30%	20%	15%	35%
Joanne	$\frac{1}{10}$	$\frac{3}{5}$	$\frac{1}{5}$	$\frac{1}{10}$
Karen	10%	32%	18%	40%

7 a 12 pears cost £2.88.
     What is the cost of 15 pears?
  b A distance of 8 km is represented by 15.2 cm on a map.
     How many cm will represent 10 km?
  c Seven books weigh 1064 g.
     What is the weight of six books?
  d With 8 gallons of petrol my car travels 248 miles. How far will it travel with 11 gallons of petrol?
  e It takes 6 minutes to hard boil three eggs. How long will it take to hard boil five eggs?

Introducing ratio

This spread will show you how to:

▶▶ Understand the idea of a ratio and use ratio notation.

▶▶ Simplify a (two-part) ratio to an equivalent ratio by cancelling.

▶▶ Understand the relationship between ratio and proportion.

▶▶ Divide a quantity in a given ratio and solve simple problems.

KEYWORDS

Compare   Ratio
Proportion   Cancel
Simplest form
Common factor

▶ **Proportion** compares the size of a part with the size of the whole.
▶ **Ratio** compares the size of two portions or parts with each other.

On this stick, 6 cm is painted red and 9 cm is painted blue.

The proportion of the stick that is blue
= 9 cm out of 15 cm
= $\frac{9}{15}$
= $\frac{3}{5}$ = 60%
3 cm in every 5 cm is blue

The ratio of red to blue
= 6 cm to 9 cm
= 6 : 9 (common factor is 3)
= 2 : 3
For each 2 cm of red there is 3 cm of blue.

The proportion of the stick that is red
= 6 cm out of 15 cm
= $\frac{6}{15}$
= $\frac{2}{5}$ = 40%
2 cm in every 5 cm is red

The ratio of blue to red
= 9 cm to 6 cm
= 9 : 6 (common factor is 3)
= 3 : 2
For each 3 cm of red there is 2 cm of blue.

The ratios 2 : 3 and 3 : 2 are different so be careful about the order.

▶ You use a ratio to compare the sizes of any two quantities.
▶ Ratios, like fractions, can be cancelled down by dividing,
for example: 6 : 15 = 2 : 5 (common factor is 3).

You can split quantities into different proportions using a ratio.

example

Pinky and Perky share £200 in the ratio 3 : 7. How much will each receive?

For every £3 Pinky gets, Perky gets £7.
The total number of parts is 3 + 7 = 10
The proportion that Pinky will get is $\frac{3}{10}$ and Perky will get $\frac{7}{10}$

$\frac{3}{10}$ of £200 = 3 × $\frac{1}{10}$ of £200 = 3 × £20 = £60
$\frac{7}{10}$ of £200 = 7 × $\frac{1}{10}$ of £200 = 7 × £20 = £140

Pinky will receive £60 and Perky £140.
(check: 60 + 140 = 200)

£200 will be shared into 10 parts so each part is
£200 ÷ 10 = £20.
Pinky has three parts = 3 × £20.

Exercise N4.5

1
a Dianne mixes 1 tin of red paint for every 2 tins of blue paint. She has 24 tins of paint altogether.
How many tins of blue paint are there?
b There are 2 men for every 3 women at the gym club. There are 15 women at the club. How many men are there?

2 Write these ratios in their simplest form:
a 9 : 15   **b** 7 : 21   **c** 15 : 85

3 Express each of these as ratios in their simplest form:
a A recipe requires 12 oz of flour for every 8 oz of butter – what is the ratio of flour to butter?
b Pedros has £300 and Carlos has £75 – what is the ratio of Carlos' money to Pedros' money?
c A father is 35 and his daughter is 14 – what is the ratio of the father's age to the daughter's age?
d A metal alloy consists of 18 kg of copper and 12 kg of tin – what is the ratio of tin to copper?
e $\frac{2}{7}$ of the population of Austria live in Vienna. What is the ratio of Austrians who live in Vienna to Austrians who don't live in Vienna?

4
a Karen and Pete share £7.20 in the ratio 4 : 5. How much money do they each receive?
b The ratio of boys to girls in a school is 7 : 8. There are 1095 pupils in the school. How many boys are there?
c The ratio of men to women at a concert was 5 : 8. There were 585 people at the concert.
How many women were there?
d The angles in a triangle are in the ratio 6 : 5 : 7. Calculate the three angles.

5 44 dog biscuits are shared between three dogs, Toby, Tess and Molly, in the ratio of their ages. In dog years, Toby is 70, Tess is 56 and Molly is 28. How many dog biscuits does each dog receive?

6
a The ratio of the number of cats to the number of dogs owned by pupils in year 7 is 5 : 3. There are 95 cats. How many animals are there altogether?
b The ratio of the number of orange flowers to the number of white flowers in a garden is 6 : 11. There are 144 orange flowers. How many white flowers are there?
c A photograph is enlarged in the ratio 13 : 27. If the length of the photograph was 351 mm, what is the length of the enlargement?
d Angela won £6512 on a TV quiz show. She saved 10 times as much as she spent. How much did she save?
e The model of an aircraft is in the scale (ratio) 1 : 24. If the real aircraft is 12.48 m long, how long is the model in centimetres?

7 The ratio of goldfish to silver fish in a pond is 3:7.
a What percentage of the fish are gold?
b How many times more silver fish are there than goldfish?

8 Find two numbers whose difference is 56 and whose ratio is 7 : 11. Make up another problem like this for your friend to solve.

9 **Investigation**
Alfredo, Bene and Carlito are 7, 5 and 3 years old respectively. They are given an allowance of £1500 a year each year to be shared in the ratio of their ages. Investigate how much each child will receive each year over the next 10 years. Write down anything you notice.

You should know how to ...

1 Recognise the equivalence of fractions, decimals and percentages.

2 Check a result by considering whether it is of the right order of magnitude.

3 Divide a quantity in a given ratio.

4 Solve word problems and investigate in the context of number.

Check out

1 a Place these fractions, decimals and percentages in order from lowest to highest.

$\frac{3}{7}$ 0.4   43% $\frac{9}{20}$ 0.39

b Karen earns £1400 per month and spends £196 on going to football.
What proportion of her income does she spend on going to football?
Express your answer as a percentage.

c Calculate 31% of £6400

d Which of these statements are true and which are false?

  i $\frac{3}{7}$ of 200 = $3 \times \frac{1}{7} \times 200$

  ii   35% of 40 = 40% of 35

  iii $\frac{48}{240} < \frac{56}{300}$

2 Check your answers to question 1.
Explain your strategies and methods of checking.

3 Lottery winnings of £4800 are divided between three friends, Ronaldo, Raul and Zinadin, in the ratio 3 : 5 : 7.

a How much money does each friend receive?

b What fraction does Raul receive?

c What percentage does Zinadin receive?

d What proportion does Ronaldo receive?

4 T-REK make T-shirts in these ranges:.

▶ three colours: red, blue, gold.

▶ three sizes: large, medium, small.

The company use these criteria to decide which types to manufacture:

▶ 25% must be red

▶ twice as many blue as gold

▶ ratio of large:medium:small is 4:3:3

▶ $\frac{3}{5}$ v-neck, $\frac{2}{5}$ round neck.

They make 2000 T-shirts.
How many will be:

a medium and blue?

b large and red?

c small and gold?

This unit will show you how to:

- ▶▶ Use letter symbols to represent unknown numbers or variables.
- ▶▶ Know the meanings of the words *term*, *expression* and *equation*.
- ▶▶ Understand that algebraic operations follow the same conventions and order as arithmetic operations.
- ▶▶ Simplify linear algebraic expressions by collecting like terms.

- ▶▶ Begin to multiply a single term over a bracket using integer coefficients.
- ▶▶ Construct and solve simple linear equations with integer coefficients and the unknown on one side only using an appropriate method.
- ▶▶ Solve word problems and investigate in the context of algebra.
- ▶▶ Present and interpret solutions in the context of the original problem.

Solving equations is all about balancing.

Before you start

You should know how to ...

1 Use algebraic conventions.

2 Simplify expressions by collecting like terms.

Check in

1 Write these sentences using algebra.

   a 1 more than x **b** 2 less than n

   c 3 times f **d** half of r

   e n less than m **f** b more than c

   g x divided by y **h** n times n

2 Write these expressions as simply as possible.

   a $a + a + a + a$

   b $3b + b + 2b$

   c $2c - c + 3c + 4c - 5c$

   d $d \times 3 + d - 2d$

   e $e + 6 + 2e - 4$

   f $3f + 13 - 2f - 1$

   g $xy + 2xy + yx - 3yx$

This spread will show you how to:
- ▶▶ Use letter symbols.
- ▶▶ Simplify linear expressions by collecting like terms.
- ▶▶ Construct and solve simple linear equations.

KEYWORDS

Equals (=)	Unknown
Expression	Adjacent
Equation	Solve

You can construct tower totals like this one:

| 6 | 3 | 8 |
| 9 | 11 |
| 20 |

You add adjacent numbers together and put the total in the box below:

6+3=9   3+8=11

9+11=20

Remember:

▶ Subtraction is the opposite of addition.
6 + 3 = 9 and 3 + 6 = 9 so 9 – 3 = 6 or 9 – 6 = 3.

This will help you solve tower totals.

example

Complete these tower totals:

a
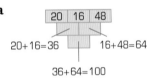

20+16=36   16+48=64

36+64=100

b

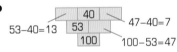

53–40=13   47–40=7

100–53=47

This tower uses the letter *n* to stand for an unknown number.

Once you know the tower total you can work out the value of *n*. First you form an expression for the total using *n*.

Add together the second tier: $n + 34 + 49$
The expression for the total is: $n + 83$

If the tower total is 100 then you can write: $n + 83 = 100$
Now you can solve the equation: $n = 100 - 83$
                                          $n = 17$

$n + 83 = 100$ is an equation.

▶ An **equation** uses an **equals** sign (=) to link two or more expressions.

Exercise A4.1

1 Complete these towers to find the tower totals.

a  25 25 25

b 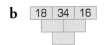 18 34 16

c 23 15 18

d 20 [ ] 18 / 35

e 12 [ ] 6 / 45

f 12 [ ] 10 / 10

g 20 10 10 20

h 3 [ ] 15 / 6 18

2 Complete these towers and work out the values of the letters.

a 3 8 x / 25
x =

b y 5 12 / 40
y =

c 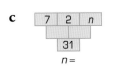 7 2 n / 31
n =

d n 6 7 / 24
n =

e x 5 8 / 20

f 18 15 t / 60

g 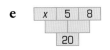 17 12 w / 45

h 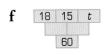 m 23 17 / 100

i 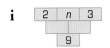 2 n 3 / 9

j 5 x 7 / 20

3 Complete these towers and work out the value of the letters.

a 3 n 5 / 14
n =

b 8 x 7 / 31
x =

c n 3 n / 26
n =

d x 7 x / 20
x =

e 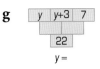 s 3s s / 80
s =

f x 2x 3x / 24
x =

g y y+3 7 / 22
y =

h a a+2 a+4 / 36
a =

i 5 8 3 / f+4
f =

j 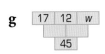 6 7 12 / c–8
c =

4 This is a 3, 2, 1 tower:

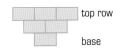 top row / base

Make your own 3, 2, 1 tower so that the base has a total of 46 and the top row adds up to 26.

5 **Challenge**
   a Make your own 3, 2, 1 tower so that the base has a total of $3n + 10$.
   b Make your own 3, 2, 1 tower so that the base has a total of $3n + 10$ and the top row adds up to $2n + 8$.

157

Algebraic operations

This spread will show you how to:
- ▶▶ Know that algebraic operations follow the same conventions and order as arithmetic operations.
- ▶▶ Simplify linear expressions by collecting like terms.
- ▶▶ Construct and solve simple linear equations.

KEYWORDS

Value	Unknown
Equation	Horizontal
Term	Vertical
Solve	

In algebra you use letters to stand for unknown numbers.
Algebra follows the same rules as number.

▶ Subtracting is the opposite of adding:

$13 + 9 = 22$ so $22 - 13 = 9$ and $22 - 9 = 13$

$x + y = 22$ so $22 - x = y$ and $22 - y = x$

> You can write $x + y = 22$ and $y + x = 22$

▶ Dividing is the opposite of multiplying:

$8 \times 5 = 40$ so $40 \div 8 = 5$ and $40 \div 5 = 8$

$ab = 40$ $\dfrac{40}{a} = b$ $\dfrac{40}{b} = a$

> This is how you write multiplication and division in algebra.

You often need these rules to solve problems in algebra.

This horizontal line has a total of 20: | 8 | x | 4 |

This vertical line has a total of 20:

Write an equation:	$8 + x + 4 = 20$
Collect like terms:	$x + 12 = 20$
The opposite of + is −:	$x = 20 - 12$
	$x = 8$

Write an equation:	$2y + y + y = 20$
Collect like terms:	$4y = 20$
the opposite of × is ÷:	$y = \frac{20}{4}$
	$y = 5$

You can check your answers are right:
If $x = 8$ then $8 + 8 + 4 = 20$

If $y = 5$ then $2y = 10$ and $10 + 5 + 5 = 20$

In a **Hot Cross**, horizontal and vertical lines are equal.
This is a **Hot Cross 20**. That means the two lines each add to 20.

Horizontal: $a + b + 6 = 20$
$a + b = 20 - 6 = 14$

Vertical: $9 + b + 8 = 20$
$b + 17 = 20$
$b = 20 - 17 = 3$

Going back to: $a + b = 14$
$a + 3 = 14$
$a = 14 - 3 = 11$

Check:
Horizontal $11 + 3 + 6 = 20$
Vertical $9 + 3 + 8 = 20$

Exercise A4.2

1 Find the value of each of these letters.
(Remember in a Hot Cross the horizontal and vertical totals are equal.)

a
```
      3
  a   6   5
      b
```
line total = 15

b
```
      2
  8   5   d
      c
```
line total = 20

c
```
      e
  f   6   8
      2
```
line total = 18

d
```
      11
  g   6   g
      h
```
line total = 20

e
```
      i
  j   j   j
      4
```
line total = 15

f
```
      3
  k   l   7
      5
```
line total = 16

g
```
      n
  8   m   4
      7
```
line total = 20

h
```
       p
  x+3  x+5  x
       x
```
line total = 38

2 For each Hot Cross find the line total and then use this to find the value of the letter.

a
```
      4
  6   3   8
      r
```

b
```
      2
  s   9   7
      13
```

c
```
      8
  5   12  u
      13
```

d
```
      6
  2r  1   8
      14
```

e
```
      w
  3   8   5
      w
```

f
```
      3
  x+3  7   6
      9
```

g
```
      2p
  15  8   3
      p
```

h
```
      9
  11  7  p+4
      12
```

3 Use the value of *x* to find the missing value, marked ?.

a
```
       3x
  4x  x+3  x−1
       ?
```
x = 5

b
```
       2x
  6   3x   7
       ?
```
x = 4

c
```
       6
  ?   3x   4
       x+3
```
x = 4

d
```
       2x
  x+4  4   ?
       x−2
```
x = 5

e
```
       x+7
  ?   x−2  2x
       x−5
```
x = 7

f
```
       10−x
  ?   3x  x+7
       2x+1
```
x = 6

g
```
       ?
  2x  x+7  3x
       x+4
```
x = 3

h
```
       x−3
  x+5  2x  x+7
       ?
```
x = 5

This spread will show you how to:
▶▶ Know that algebraic operations follow the same conventions and order as arithmetic operations.
▶▶ Begin to multiply a single term over a bracket.

KEYWORDS
Brackets   Partition
Expression

Panic!!
Charlie is at the supermarket checkout.
He wants to buy eight bottles of Cola.
They cost 68p each and he has £5.
Has he got enough money?

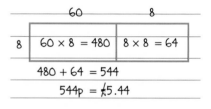

He tries to work out the cost in his head but there are too many sums.

> £5 is 500p.
> 68 times 8 is, erm...

He estimates the cost but it's too close to call.

> Seven 8s are 56, so
> 70×8 equals 560.
> Oh dear, that's £5.60.

He finds a piece of paper and asks for a pen.

	60	8
8	60 × 8 = 480	8 × 8 = 64

480 + 64 = 544

544p = £5.44

The grid method is useful for doing complex multiplications. In the grid method you **partition** large numbers into parts, usually multiples of 10:

> Partition means split up.

To find 36 × 8 you partition 36 into 30 + 6:

240 + 48 = 288

	30	6
8	30×8 =240	6×8 =48

To calculate 546 × 7 you partition 546 into 500 + 40 + 6:

3500 + 280 + 42 = 3822

	500	40	6
7	500×7 =3500	40×7 =280	6×7 =42

The grid method makes it easy to remove, or **expand** brackets in algebra.

To work out $(6x + 5) \times 4$ you partition $(6x + 5)$ into $6x + 5$:

	6x	5
4	6x×4 =24x	5×4 =20

$4(6x + 5) = 24x + 20$

▶ You can leave out the × in algebraic expressions:
$(6x + 5) \times 4$ is $4(6x + 5)$

Exercise A4.3

1 Use the grid method to multiply these numbers (the first one has been partly done for you).

a $37 \times 6 = (30 + 7) \times 6$

	30	7	
6	30×6 $=$	7×6 $=$	$=$

with $\oplus$ between the cells

b $58 \times 3 = ($ $) \times 3$
c $62 \times 5 = ($ $) \times 5$
d $71 \times 6 =$
e $59 \times 4 =$
f $74 \times 8 =$
g $84 \times 4 =$
h $27 \times 8 =$
i $39 \times 9 =$

2 Use the grid method to multiply these algebraic expressions (the first one has been partly done for you).

a $4(5t + 9) = (5t + 9) \times 4 =$

	5t	9	
4	$5t \times 4$ $= 20t$	9×4 $= 36$	$= 20t + 36$

with $\oplus$ between the cells

b $8(7t + 4) = (7t + 4) \times 8$
c $3(5t + 8) = (5t + 8) \times 3$
d $6(7t + 1) =$
e $5(6t + 2) =$
f $6(3t + 7) =$
g $8(2t + 7) =$
h $4(8t + 4) =$
i $9(3t + 9) =$

3 Use the grid method to expand these brackets:

a $5(3t + 2) = (3t + 2) \times 5$
b $3(6t + 4) = (6t + 4) \times 3$
c $2(9t - 1) =$
d $6(3t + 7) =$
e $4(4t - 3) =$
f $5(3t - 6) =$
g $5(2t + 4) =$
h $3(6t - 4) =$
i $2(3x + 2) =$
j $5(2x + 7) =$
k $3(9x - 7) =$
l $6(3p + 2) =$

4 Work out what fits into the brackets.

a ($\quad$) $\times 3 = 3t + 6$
b ($\quad$) $\times 5 = 5t - 15$
c ($\quad$) $\times 4 = 8t + 4$
d $5($ $) = 5t - 25$
e $3($ $) = 9t - 12$
f $6($ $) = 24t + 18$
g $3($ $) = 24t - 3$
h $7($ $) = 35x + 14$
i $3($ $) = 15t - 24$

5 Here are 16 expressions.
They each have a matching pair.

For example, $24x + 30 = 6(4x + 5)$

Copy the two lists and complete the matching diagram.

$24x + 30$	$4(6x + 3)$
$18x + 24$	$9(2x + 4)$
$18x + 12$	$6(3x + 4)$
$24x + 36$	$6(4x + 5)$
$18x + 36$	$6(3x + 2)$
$24x + 12$	$12(2x + 3)$
$24x + 18$	$6(4x + 3)$

A4.4 Solving equations

This spread will show you how to:
▶▶ Construct and solve linear equations.

KEYWORDS

Equation   Unknown
Term   Value
Expression   Solve

You can use algebra to help solve problems involving unknown quantities.

▶ To find the value of a quantity you:
  ▶ let a symbol stand for the unknown quantity
  ▶ construct an expression using that symbol
  ▶ form an equation from that expression
  ▶ solve the equation to find the value.

An expression is a collection of letter and number terms.
An equation has an = sign and can be solved to find an unknown value.

example

Mohammed thinks of a number.

He subtracts 3.
His answer is 12.

What was the number he thought of?

...if I take away 3, I get 12.

The unknown quantity is the number he started with. Let that be n.

Construct an expression:	subtract 3	$n - 3$
Form an equation:	the answer is 12	$n - 3 = 12$
Solve the equation:	the opposite of − is +	$n = 12 + 3$
		$n = 15$

Check the answer: $15 - 3 = 12$

Mohammed thought of 15.

example

One angle in an isosceles triangle is 110°.
What are the other two angles?

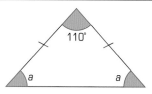

The unknown quantity is the size of the equal angles.
Let each angle be a.

Construct an expression for the angle sum:		$a + a + 110°$
Simplify the expression:		$2a + 110°$
Form an equation:	angle sum is 180°	$2a + 110° = 180°$
Solve the equation:	the opposite of + is −	$2a = 180° - 110° = 70°$
	the opposite of × is ÷	$a = 70 ÷ 2 = 35°$

Check the answer: $110° + 35° + 35° = 180°$ and two angles are equal.

The other two angles are 35° and 35°.

Exercise A4.4

1 Solve these equations to find the values of x.

a	$x + 18 = 20$	**b**	$4x = 36$	**c**	$16 - x = 10$
d	$2x + 1 = 5$	**e**	$3x - 4 = 2$	**f**	$2x + 7 = 15$
g	$3x - 1 = 11$	**h**	$2x - 7 = 21$	**i**	$4x - 3 = 5$
j	$18 = 2x + 10$	**k**	$3x + 7 = 22$	**l**	$5 + 10x = 25$
m	$3x + 1.5 = 10.5$	**n**	$1.5x + 3 = 6$	**o**	$8x - 5 = 15$

In questions 2 to 10 you must
▸ construct an expression
▸ form an equation
▸ solve the equation.
Show all the steps in your working.

2 Jennifer thinks of a number, doubles it and the answer is 18.
What was the number?

3 Martin thinks of a number, subtracts 15 and the answer is 14.
What was the number?

4 Claudette thinks of a number, doubles it and adds 4. The answer is 18.
What was the number?

5 Joshir thinks of a number, multiplies it by 3 and subtracts 5. The answer is 25.
What was the number?

6 Sean thinks of a number, halves it and adds 8. The answer is 20.
What was the number?

7 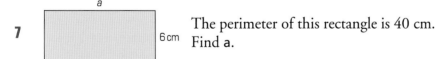 The perimeter of this rectangle is 40 cm.
Find **a**.

8 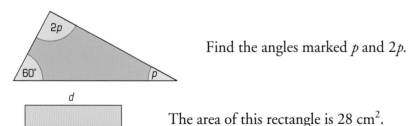 Find the angles marked p and $2p$.

9 The area of this rectangle is 28 cm^2.
Find d.

10 A spacecraft travels for 2 days at a constant speed and covers a distance of 720 000 miles.
On average, how many miles per hour did it travel?

You should know how to ...

1 Use letter symbols to represent unknown numbers or variables.

Remember:

▸ $3 \times x = 3x$

▸ $3 \div x = \frac{3}{x}$

2 Understand that algebraic operations follow the same conventions and order as arithmetic operations.

Remember:

▸ subtraction is the opposite of addition

▸ division is the opposite of multiplication.

3 Construct and solve simple linear equations.

4 Solve word problems and investigate in the context of algebra.

Check out

1 Write these sentences using algebra:

a x less than 10

b double n and add 6

c half m and subtract 7

d 5 more than triple p

e 3 less than double x

f 6 more than y then double

g 3 less than n then halve

h 5 more than double t then halve

2 Copy and complete these pairs of equations. For each pair:

▸ fill in the missing information

▸ find the value of the unknown.

a $x + 6 = 10$ so $10 - \square = x$

b $y - 5 = 12$ so $12 \; \square \; 5 = y$

c $2 + h = \square$ so $9 \; \square \; \square = h$

d $m \div 2 = \frac{m}{2} = 8$ so $8 \times \square = m$

e $n \div 3 = \frac{n}{3} = \square$ so $5 \; \square \; \square = n$

f $3c = 5.4$ so $5.4 \div 3 = \square$

g $n + 3 = 5$ so $5 \; \square \; \square = \square$

h $b - 6 = 12$ so $\square \square \square = \square$

3 Construct an equation in n and solve it to find the original number:

a I think of a number, multiply it by 5 then add 3. My answer is 8.

b I think of a number, multiply it by 3 then subtract 10. My answer is 8.

c I think of a number, divide it by 2 then add 3. My answer is 8.

4 Five years ago, Aren was 20 years younger than his father.

This year he will be half his fathers' age.

How old is Aren?

This unit will show you how to:

▶▶ Understand and use the language and notation associated with reflections, translations and rotations.

▶▶ Use conventions and notation for 2-D coordinates in all four quadrants.

▶▶ Recognise and visualise the transformations and symmetries of a 2-D shape.

▶▶ Solve word problems and investigate in the context of shape and space.

▶▶ Begin to generalise and to understand the significance of a counter-example.

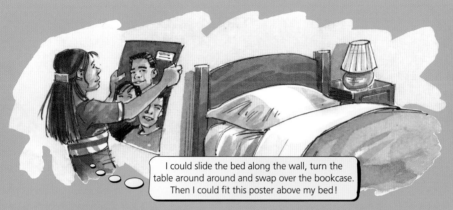

I could slide the bed along the wall, turn the table around around and swap over the bookcase. Then I could fit this poster above my bed!

You can transform your bedroom by moving the furniture around.

Before you start

You should know how to ...

1 Read and plot coordinates in all four quadrants.

2 Recognise and name common 2-D shapes.

Check in

1 Here are the points of three vertices of a square: ($^-$1, 1) (2, 5) (6, 2).
What are the coordinates of the fourth vertex?
Plot the points on a coordinate grid.

2 Name these shapes.
Be as specific as possible.

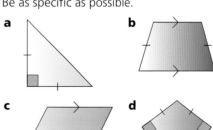

a

b

c

d

54.1 Reflection and symmetry

This spread will show you how to:
- ▶▶ Understand reflection in two dimensions.
- ▶▶ Reflect a shape in a horizontal or vertical mirror line.
- ▶▶ Read and plot points using coordinates in all four quadrants.

KEYWORDS

Transformation   Object
Mirror line   Image
Axis of symmetry
Reflection symmetry

This shape has been folded:

The two halves are **congruent**. They are exactly the same:

The fold line is a line of symmetry. The shape has reflection symmetry:

When you reflect a shape, or object, in a mirror the reflection, or image, will be congruent:

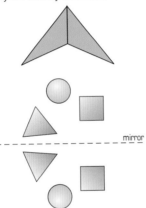

mirror

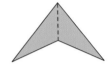

You can see a reflection of yourself in a mirror.

You can produce patterns using reflections:

The shapes are **equidistant** from the mirror line.

▶ You can reflect a shape on a coordinate grid.
The original shape is the object and the reflection is the image.

Reflection is a self-inverse transformation: you reflect the image in the mirror line to get back to the original shape.

This shape is reflected in the *x*-axis:

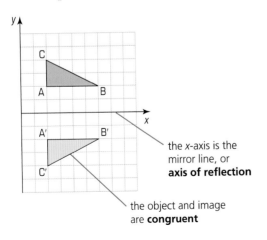

the *x*-axis is the mirror line, or **axis of reflection**

the object and image are **congruent**

This shape is reflected in the *y*-axis:

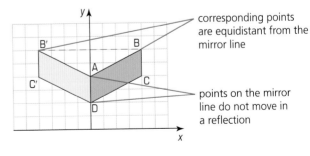

corresponding points are equidistant from the mirror line

points on the mirror line do not move in a reflection

▶ You specify or describe a reflection using the mirror line or axis of symmetry.

Exercise S4.1

1 Copy each of these shapes and mark all the lines of symmetry:

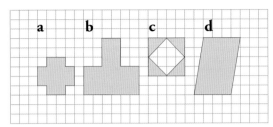

2 In these questions the dotted line is a line of symmetry.
Copy the shapes onto squared paper.
Reflect the shape in the line of symmetry.

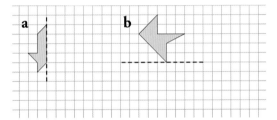

3 Copy these shapes onto squared paper.
There are 2 lines of symmetry for each shape.
Reflect each shape in the lines of symmetry.

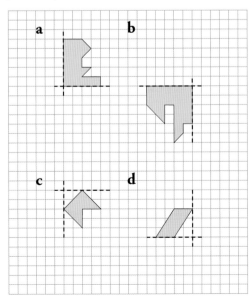

4 These questions involve parallel mirrors.
Reflect the shape through each mirror.
Describe any patterns you notice.

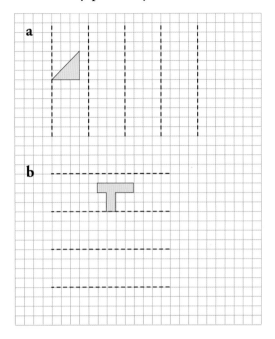

5 Copy each diagram. Shade in the necessary squares to make each pattern symmetrical about the mirror lines.

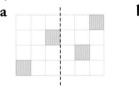

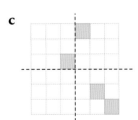

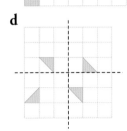

6 Shade in 3 of the squares on a copy of this grid.
Complete the pattern so that it is symmetrical about the two mirror lines.

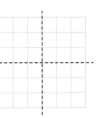

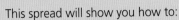

S4.2 Reflecting shapes

This spread will show you how to:
- ▶▶ Understand reflection in two dimensions.
- ▶▶ Construct the reflections of shapes in mirror lines placed at different angles.

▶ You can reflect a shape on a coordinate grid.
The original shape is the object and the reflection is the image.

▶ You specify or describe a reflection using the mirror line.

Some shapes can be quite tricky to reflect:

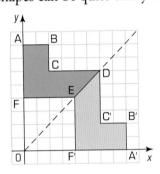

Tricky shapes often produce the best patterns!

You can check your reflection using a mirror if you have one handy.

▶ To check a shape is reflected correctly, consider:
- ▶ Are the object and image congruent?
- ▶ Are corresponding points equidistant?
- ▶ If you reflect the image in the mirror line, does it reflect back to the original shape?

It can help to turn the page round so the mirror line is upright.

example

Reflect this shape in line A.
Then reflect the image in line B.

The lines are called axes of symmetry.

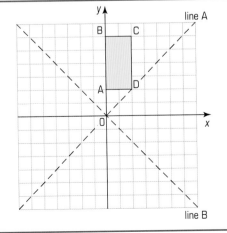

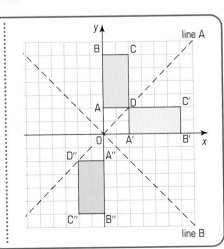

Exercise S4.2

1 On a 5 cm by 5 cm squared grid, draw a diagonal line.
Shade in three squares anywhere on your grid but not crossing the diagonal line.

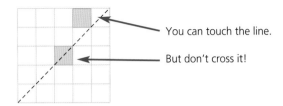

You can touch the line.

But don't cross it!

   a The diagonal line is the mirror line.
      Draw the reflections of your squares in the mirror line.
   b Now repeat with three different squares.

2 On a 5 cm by 5 cm squared grid, draw a diagonal line.
Shade this hexagon on your grid.

Follow these rules:

   ▶ It can be above the diagonal or below it.   ▶ It can touch the diagonal but must not cross it.

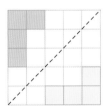 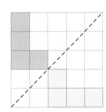 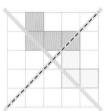

   a The diagonal line is the mirror line.
      Draw the reflection of your hexagon in the mirror line.
   b Now shade the hexagon in a different place and draw its reflection.
      Try as many different ways as you can.

3 Copy these shapes onto squared paper.
The dotted lines are lines of symmetry.
Reflect each shape in the lines of symmetry.

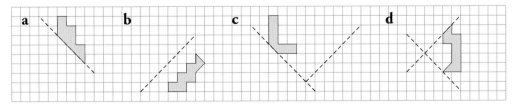

S4.3 Translating shapes

This spread will show you how to:
▶️ Understand translation.
▶️ Translate shapes on a coordinate grid.

KEYWORDS
Object   Coordinates
Image   Congruent
Translation

This shape looks like a reflection in the *x*-axis.

The object and image are congruent but ... it is not a reflection.

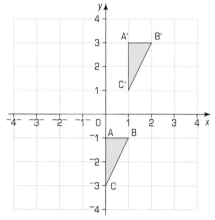

To map the object onto the image you slide the object ... 1 unit to the right ... and then 4 units up.

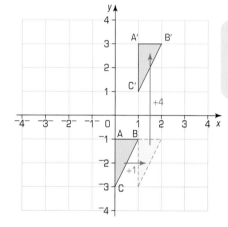

This sliding movement is called a **translation**.

▶ A translation moves the object:
  ▶ a specific distance left or right
  ▶ a specific distance up or down and then.

To get back to the original object you move the image an equal distance in the opposite direction.

---

example

▶ Draw the triangle with coordinates (1, 3) (2, 3) and (2, 5).
▶ Translate it 2 units to the right and 3 units down.
▶ State the coordinates of the image's vertices and describe the translation that will take it back to where it started.

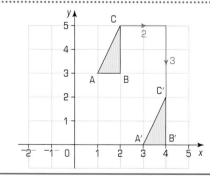

Notice that you add 2 to the *x* coordinates and subtract 3 from the *y* coordinates.

The vertices of the image are: A′ (3, 0), B′ (4, 0) and C′ (4, 2)
To get back you move 2 units to the *left* and 3 units *up*.

▶ A translated object and its image are:
  ▶ congruent
  ▶ the same orientation.

Exercise S4.3

1

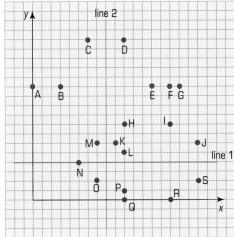

Identify pairs of points reflected in:
a line 1   **b** line 2

2 Copy these axes onto squared paper.
Draw the rectangle and label it R.
Draw and label the lines X and Y.

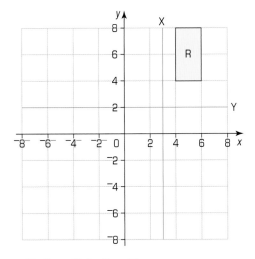

a Reflect R in line X.
Label the new shape R′

b Reflect R in line Y.
Label the new shape R″

c Translate R five squares to the left and
six squares down.
Label the new shape R‴

3 Draw axes from ⁻12 to 12.
a On your axes draw the shape A with
coordinates

$(0, 2)$ $(0, 7)$ $(5, 7)$ $(5, 4)$
Name the shape.

b Draw:
▶ line X which is vertical and passes
through $(3, 0)$
▶ line Y which is horizontal and passes
through $(0, ⁻2)$

c Reflect A in line X.
Label the new shape A′

d Reflect A in line Y.
Label the new shape A″

e Translate A two units to the right and
one unit down.
Label the new shape A‴

4 Draw axes from ⁻7 to 7.
a On your axes draw the shape B with
coordinates

$(⁻2, 2)$ $(⁻2, 6)$ $(3, 6)$ $(5, 2)$
Name the shape.

b Draw:
▶ line X which is vertical and passes
through $(⁻1, 0)$
▶ line Y which is horizontal and passes
through $(0, 0)$

c Reflect B in line X.
Label the new shape B′

d Reflect B in line Y.
Label the new shape B″

e Translate B three squares to the left
and five squares down.
Label the new shape B‴

Rotating shapes

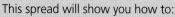

This spread will show you how to:
▶ Understand rotation.

KEYWORDS
Centre of rotation
Congruent   Rotation

This object and its image are congruent.

Each shape has a different orientation
so it is not a translation.

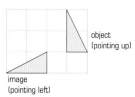

The corresponding points are not equidistant
from a mirror line so it is not a reflection.

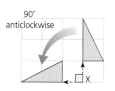

To map the object onto the image you
turn it anticlockwise through 90°.

This turning movement is called
a rotation.

The point X is the centre of rotation.

▶ A rotation moves the object by turning about a fixed point.
▶ To specify or describe a rotation you state:
  ▶ the centre of rotation and
  ▶ the anticlockwise angle.

You rotate the image clockwise
to get back to where you
started.

The centre of rotation can be ...

... part of the shape

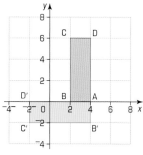

Rotation of +90° about A

... inside the shape

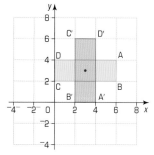

Rotation of +270° about X

... outside the shape.

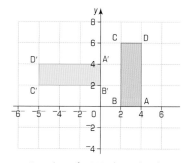

Rotation of +90° about (0, 0)

You find the angle of rotation by joining
corresponding points to the centre of
rotation:

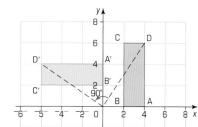

Exercise S4.4

For questions 1–3 you will need to draw axes from ⁻3 to 3.

1 **a** On a grid, draw shape A with coordinates (0, 3), (0, 0), (2, 0)
   b Rotate A about the point (0, 0) through 90° anticlockwise.
      Label the new shape A′. Write down the coordinates of its vertices.
   c Rotate A′ about the point (0, 0) through 90° anticlockwise.
      Label the new shape A″. Write down the coordinates of its vertices.
   d Rotate A″ about the point (0, 0) through 90° anticlockwise.
      Label the new shape A‴. Write down the coordinates of its vertices.
   e What rotation takes A‴ back to A′? Write down as many ways as you can find.

2 **a** On your grid, draw shape B with coordinates (0, 1), (1, 0), (3, 2), (2, 3).
      Name shape B.
   b Rotate B about the point (0, 0) through 90° anticlockwise.
      Label the new shape B′. Write down the coordinates of its vertices.
   c Rotate B′ about the point (0, 0) through 90° anticlockwise.
      Label the new shape B″. Write down the coordinates of its vertices.
   d What rotation takes B″ back to B? Is there more than one way?

3 **a** On a new grid, draw shape C with coordinates (1, 1), (1, 2), (3, 2), (3, 3)
   b Rotate C about the point (1, 1) through 90° anticlockwise.
      Label the new shape C′. Write down the coordinates of its vertices.
   c Rotate C′ about the point (1, 1) through 90° anticlockwise.
      Label the new shape C″. Write down the coordinates of its vertices.
   d Rotate C″ about the point (1, 1) through 90° anticlockwise.
      Label the new shape C‴. Write down the coordinates of its vertices.
   e What rotation takes C‴ back to C′? Write down as many ways as you can find.
   f Describe what happens to the coordinates of the vertices after each rotation.

4 Copy these shapes onto isometric paper.
Rotate each shape about the given centre through 120° anticlockwise.
Repeat each rotation until the shape is back in its original position.

a
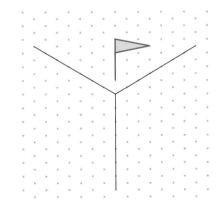

b
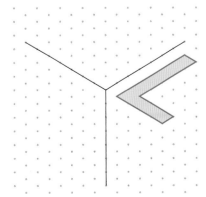

This spread will show you how to:
▶▶ Recognise and visualise symmetry of 2-D shapes.

KEYWORDS
Line of symmetry
Reflection symmetry
Rotation symmetry
Rotate   Symmetry

This shape folds so that the two halves fit together exactly.

The shape has reflection symmetry.

The crease line is the line of symmetry.

It is reflection symmetry as the line of symmetry is a mirror line.

▶ A shape has reflection symmetry if it has a line of symmetry.
▶ A line of symmetry bisects a shape so that one half reflects onto the other.

example

Find all the lines of symmetry of these shapes:

a   b

There are no lines of symmetry.   There is one line of symmetry.

This shape has no reflection symmetry but it looks symmetrical.
Its symmetry is rotational.

▶ A shape has rotational symmetry if it fits onto itself more than once in a 360° turn.
▶ The number of times it fits onto itself is the order of rotational symmetry.

example

What is the order of rotational symmetry of these shapes?

a square

a   90°   90°   90°   90°

The order is 4.

b arrowhead

b   90°   90°   90°   90°

It has rotational symmetry of order 1.

Exercise S4.5

1 For each of these shapes:
  a What is the order of rotational symmetry?
  b How many lines of symmetry does it have?
  c Name the shape.

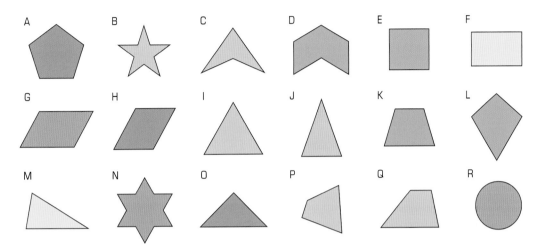

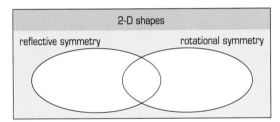

2 Using your results from question 1, place each of the shapes in this diagram.
Just write the letters, not the actual names.

| 2-D shapes |
| reflective symmetry   rotational symmetry |

Shapes with no symmetry go
outside the bubbles.

3 Which of the letters in the box
have:
  a rotational symmetry
  b reflection symmetry
  c no symmetry
  d reflection and rotational symmetry?

A D E H M

N O S T U

V W X Y Z

4 Join four identical squares so that the edges fit exactly.
Make patterns with:
  a reflection symmetry
  b rotational symmetry
Repeat with five squares, then six squares.

S4.6 **Transformations**

This spread will show you how to:

▶▶ Recognise and visualise transformations of 2-D shapes.

KEYWORDS

Congruent   Rotation

Translation   Reflection

Transformation

The grid shows some congruent shapes.

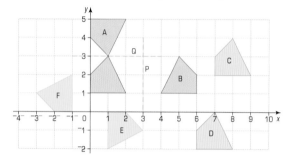

You can describe how to move from one shape to another using a transformation. The object is transformed onto the image.

These are the transformations you should know:

Reflection

▶ You specify or describe a reflection using the mirror line or axis of reflection.

The green shapes show a reflection – the axis of reflection for shape A is the line Q. The axis of reflection for B is line P.

Translation

▶ A translation moves a shape:
  ▶ a specific distance left or right
  ▶ a specific distance up or down.

A translation is a slide.

The red shapes show a translation.
For shape C, you move 7 to the right and 1 up.
For shape D, you move 6 to the right and 3 down.

Rotation

▶ To specify or describe a rotation you state:
  ▶ the centre of rotation and
  ▶ the anticlockwise angle.

A rotation is a turn.

The yellow shapes show a rotation – you move +90° about (0, 0) for shape F (or +270° about (0, 0) for shape E).

Exercise S4.6

You need copies of this grid for this exercise.

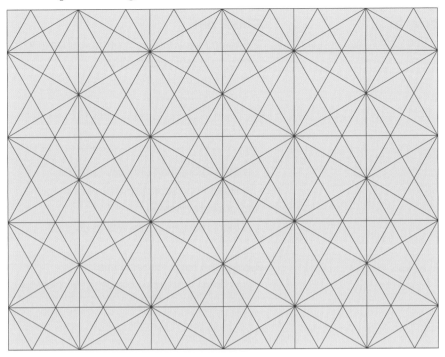

1 Which of these shapes can you find on the grid?
Shade and label each of the shapes.

Isosceles triangle	Parallelogram	Scalene triangle
4-sided arrowhead	Rhombus	5-pointed star
6-sided arrowhead	Equilateral triangle	6-pointed star
Square	Isosceles trapezium	Right-angled triangle
Rectangle	Kite	Trapezium

2 Choose one of the shapes you found in question 1.
  a Shade your shape on a new grid.
  b Shade in any translations of the shape that you can find.
     Check they are all translations of your shape.

3 Choose one of the shapes you found in question 1.
  a Shade your shape on a new grid.
  b Shade in any reflections of the shape that you can find.
     Draw in all the mirror lines.
  c Find the reflections when you reflect your shape in parallel mirrors. Use horizontal and
     then vertical mirrors. Draw in all the mirror lines.

4 Repeat questions 2 and 3 for different shapes.

5 Can you find any rotations of your chosen shape?

You should know how to ...

Solve word problems and investigate the context of shape and space.

Check out

1 Add one square to each of these shapes so that they have reflection symmetry:

a   b

Is there more than one way to do this?

Now add one square so that each shape has rotational symmetry.

Is there more than one way to do this?

2 Imagine a large red rectangle.

▶ Now imagine two congruent smaller black right-angled triangles.

▶ Slide one of the triangles so that the right angle fits into a corner of the rectangle.

▶ Now slide the other triangle so that the right angle fits into a different corner.

▶ Sketch the red shape left.

▶ Name and describe your shape.

▶ Are there any other possibilities?

▶ What if the triangles were not congruent?

This unit will show you how to:

▶▶ Round positive whole numbers to the nearest 10, 100 or 1000 and decimals to the nearest whole number or one decimal place.

▶▶ Recognise and use multiples, factors, highest common factor and lowest common multiple, and primes; use simple tests of divisibility.

▶▶ Calculate simple fractions of quantities and measurements; add and subtract fractions.

▶▶ Recognise the equivalence of percentages, fractions and decimals.

▶▶ Consolidate the rapid recall of number facts.

▶▶ Consolidate and extend mental methods to include decimals, fractions and percentages.

▶▶ Make and justify estimates and approximations of calculations.

▶▶ Multiply and divide three-digit by two-digit whole numbers; extend to multiplying and dividing decimals with one or two places by single-digit whole numbers.

▶▶ Check a result by considering whether it is to the right order of magnitude.

▶▶ Carry out calculations with more than one step using brackets and the memory.

▶▶ Interpret the display of a calculator.

▶▶ Solve word problems and investigate in the context of number.

▶▶ Break a complex calculation into simpler steps, choosing and using appropriate and efficient operations, methods and resources.

Well, I've got £50 to spend. There's 15% off everything. I wonder how many copies of the CD I can buy ...

If you understand percentages you can calculate discounts in your head.

Before you start

You should know how to ...

1 Use the correct order of operations.

2 Convert one metric unit to another.

3 Find a fraction and a percentage of an amount

Check in

1 Calculate:

   a $3 + 4 \times 5$ **b** $0.3 \times 8 - 0.6 \times 3$

   c $(73.2 - 14) \times \frac{5}{2} + 31$

2 Convert these measurements:

   a 300 mm to cm   **b** 0.014 km to m

   c 423 ml to litres   **d** 68 g to kg

3 Calculate:

   a $\frac{2}{5}$ of 640 apples   **b** 20% of 528 m

Rounding

This spread will show you how to:

▶▶ Use rounding to approximate.

▶▶ Round postitive whole numbers to the nearest 10, 100 or 1000.

▶▶ Round decimals to the nearest whole number or to 1 dp.

Sometimes it is not important to know an exact number.

There were 11 373 at the match.

The lottery jackpot is £12 103 567.54.

About 10 000 were at the match.

The jackpot is about £12 000 000.

▶ You find the approximate size by rounding to the nearest 1000 ... 100 ... 10 ... 1 ... 0.1 ... 0.01 and so on, depending on how accurate you need to be.

---

example

Round 2748.37 to the nearest: **a** 1000   **b** 100   **c** 10   **d** 1   **e** 0.1

a 2748.37 is between 2000 and 3000
The 7 is more than 5 so it is nearer 3000

b 2748.37 is between 2700 and 2800
The 4 is less than 5 so it is nearer 2700

c 2748.37 is between 2740 and 2750
The 8 is more than 5 so it is nearer 2750

d 2748.37 is between 2748 and 2749
The 3 is less than 5 so it is nearer 2748

e 2748.37 is between 2748.3 and 2748.4
The 7 is more than 5 so it is nearer 2748.4

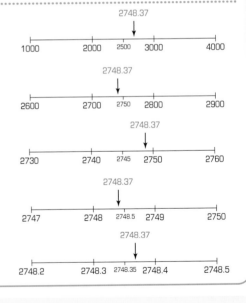

▶ When you round a number to a degree of accuracy, look at the next digit.
If it is 5 or more you round up. For example, 12.57 is 12.6 to 1 dp.

---

example

Round: **a** £327.48 to the nearest £1   **b** 273.9837 to 1 dp

a To round to the nearest unit, look at the tenths: £327.48 ≈ £327 (to the nearest £1)

b To round to the nearest 1 dp, look at the 2nd dp: 273.9837 ≈ 274.0 (to 1 dp)

Exercise N5.1

1   Round each of these numbers **a** to the nearest 100 and **b** to the nearest 10.
    i 253   **ii** 731   **iii** 1456.8
    iv 15 289   **v** 199   **vi** 3456 km
    vii 78.35 m   **viii** 3298.67 g

2   Round each of these numbers **a** to the nearest whole number and **b** to one decimal place.
    i 3.78   **ii** 3.45   **iii** 3.98
    iv 2.734   **v** 11.6136   **vi** 245.07 m
    vii 32.751 kg **viii** 13.396 litres

3   Here are the distances run by four endurance athletes in 24 hours:
    Abdul   99.73 km
    Michael   98 735 m
    Paul   99.368 km
    Kevin   99 486 m
    a Round each athlete's distance to the nearest kilometre.
    b Use these results to put the distances in order from lowest to highest.
    c What would be a better way of rounding the numbers?

4   **a Puzzle**
    Round each number to a different degree of accuracy to make five new numbers. These numbers must add to make a total of 1736.9

    Numbers

237.64	49.8	873.71
	23.927	462.6

    Degrees of accuracy

nearest 100	nearest 1000	nearest 10
	nearest 1	nearest 0.1

    b Invent a similar puzzle of your own.

5   For each of the following problems give an answer to the nearest whole number, and then explain if your answer is sensible. (You may use a calculator if necessary.)
    a 108 children in Year 7 are going by coach on the school trip. Each coach will hold 48 pupils.
    How many coaches will be required?
    b Karen has £312. A rail ticket to Preston costs £40. How many can she buy?
    c Jonathon has 108 metres of tape which he needs to cut into 48 metre lengths. How many lengths can he cut off?
    d Chicky has 312 eggs. A tray will hold up to 40 eggs. How many trays will be needed to hold all the eggs?

6   Write down the largest and smallest numbers that could be rounded to:
    a 30 (nearest 10)
    b 7.3 (1 decimal place)

7   **a** Copy and complete this table:
        Write down anything you notice.

Number	Nearest 10	Nearest whole number	Nearest 1 dp
13.85			
13.034			
13.446			
13.5012			

    b Copy and complete this table:
        Write down anything you notice.

Number	Nearest 10	Nearest whole number	Nearest 1 dp
8.45			
12.673			
10.0398			
9.983			

8   **Investigation**
    Investigate how long it would take you to count to a million.

This spread will show you how to:
▶▶ Recognise and use multiples, factors and primes.
▶▶ Consolidate the rapid recall of number facts and use known facts to derive unknown facts.

KEYWORDS
Highest common factor
Lowest common multiple
Product   Remainder
Prime

Remember:

▶ Any whole number can be written as the product of two factors.
For example: $12 = 3 \times 4$ so 3 and 4 are factors of 12.

Factors come in pairs:

$12 = 1 \times 12$ $12 = 2 \times 6$ $12 = 3 \times 4$

The factors of 12 are 1, 2, 3, 4, 6, 12.
They are the numbers that divide into 12 with no remainder.

▶ If a number has only two factors, the number is a prime number.
For example, $5 = 1 \times 5$ and $17 = 1 \times 17$ are both prime numbers.

The highest common factor (HCF) of two numbers is the highest number in both factor lists:

The factors of 12:   1   2   3   4   6   12
The factors of 18:   1   2   3   6   9   18

1, 2, 3 and 6 are common factors of 12 and 18. The HCF is 6.

Remember:

▶ A multiple of 12 is $12 \times$ a number, or $12n$. It is a number in the 12 times table.

The multiples of 12 are 12, 24, 36, 48, 60, ...
They are the numbers that divide by 12 with no remainder.

The lowest common multiple (LCM) of two numbers is the lowest number in both multiple lists:

The multiples of 12:   12   24   36   48   60   72   ...
The multiples of 18:   18   36   54   72   90   108   ...

36 and 72 are common multiples of 18. The LCM is 36.

Exercise N5.2

1 Find all the factors of:

   a 20   **b** 36   **c** 40   **d** 43

   e 66   **f** 100   **g** 132   **h** 256

   i 324   **j** 221

2 **Eratosthenes' sieve**

(You will need a 1–100 number square.)

- ▶ 2 is the lowest prime number. Cross out all the multiples of 2 except for the number 2.
- ▶ 3 is the next number not crossed out. It is the next prime number. Cross out all the multiples of 3 except for the number 3.
- ▶ 5 is the next number not crossed out. It is the next prime number. Cross out all the multiples of 5 except for the number 5.
- ▶ And so on …

Use Eratosthenes' sieve to find all the prime numbers up to 100.

3 **Investigation**:

What number less than 100 has the most factors?

4 In these arithmagons the numbers in the squares are the products of the numbers on each side.

Solve these arithmagons.

a

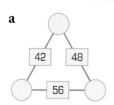

b

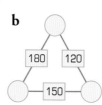

c

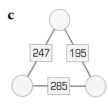

5 Cancel these fractions to their simplest forms.

   a $\frac{6}{8}$ **b** $\frac{25}{30}$ **c** $\frac{18}{24}$ **d** $\frac{15}{25}$

   e $\frac{117}{169}$ **f** $\frac{216}{414}$ **g** $\frac{336}{273}$ **h** $1\frac{156}{312}$

6 Find the highest common factor (HCF) and lowest common multiple (LCM) of each of these pairs of numbers:

   a 8 and 6   **b** 25 and 30

   c 18 and 24   **d** 15 and 25

   e 45 and 72   **f** 42 and 63

   g 36 and 60   **h** 28 and 16

7 **a** Two hands move around a dial. The faster hand moves around in 18 seconds, and the slower in 26 seconds. If the two hands start together at the top of the dial, how many seconds does it take before they are next together at the top?

   b A bathroom wall measures 225 cm by 270 cm. What is the largest size of square tile that can be used to cover the wall, without needing to break any of the tiles?

   c In a 5000 m race the leading runner is running at 66 seconds per lap, whilst the slowest runner is running at 72 seconds per lap. After how many laps will the leading runner overtake the slower one?

8 **Investigation**

This expression $n^2 - n + 41$ generates prime numbers for some whole number values of n.

For example, if $n = 3$,
$$n^2 - n + 41 = 3^2 - 3 + 41$$
$$= 47 \text{ which is a prime number}$$

Find the lowest whole number value of n which does **not** generate a prime number.

This spread will show you how to:
- ▶▶ Consolidate and extend strategies for mental multiplication and division.
- ▶▶ Consolidate the rapid recall of number facts and use known facts to derive unknown facts.
- ▶▶ Use tests of divisibility.

KEYWORDS

Divisibility	Partition
Factor	Sum
Multiply	

If you can calculate in your head then you can work out problems wherever you are.

Here are two useful methods for multiplying in your head:

Using factors to simplify numbers

Break down the numbers into factors you can multiply with easily:

$0.7 \times 14 = 0.7 \times 7 \times 2$
$7 \times 7 = 49$ so $0.7 \times 7 = 4.9$
$0.7 \times 14 = 4.9 \times 2$
$\qquad = 9.8$

$1.6 \times 40 = 1.6 \times 10 \times 4$
$1.6 \times 10 = 16$
$1.6 \times 40 = 16 \times 4$
$\qquad = 64$

Using partitioning

Break down the numbers by partitioning to make them easier to multiply:

$9 = 10 - 1$

$6.4 \times 9 = 6.4 \times 10 - 6.4 \times 1$
$\qquad = 64 - 6.4$
$\qquad = 57.6$

$18 = 20 - 2$

$3.7 \times 18 = 3.7 \times 20 - 3.7 \times 2$
$\qquad = 74 - 7.4$
$\qquad = 66.6$

Remember:
$7 \times 8 \qquad = 56 \quad$ so $\quad 56 \div 8 \qquad = 7$
$7 \times 4 \times 2 \quad = 56 \quad$ so $\quad 56 \div 4 \div 2 \quad = 7$

This will help you use factors to divide in your head:
$144 \div 6 = 144 \div 2 \div 3$
$\qquad = 72 \div 3$
$\qquad = 24$

When the numbers are large you can check whether they will divide exactly by using a divisibility test:

$\div 2$ the number ends in 0, 2, 4, 6 or 8
$\div 4$ the last two digits divide by 4
$\div 8$ half the number divides by 4
$\div 5$ the number ends in 0 or 5

$\div 3$ the sum of the digits divides by 3
$\div 6$ the number divides by 2 and 3
$\div 9$ the sum of the digits divides by 9

3456: $3 + 4 + 5 + 6 = 18$ so it divides by 9

Exercise N5.3

1 Calculate these mentally.
   a 12×20 **b** 23×30 **c** 14×6
   d $360 \div 4$ **e** $300 \div 20$ **f** $72 \div 6$

2 **Investigation**

> The number 24 divides exactly by each of its digits: $24 \div 2 = 12$ $24 \div 4 = 6$
> It also divides exactly by the sum of its digits $(2 + 4 = 6)$: $24 \div 6 = 4$

Find five more numbers that divide by each of their digits and by the sum of their digits.
Write down anything you notice.

3 Calculate these mentally. You may need to make some jottings.
   a 4.3×20 **b** 2.9×70
   c 3.4×9 **d** 1.4×6
   e $114 \div 6$ **f** $548 \div 4$
   g $192 \div 12$ **h** $153 \div 9$

4 Solve these arithmagons – the numbers in the squares are the products of the numbers on each side.

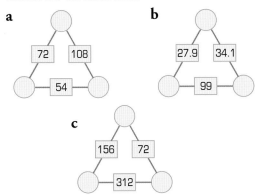

5 **Puzzle**
Write any 3-digit number, for example:
376
Work out the sum of the digits:
$3 + 7 + 6 = 16$
Subtract the sum of the digits from the original number: $376 - 16 = 360$
Is the answer always divisible by 9?

6 **Game**
The first player picks a number from the board – this is their target number.

12.6	10.8	22.4	12.8	52.5	15.6
54.6	21	27	39	44.8	64.5
7.2	14.4	51.6	84	21.6	58.5
23.4	34.4	60.2	36.4	31.5	56
35	13.5	46.8	68.8	14	41.6
26	25.6	25.5	13.6	67.2	48

They select a number from Group A and a number from Group B which they think when multiplied together will make the target number.

Group A		Group B	
2.1	3.2	4	6
3.9	4.3	8	10
5.6	2.6	12	14
1.7	1.8	15	16
0.9	3.5		

The second player works out the multiplication (and checks using a calculator if necessary).

If the first player is correct they can claim that number on the board.

The winner is the first person to claim 4 numbers on the board that are in a line either horizontally, vertically or diagonally.

7 Find the missing number in each of these calculations. You should do all calculations mentally, but you may need to make some jottings.
   a $12 \times ? = 408$ **b** $? \times 8 = 33.6$
   c $? \div 15 = 4.3$ **d** $120.6 \div ? = 6.7$
   e $24 \times ? = 552$ **f** $? \div 6.4 = 30$

This spread will show you how to:

▶▶ Refine written methods of multiplication and division of whole numbers to ensure efficiency, and extend to decimals.

▶▶ Make and justify estimates and approximations.

KEYWORDS

Approximately equals (≈)

Multiply

Some calculations take too long to do in your head and it is easy to make a mistake.

You can do more complex calculations on paper.
You should always find an approximate answer first.

▶ A good approximation is close to the answer and is easy to calculate:

47.34 × 24.8 ≈ 50 × 20 = 1000	Easy to carry out but very crude – reasonable
47.34 × 24.8 ≈ 47 × 25 = 1175	Hard to carry out but very close – good
47.34 × 24.8 ≈ 50 × 25 = 1250	Easy to carry out and close – the best approximation

Remember:
≈ means approximately equals.

There are two good methods for multiplying:

example

Calculate   8 × 3.45

It's easy to make a mistake unless you write it down.

First consider whether you can carry it out in your head:
8 × 3.5 − 8 × 0.05 is too complex.

Approximate: $8 \times 3.45 \approx 10 \times 3 = 30$

It is usually easier to work with whole numbers than with decimals.

$$3.45 = 345 \div 100$$
So $8 \times 3.45 = 8 \times 345 \div 100$

Using the **grid method**:
Partition 345 into 300 + 40 + 5:

	300	40	5
8	8 × 300 = 2400	8 × 40 = 320	8 × 5 = 40

8 × 345 = 2400 + 320 + 40
= 2760
8 × 3.45 = 2760 ÷ 100
= 27.6

Using the **standard method**:

```
              345
          ×     8
8 × 300      2400
8 × 40        320
8 × 5      +   40
8 × 345      2760
```

8 × 345 = 2760 so 8 × 3.45 = 27.6

Exercise N5.4

1 Calculate the following. You may be able to do some of these questions mentally. For others you will probably need to use a written method.

   a 13×11 **b** 0.6×8 **c** 1.3×15
   d 2.3×6 **e** 4.2×19 **f** 7.5×8
   g 6.7×20 **h** 8.4×60

2 **Game**
This is a game for two players. Each player has a 0–9 dice and a copy of these two multiplications.

The first player rolls the dice and writes the number in one of the boxes of their own multiplications or one of their opponent's. The second player rolls the dice and does likewise. After all the boxes have been filled the players work out each of their multiplications, and check their opponent's.
Each player adds their own two answers together. The winner is the player who makes a total nearest to 1300.

3 **Puzzle**
Copy and complete this multiplication grid.

×			27.8	
3	39.6			
4			13	
7				
			29.25	

Write down any strategies you used.

4 **Investigation**
Here is a list of five numbers.
    3 2.6 8 3.72 6
▸ Multiply the first two numbers.
▸ Multiply the second and third numbers.
▸ Multiply the third and fourth numbers.
▸ Multiply the fourth and fifth numbers.
▸ Add together the four answers.
▸ Rearrange the numbers and repeat this process to get a new total. What is the largest total you can make?

5 Find two numbers, one of which is a whole number and one of which is a decimal to 2 dp, whose sum is 20.67 and whose product is 48.06

6 **a** A map has a scale of 1 cm to 5 km. A journey measured on the map is 8.32 cm. What is the length of the real journey in kilometres?
  b Micky LeDrag smokes one packet of 20 cigarettes a day. Each packet costs £4.43. How much does it cost him to smoke for:
    i 1 week
    ii 4 weeks
    iii 1 year
    iv 40 years?
  c I pay for 17 packets of crisps with a £10 note. Each packet of crisps costs £0.42. How much change do I receive?

7 **Puzzle**
Use the numbers 5, 7, 3, 2.65, 4.32 and 7.29 to solve each of the following problems – each number can be used only once in each question.
  a $? \times ? + ? = 22.87$
  b $? \times ? + ? \times ? = 26.21$
  c $? \times (? + ?) + ? \times ? = 60.06$

This spread will show you how to:

▶▶ Refine written methods of division of whole numbers to ensure efficiency, and extend to decimals.

▶▶ Interpret the display on a calculator in different contexts.

▶▶ Use checking procedures.

KEYWORDS

Exactly	Remainder
Multiples	Round
Nearest	Subtract
Quotient	

You can carry out more complex divisions on paper.
The method of repeated subtraction is useful:

Approximate: $139.36 \div 8 \approx 150 \div 10 = 15$

Now subtract multiples of 8 from 139.36:

```
8)139.36
 −  80.00      8 × 10 = 80
    59.36
 −  56.00      8 × 7 = 56
     3.36
 −   3.20      8 × 0.4 = 3.2
     0.16
 −   0.16      8 × 0.02 = 0.16
     0.00
               8 × 17.42 = 139.36
     so        139.36 ÷ 8 = 17.42
```

Think $8 \times 0.1 = 0.8$
$8 \times 0.2 = 1.6$
$8 \times 0.3 = 2.4$
$8 \times 0.4 = 3.2$
$8 \times 0.5 = 4.0$ too big

Think $8 \times 0.01 = 0.08$
$8 \times 0.02 = 0.16$ exactly!

▶ You can check a division by multiplying:

Check $139.36 \div 8 = 17.42$ by calculating 8×17.42

The result of a division is called the **quotient**.
The quotient may have a decimal or fractional part.
You may need to round it depending on the question.

You can multiply the decimal part of the quotient by the divisor to find the remainder.
Example $7 \div 2 = 3.5$
$0.5 \times 2 = 1$
$7 \div 2 = 3$ rem 1

example

a Multi-packs contain seven packets of crisps. How many multi-packs can you make from 80 packets of crisps and how many are left over?

b How many minutes is 453 seconds?

....

a $80 \div 7 = 11.4285 \ldots$ so you can make 11 multi-packs.
$11 \times 7 = 77$ packets so there are 3 packets left over.

11.4285 ... would round to £11.43 to the nearest penny.

b $453 \div 60 = 7.55$ minutes.
60 seconds = 1 minute so 0.55 minutes = 0.55×60 seconds = 33 seconds
So 453 seconds = 7 minutes and 33 seconds

Exercise N5.5

1 Calculate the following.
   a 0.3×8 **b** 0.6×5
   c 0.02×7 **d** 0.08×7
   e 0.05×9 **f** $390 \div 26$
   g $899 \div 31$ **h** $780 \div 25$

2 **Puzzle**
Work out each of these divisions, and then rearrange the quotients in order from lowest to highest to discover a famous character.

R	$74.5 \div 5$	E	$284.4 \div 9$
T	$211.2 \div 8$	H	$86.1 \div 7$
A	$96.6 \div 7$	T	$198.8 \div 7$
R	$127.8 \div 9$	O	$191.2 \div 8$
R	$202.8 \div 6$	Y	$109.8 \div 6$
P	$157.6 \div 8$		

3 Copy and complete this bill from Alfred's Abrasives company.

Item	Cost per item	Number of items	Total cost
Angry paper	£17.22	8	
Cross stone		7	£100.38
Surly rub		5	£ 63.35
Nasty discs		8	£301.68
Unpleasant rolls	£23.64	3	
Biting pads	£33.23		£132.92
		Total	

4 Miguel chooses a number from Box A and divides it by a number from Box B.

Box A		Box B	
87.36	114.24	6	8
	141.12	5	4

Which numbers would give:
   a the largest quotient
   b a quotient of exactly 19.04
   c the quotient with the largest remainder
   d the quotient with the smallest remainder
   e the smallest quotient?

5 **a** Use a calculator to work out each of these divisions. Express the remainder part of the quotient as a whole number.
     i $723 \div 17$ **ii** $1786 \div 47$
     iii $3987 \div 27$ **iv** $8945 \div 38$
  b Explain how you changed the decimal part of the quotient into a whole number remainder.

6 Solve each of the following problems, deciding whether to give the answer with a remainder, as a fraction or as a decimal, whether to round up or down and what degree of accuracy is required.
  a Granny Monika shares £500 between her three grandchildren in the ratio of their ages. Mandy is 18, Peter is 15 and Joanne is 9. How much money will they each receive?
  b It is 14 : 00 on the 7th March 2007. The Mars Lander will touch down in precisely 400 hours. At what time and date will it touch down?
  c A length of carpet 14 metres long and 1 metre wide needs to be cut into 9 equal sized pieces to make carpet tiles which are also 1 metre wide. How long will each carpet tile be?
  d Vegetable pies are sold in packets of 9. Karen needs 200 pies for a pie and peas charity evening. How many packets does she need to buy?

7 On a Wednesday evening William Gnomaitz records the time of each TV programme he watches, including the adverts. Here are his results:

Children's TV	27 mins
Film	1 hour 48 mins
News	18 mins 30 seconds

Calculate the total time William spent watching TV.

This spread will show you how to:
▶▶ Compare two or more simple fractions.
▶▶ Add and subtract simple fractions.
▶▶ Recognise equivalent fractions.

KEYWORDS
Compare   Equivalent
Greater than (>)
Less than (<)
Lowest common multiple

Equivalent fractions describe the same proportion:

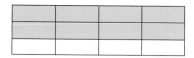

$\frac{2}{3}$ of the rectangle is shaded.
$\frac{8}{12}$ of the rectangle is shaded.

$\frac{2}{3}$ and $\frac{8}{12}$ are equivalent.

You can multiply to find equivalent fractions: $\frac{1}{3}$ $\xrightarrow{\times 2}$ $\frac{2}{6}$ $\xrightarrow{\times 4}$ $\frac{8}{24}$

Equivalent fractions will help you compare fractions with different denominators.

Which is bigger, $\frac{3}{5}$ or $\frac{5}{8}$?

Find equivalent fractions with denominator 40:

$\frac{3}{5} \xlongequal{\times 8} \frac{24}{40}$ $\frac{5}{8} \xlongequal{\times 5} \frac{25}{40}$

$\frac{25}{40} > \frac{24}{40}$

so $\frac{5}{8} > \frac{3}{5}$

Multiples of 5:
5, 10, 15, 20, 25, 30, 35, 40
Multiples of 8:
8, 16, 24, 32, 40
40 is the lowest common multiple.

In fact, $\frac{5}{8}$ is $\frac{1}{40}$ more than $\frac{3}{5}$!

You can use the same method to add or subtract fractions with different denominators:

▶ To add or subtract fractions:
  1 Find equivalent fractions with a common denominator.
  2 Add or subtract the numerators.

Work out $\frac{3}{4} + \frac{2}{3}$

The LCM of the denominators is 12.

$\frac{3}{4} \xlongequal{\times 3} \frac{9}{12}$ $\frac{2}{3} \xlongequal{\times 4} \frac{8}{12}$

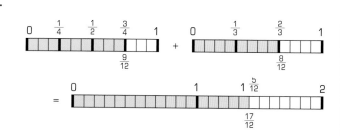

$\frac{3}{4} + \frac{2}{3}$

$= \frac{9}{12} + \frac{8}{12}$

$= \frac{17}{12} = 1\frac{5}{12}$

Exercise N5.6

1 Copy and complete these equivalent fractions.

a $\frac{2}{3} = \frac{?}{15}$ **b** $\frac{3}{5} = \frac{?}{15}$

c $\frac{3}{8} = \frac{?}{48}$ **d** $\frac{4}{9} = \frac{?}{171}$

e $\frac{7}{5} = \frac{28}{?}$ **f** $\frac{?}{3} = \frac{34}{51}$

2 What fraction of:

a 120 is 35
b 2 hours is 42 mins
c 3 km is 550 metres
d 7 kg is 2400 grams
e 500 ml is 2.4 litres
f a right angle is 72 degrees?

Leave your answers as fractions expressed in their simplest form.

3 Insert >, < or = in between each of these pairs of fractions.

Show your working out clearly for each question.

a $\frac{3}{5}$ $\frac{2}{3}$ **b** $\frac{3}{4}$ $\frac{21}{28}$

c $\frac{2}{5}$ $\frac{3}{7}$ **d** $\frac{15}{7}$ $2\frac{1}{4}$

e $1\frac{3}{8}$ $\frac{22}{14}$ **f** $\frac{2}{3}$ $\frac{16}{20}$

4 Which of these fractions is nearer to 1: $\frac{5}{6}$ or $\frac{6}{7}$? Explain your reasoning.

5 **Puzzle**

Find a fraction which is smaller than $\frac{14}{17}$ but larger than $\frac{9}{11}$.

6 Work out the following, leaving your answers as mixed numbers where appropriate.

a $\frac{2}{9} + \frac{5}{9}$ **b** $2\frac{2}{5} - \frac{4}{5}$

c $\frac{2}{3} + \frac{3}{5}$ **d** $\frac{11}{5} - \frac{4}{3}$

e $\frac{3}{4} + \frac{1}{3}$ **f** $\frac{5}{8} - \frac{2}{3}$

g $\frac{17}{11} + \frac{4}{9}$ **h** $3\frac{4}{17} - \frac{19}{12}$

7 **Game**

(You will need a set of Fraction cards and grid N5.6F)

This is a game for two players.
Each player is dealt 10 cards.
The first player puts a card down on the grid.

The second player now places a card down on the same grid.
This continues until one person cannot place a card or the grid is full.
The last person to place a card **wins** all the cards that have been placed on the grid. These cards are saved face down in a pile by the winner.

The game continues with an empty grid. The first card is placed by the player who lost the previous round.

The game ends when one player has played all their cards. The winner is the player who has won the most cards.

8 **Puzzle**

Put these fractions into groups of three so that each group has a total of 1.

$\frac{7}{12}$ $\frac{1}{3}$ $\frac{1}{5}$ $\frac{1}{24}$ $\frac{2}{9}$

$\frac{1}{2}$ $\frac{1}{5}$ $\frac{1}{3}$ $\frac{13}{35}$ $\frac{3}{8}$

$\frac{1}{8}$ $\frac{4}{9}$ $\frac{7}{15}$ $\frac{3}{7}$ $\frac{3}{8}$

9 **Investigation**

Investigate what happens when you add ...

$\frac{1}{2} + \frac{1}{4}$

$\frac{1}{2} + \frac{1}{4} + \frac{1}{8}$

$\frac{1}{2} + \frac{1}{4} + \frac{1}{8} + \frac{1}{16}$ ...

Explain what happens to the total.

10 **Puzzle**

If $\frac{1}{p} - \frac{1}{q} = \frac{1}{4}$ find the values of p and q.

Converting fractions, decimals and percentages

This spread will show you how to:
▶▶ Recognise the equivalence of fractions, decimals and percentages.
▶▶ Use checking procedures.

Fractions, decimals and percentages are all ways of expressing a part of a whole.
If you can convert between them you will find it easier to calculate part of a quantity.

Here are some of the methods you can use:

Mental methods

You should know that
$\frac{1}{10} = 0.1 = 10\%$
$\frac{2}{10} = 0.2 = 20\%$
$\frac{1}{4} = 0.25 = 25\%$
$\frac{1}{3} = 0.333\ldots = 33\frac{1}{3}\%$

0	1/5	2/5	3/5	4/5	1
0	0.2	0.4	0.6	0.8	1
0	20%	40%	60%	80%	100%

So you also know that:

▶ $\frac{3}{5}$ is $3 \times \frac{1}{5}$

          so

▶ 64.5% is 645% ÷ 10

          so

▶ 0.53 is $\frac{53}{100}$ = 53%

▶ $\frac{7}{10} = 7 \times \frac{1}{10} = 7 \times 10\% = 70\%$

$\frac{1}{5} = \frac{2}{10} = 0.2 = 20\%$
$\frac{3}{5} = \frac{6}{10} = 0.6 = 60\%$
$645\% = \frac{645}{100} = 6.45$
$64.5\% = 6.45 \div 10 = 0.645$

Written methods

▶ $\overset{\times\,5}{\overset{\frown}{\underset{\underset{\times\,5}{\smile}}{\frac{13}{20}}}} = \frac{65}{100} = 65\%$

▶ $0.32 = \frac{32}{100}$

$\overset{\div\,4}{\overset{\frown}{\underset{\underset{\div\,4}{\smile}}{\frac{32}{100}}}} = \frac{8}{25}$

▶ $42\% = \frac{42}{100}$

$\overset{\div\,2}{\overset{\frown}{\underset{\underset{\div\,2}{\smile}}{\frac{42}{100}}}} = \frac{21}{50}$

Calculator methods

▶ $\frac{3}{7} = 3 \div 7 = 0.4285\ldots$
              $\approx 0.43 = 43\%$

You can check this:
You know that
$\frac{3}{7} < \frac{1}{2}$ and $\frac{3}{7} > \frac{1}{4}$
So $\frac{1}{4} < \frac{3}{7} < \frac{1}{2}$
and $0.25 < \frac{3}{7} < 0.5$

▶ $\frac{4}{9} = 4 \div 9 = 0.444\ldots$
              $\approx 0.44 = 44\%$

You can check this:
You know that
$\frac{4}{9} < \frac{1}{2}$ and $\frac{4}{9} > \frac{1}{3}$
So $\frac{1}{3} < \frac{4}{9} < \frac{1}{2}$
and $0.333\ldots < \frac{4}{9} < 0.5$

Exercise N5.7

1 Copy and complete these equivalent fractions, decimals and percentages. You should be able to work them out without using a calculator.

Fraction	Decimal	Percentage
$\frac{3}{4}$		
	0.8	
		45%
$\frac{13}{20}$		
	0.64	

2 Copy and complete this table. Use the most effective method to convert between fractions, decimals and percentages

Fraction (in its simplest form)		$\frac{7}{9}$		$\frac{13}{10}$	
Decimal (up to 3 dp)	0.72			0.475	
Percentage (to 1 dp)			95%		37.5%

3 Insert > , < or = in between each of these pairs of fractions and decimals. Show your working out clearly for each question.

a $\frac{3}{5}$ 0.6   **b** $\frac{3}{4}$ 0.72

c $\frac{2}{5}$ $\frac{25}{65}$ **d** 0.32   0.4

e $\frac{15}{9}$ $1\frac{3}{5}$ **f** $1\frac{3}{8}$ 1.35

g $\frac{2}{3}$ 0.65   **h** 0.44 $\frac{17}{40}$

4 Calculate the following, showing all your working and explaining your reasoning.

a Which of these fractions is nearer to 1: $\frac{7}{8}$ or 0.85?

b Find a fraction which is smaller than $\frac{13}{19}$ but larger than 0.65

5 Calculate the following, in each case showing all your working out and explaining your answers.

a Jean scores 48% in his French exam and gets $\frac{26}{54}$ in his German exam. In which subject did he do the best?

b In a school survey 73% of the pupils said they liked eating meat. In Peter's class $\frac{22}{29}$ pupils said they liked meat. How do the results of Peter's class compare with the rest of the school?

c Is 123% of £750 more or less than $\frac{21}{17}$ of £750?

6 What fraction of:

a 130 is 45

b 3 hours is 63 mins

c 5 km is 1740 metres

d 8 kg is 2750 grams

e a complete turn is 125 degrees?

Leave your answers as fractions expressed in their simplest form.

f Put the fractions in order. Check your answer by expressing each fraction as a percentage to 1 dp.

7 A Feeler gauge is used to measure the thickness of gaps inside engines and other pieces of machinery.

There are 3 strips on the gauge of thickness $\frac{1}{2}$ cm, $\frac{1}{4}$ cm and $\frac{1}{10}$ cm.

To check a gap of $\frac{3}{4}$ cm, the $\frac{1}{2}$ cm and $\frac{1}{4}$ cm strips would be used together.

a Write down all the possible gaps that can be measured with the feeler gauge.

b Two new strips are added to the feeler gauge measuring 0.3 cm and 1.5 cm. Write down all the gaps that can be measured with the new feeler gauge.

c Design a feeler gauge to measure all gaps between 0 and 1 cm in steps of 0.05 cm.

Calculating parts of quantities

This spread will show you how to:

▶▶ Calculate fractions of numbers, quantities or measurements.

▶▶ Multiply a fraction by an integer or an integer by a fraction.

▶▶ Calculate percentages of numbers, quantities and measurements.

KEYWORDS

Amount	Estimate
Decimal	Greater than
Fraction	Less than
Percentage	

▶ To find $\frac{1}{6}$ of an amount you divide the amount into 6 equal parts.

$\frac{1}{6}$ of an amount = amount ÷ 6.

This will help you calculate any fraction of an amount.

$$\frac{1}{5} \text{ of } 45 \text{ kg} = \frac{1}{5} \times 45 \text{ kg}$$
$$= 45 \text{ kg} \div 5$$
$$= 9 \text{ kg}$$

$$\frac{3}{5} \text{ of } 165 \text{ cm} = 3 \times \frac{1}{5} \text{ of } 165 \text{ cm}$$
$$= 3 \times 165 \text{ cm} \div 5$$
$$= 3 \times 33 \text{ cm}$$
$$= 99 \text{ cm}$$

Or you can convert the fraction to a decimal:
$$\frac{3}{20} \text{ of } £414 = 3 \div 20 \times £414$$
$$= 0.15 \times £414$$
$$= £62.10$$

▶ Finding 10% of an amount is the same as finding $\frac{1}{10}$th of the amount.

This can help you find other percentages of amounts:

$$10\% \text{ of } 45 \text{ kg} = \frac{1}{10} \text{ of } 45 \text{ kg}$$
$$= 45 \text{ kg} \div 10$$
$$= 4.5 \text{ kg}$$

$$70\% \text{ of } 135 \text{ cm} = 7 \times 10\% \text{ of } 135 \text{ cm}$$
$$= 7 \times 13.5 \text{ cm}$$
$$= 94.5 \text{ cm}$$

Or you can convert to a fraction or a decimal:

$$12\% \text{ of } 45 \text{ m} = \frac{12}{100} \text{ of } 45 \text{ m}$$
$$= 12 \times \frac{1}{100} \times 45 \text{ m}$$
$$= 12 \times 0.45 \text{ m}$$
$$= 5.4 \text{ m}$$

$$17\% \text{ of } £534 = \frac{17}{100} \text{ of } £534$$
$$= \frac{17}{100} \times £534$$
$$= 0.17 \times £534$$
$$= £90.78$$

You should always check your answer using a simple estimate.

You can jot down the numbers if it helps:

Joe works out that $\frac{3}{7}$ of £301 is £129. He checks his answer using facts he knows:

$\frac{3}{7} < \frac{1}{2}$	$\frac{1}{2}$ of £300 ≈ £150
$\frac{3}{7} > \frac{1}{4}$	$\frac{1}{4}$ of £300 ≈ £75

$\frac{1}{4} < \frac{3}{7} < \frac{1}{2}$ and £75 < £129 < £150

$\frac{3}{7}$ is nearer $\frac{1}{2}$ and £129 is nearer £150 so his answer seems about right.

Exercise N5.8

1 Calculate the following.
  a $\frac{1}{5}$ of 235 m   **b** 10% of £14.30
  c $\frac{1}{3}$ of 261 cups   **d** 25% of 240 cm
  e $\frac{2}{5}$ of 780 grains of rice
  f 20% of 730 people
  g 5% of 420 baked beans
  h 60% of 345 mints

2 You can work out some of these questions mentally, some using written methods and for others you may need to use a calculator.
  a $\frac{9}{20}$ of £765
  b 38% of 450 bread rolls
  c 13% of 17 m   **d** $\frac{7}{12}$ of 864 g
  e $\frac{2}{9}$ of 513 words   **f** 11% of €630
  g $\frac{11}{15} \times 705$ bulbs   **h** 115% of $1430
  i $\frac{4}{5}$ of 45 mm   **j** $1\frac{3}{8}$ of 2123 m
  k $3\frac{3}{5} \times 215$ files   **l** $0.8 \times £230$

3 **a** Work out $\frac{3}{5}$ of 45% of $6912
  b Is 35% of 60 the same as 60% of 35? Explain your answer.
  c A rectangular piece of paper measures 42 cm by 61 mm. $\frac{1}{7}$ of the paper is painted red. What is the area of the paper that is not painted red?
  d Lost year Joanne sold £11 658 400 of computer hardware. This year she hopes to increase the sales of her company by 14%. What value of sales does she hope to have this year (to the nearest £100)?

4 **a** 14% of a 250 g cake is fat. How many grams of cake are not fat?
  b $\frac{3}{11}$ of the pupils in Year 7 support their local football team. Of the remaining pupils in Year 7, 50 support Premiership teams, 26 said they do not support any particular team and 20 said they do not like football. How many pupils are there in Year 7?

5 This table shows the number of certificates won by different tutor groups in Year 7.

Tutor group	Number of pupils	English certificates	Maths certificates	Science certificates
7 Up	27	15	23	7
7 Tyone	29	16	25	8
7 Magnificent	32	17	27	8
7 Secret	30	16	24	7

  a What percentage of 7 Up won English certificates?
  b What percentage of 7 Magnificent won Science certificates?
  c Which tutor group had the highest proportion of Maths certificates?
  d Which tutor group had the lowest proportion of Science certificates?
  e Which tutor group did the best overall? Explain your answer.

6 Calculate the following amounts, giving your answers in the units indicated.
  a $\frac{3}{7}$ of 3948 mm (centimetres)
  b 23% of 2 hours (minutes and seconds)
  c 132% of 37 000 000 mm (kilometres)

7 **Investigation**
Keep going round the triangle calculating the fraction or percentage of the amount.

Start with £100
40%
180%
$\frac{6}{5}$

  a What is happening to the amount each time you go around the triangle? Explain your answer.
  b Will your amount of money ever reach zero?

You should know how to ...

1 Extend mental methods of calculation to include fractions, decimals and percentages.

2 Refine written methods of multiplication and division, and extend to decimals.

3 Check a result by considering whether it is of the right order of magnitude.

4 Recognise the equivalence of fractions, decimals and percentages.

5 Break a complex calculation into simpler steps, choosing and using appropriate and efficient operations and methods.

6 Solve word problems and investigate the context of number.

Check out

1 a Copy and complete the table using mental methods:

Fraction	Decimal	Percentage
		27%
$\frac{3}{8}$		
		40%
	1.25	

  b Explain your working.
  c Calculate 15% of £25.

2 Calculate:
  a 5.37×9 **b** 483.6×7
  c 4.97×28 **d** $1035 \div 23$
  e $86.8 \div 7$ **f** $213.12 \div 9$
  Give your answers as a decimal where appropriate.

3 Check your results to question 1 and 2. Show all your working.

4 $\frac{3}{20} = 0.15 = 15\%$
  Describe different methods for converting from:
  a a fraction to a decimal
  b a decimal to a percentage
  c a percentage to a decimal

5 a Calculate $\frac{2}{5}$ of 45% of $\frac{3}{8}$ of £4000.
  b Make up word problems for this calculation:
    35% of 250 = 87.5
  c The value of a property increases by 10% each year for 5 years.
    'After 5 years the property is worth 50% more.'
    Explain why this statement is untrue.

6 Which is the larger amount:
  ▶ 40% of £5 or
  ▶ 50% of £4?

Analysing statistics

This unit will show you how to:

▶▶ Decide which data would be relevant to an enquiry and possible sources.

▶▶ Plan how to collect and organise small sets of data.

▶▶ Design a data collection sheet or questionnaire to use in a simple survey

▶▶ Calculate statistics for small sets of discrete data.

▶▶ Construct graphs and diagrams to represent data.

▶▶ Interpret diagrams and graphs, and draw conclusions.

▶▶ Compare two simple distributions using the range and one of the mode, median or mean.

▶▶ Write a short report of a statistical enquiry and illustrate with appropriate diagrams, graphs and charts

▶▶ Solve word problems and investigate in the context of handling data.

▶▶ Represent problems mathematically, making correct use of symbols, words, diagrams, tables and graphs.

▶▶ Present and interpret solutions in the context of the original problem.

▶▶ Explain and justify methods and conclusions.

Good research starts with good questions. There are plenty of ways to gather data, including using your own surveys or the internet.

Before you start

You should know how to ...

1 Order numbers.

2 Round numbers to 1 or 2 decimal places.

Check in

1 Write these numbers in size order, starting with the smallest:

52.9, 52, 35.2, 52.1 and 53.92

2 Write these numbers to the accuracy stated:

a 4.321 (1 dp) b 12.564 (1 dp)
c 123.456 (1 dp) d 8.036 (2 dp)
e 0.507 (2 dp) f 5.004 (1 dp)

This spread will show you how to:
- ▶▶ Decide which data would be relevant to the enquiry and possible sources.
- ▶▶ Plan how to collect and organise the data and design suitable data collection sheets and tables.

KEYWORDS
Data collection sheet
Average
Data

Anytown Marketing Board wants to increase tourism.

They are putting together a brochure for the region and want to include information about the weather.

They decide that the most important weather features are:
- ▶ temperature
- ▶ rainfall
- ▶ sunshine

They decide to collect this data for each month:
- ▶ the average daily number of hours of sunshine
- ▶ the total monthly rainfall (mm)
- ▶ the average temperature (°C)

Jack agrees to collect the data using the internet and local newspaper records.
This is **secondary data** as it already exists.

He collects two sets of data – for 2000 and 1990 (because a single set of data might not be representative).
Here is his a data collection sheet:

	Year	Jan	Feb	Mar	Apr	May	Jun	July	Aug	Sep	Oct	Nov	Dec
Average temp (°C)	1990	3.8	4	5.8	7.9	11	14	17	16	14	11	6.6	4.7
	2000	4.3	4.2	5.9	6.8	9.2	12	15	15	13	10	7	5.3
Monthly rainfall (mm)	1990	78	51	60	54	55	57	45	56	68	73	78	79
	2000	63	49	48	46	54	50	70	72	63	74	70	68
Average daily sunshine (hrs)	1990	2.1	2.3	3.4	3.6	4.4	5.9	7.3	6.8	5.2	4.8	3.5	2.6
	2000	1.7	2.5	3.5	3.6	4.2	5.8	7.2	6.5	5	4.7	3.2	2.5

- ▶ To collect the right data for your enquiry:
  1. Decide which data is relevant
  2. Research possible sources of the data
  3. Plan and design a data collection sheet

Now they have the data they have to decide on the best way to present it.

Exercise D3.1

1 Decide which data you would need to investigate these questions. Suggest possible *sources* for the data. State whether you would be using *primary* data or *secondary* data.

 a Is there a difference between boys' and girls' reading habits?
 b Do school students watch more television if they have a TV in their bedroom?
 c What percentage of people in the UK live in cities? How does this compare with some other countries?
 d Which are the hottest parts of Great Britain? Which are the wettest?
 e Does background music help people to concentrate when working? Does the type of music matter?
 f How have life expectancies changed in the UK over the last 100 years? How does this compare with other countries?

2 For each of the parts of question 1, design a questionnaire or data collection sheet which you could use to organise the data.

3 Martine is watching *Top of the Pops* with her family.
 Her father says:

> When I was your age, you'd have to sell far more singles to get to number one than you do nowadays.

Martine isn't convinced.

 a What data could she collect to find out whether her father is right?
 b Is the data Martine needs *primary* data or *secondary* data?
 c Where could she get the data from?
 d Design a questionnaire or data collection sheet she could use.

4 Daryl and Marcia are talking about the clothes shopping they did at the weekend.
 Daryl says:

> All these designer labels are just a big con. After all, designer clothes aren't any *better* than cheaper makes. Cover up the label, and most people couldn't tell the difference!

Marcia decides to test Daryl's claim. Explain carefully how she could go about this.

Jack will present the data to the Board members.
They then have to decide how to present the data to encourage people to visit.
He can use:

Pie charts

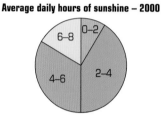

Average daily hours of sunshine – 2000

You can see that most months have an average of more than 2 hours' sunshine, and half the months have more than 4 hours sunshine.
The chart does not tell you which months have the most sunshine.

▶ A pie chart is useful for comparing a category with the whole.

If there are too many categories it is harder to interpret:

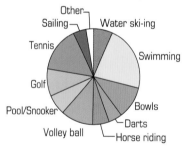

Sports played on holiday

This pie chart shows the results of a survey about the sports people played on holiday. Although it is possible to draw some conclusions, the large number of categories make the diagram hard to interpret.

Bar charts

▶ A bar chart is useful for comparing one category with another.

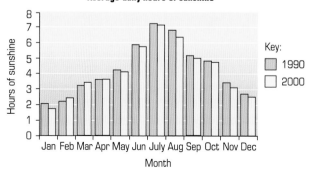

Average daily hours of sunshine

Key:
■ 1990
□ 2000

This bar chart makes it easy to see how one month's data compares with any other. It is also easy to compare the data for 1990 and 2000. Bar charts can still be quite easy to interpret when there are a large number of categories.

Exercise D3.2

1 Nazim travels to work by train. Each week he records how many trains have been late. He does this each week for 20 weeks. The chart shows his results:

Late arrivals each week

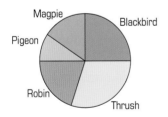

a Nazim says that a *good* week is when his train is only late once, or not at all. How many good weeks were there?
b What was the *modal class* of the data?
c Explain why you cannot use the chart to work out the total number of late arrivals in the 20 weeks.

2 This pie chart represents the birds that Sandra saw in her garden during a one-hour survey.

a What was the most common type of bird?
Sandra saw 5 blackbirds during the hour.
b How many birds did she see altogether?
c Copy and complete the table below:

Bird	Blackbird	Thrush	Robin	Pigeon	Magpie
Frequency					

3 Draw a bar chart for the data in the pie chart in question 2.
What are the advantages and disadvantages of the pie chart and the bar chart for displaying these data?

4 This table shows the results of a class survey about pets.
People were asked to tick boxes to show which type of pets they owned.

Type of pet	Cat	Dog	Rabbit	Hamster	Bird	Other
Number of owners	12	8	4	6	2	7

a Construct a bar chart to represent these results.
b Explain why you cannot use the data to:
   i   find out how many people there are in the class
   ii work out how many pets there were altogether

5 There were 48 entrants in the first round of the 200 metres race at a school's athletics event. The first heat times (in seconds, to the nearest 0.1 s) for the 48 competitors are shown below.

30.7	29.7	29.6	30.3	31.1	33.8
29.1	31.1	26.6	29.2	30.8	28.4
29.1	32.9	29.8	28.7	27.1	31.5
29.4	27.6	31.5	28.3	28.5	29.5
30.6	28.8	32.3	32.5	28.5	28.2
32.2	28.9	29.0	30.2	31.0	28.8
28.0	31.6	31.6	28.1	28.3	27.5
32.1	28.5	26.8	32.7	29.6	30.4

Organise the data into suitable categories, and plot a bar chart.

Comparing data using diagrams

This spread will show you how to:
- ▶▶ Construct graphs and diagrams to represent data and identify key features.
- ▶▶ Interpret diagrams and graphs, and draw inferences.

KEYWORDS

Bar chart
Represent
Interpret

Diagrams show trends and help you generalise.
Jack has prepared these diagrams to show the monthly rainfall figures:

Comparative bar chart

Component bar chart

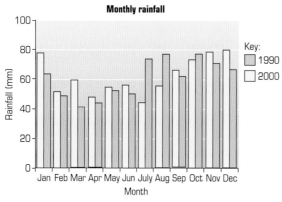

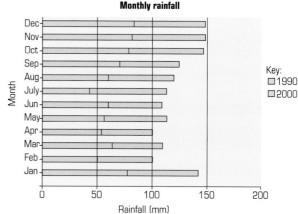

This graph makes it easy to:
- ▶ compare the two years.
It is harder to:
- ▶ see the overall trend.

This graph makes it easy to:
- ▶ generalise – the spring months are the driest.
It is harder to:
- ▶ see the trend for a particular year – especially 2000!

The Board believes sunshine, rainfall and temperature are good indicators of the weather.
They analyse the temperature data alongside the sunshine.
The data sets use the same scale so they fit on the same diagram even though they use different units. It is harder to compare the rainfall on the same diagram.

Comparative bar chart for 1990

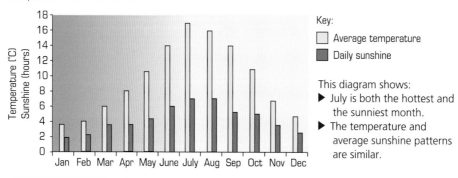

Key:
- ☐ Average temperature
- ■ Daily sunshine

This diagram shows:
- ▶ July is both the hottest and the sunniest month.
- ▶ The temperature and average sunshine patterns are similar.

▶ To compare data on a diagram the data should use the same scale.

Exercise D3.3

1 This bar chart shows the number of books read in the past month by the students in class 7R.

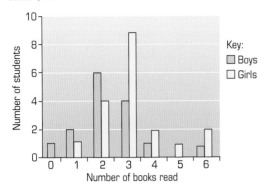

a How many girls had read 3 books or more in the last month?
b How many boys had read at least 3 books over the same period?
c What was the maximum number of books that anybody had read in the class?
d Why can you *not* say that 'the girls in 7R read more than the boys'?

2 In a maths exam, students are given a grade from Table A.

Table A

Fail	Less than 40%
Pass	41% to 60%
Credit	61% to 80%
Distinction	81% and above

Table B shows the number of students in two classes who were awarded each grade.

Table B

Grade	Fail	Pass	Credit	Distinction
Class 7A	2	8	14	6
Class 7B	4	6	19	11

Show the results for both classes on the same bar chart.

3 Two maths groups take the same exam described in question 2. The table shows the percentage marks they obtained.

Class 7C – percentage marks

39	91	80	39	28	45	63	22	55	39	33	39
81	39	94	47	43	78	25	87	64	30	46	98

Class 7D – percentage marks

28	50	83	83	55	28	60	41	27	52	79	23
56	45	22	27	75	67	54	60	62	62	26	74

a Design a data collection sheet to record the number of pupils in each class who obtained each of the different grades for the exam.
b Use this information to produce a comparative bar chart for the data.
c Use the same data to produce a component bar chart.
d Write about the two different charts, explaining the features which each of them shows up best.

4 The line graph below shows the average maximum temperatures in Sydney and Oxford.

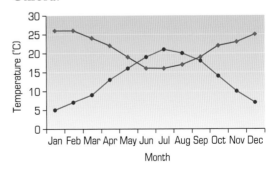

Write a short report comparing the monthly maximum temperatures in Oxford and Sydney.

This spread will show you how to:
▶▶ Calculate statistics from data, finding the mode, mean, median and range.
▶▶ Compare two simple distributions using the average and range.

KEYWORDS

Average   Modal class
Mean   Range
Median   Represent
Mode   Statistics

Diagrams illustrate data visually so you can see the results at a glance.

Now the Board wants to summarise the findings for the brochure.
You summarise data using an average and a measure of spread.

Measures of average use a single value to represent the data.
You have to choose the most appropriate average to use.

▶ The **mean** of a set of data is the sum of all the values divided by the number of values.
▶ The **median** is the value in the middle of the data.
  The data must be arranged in order first.
▶ The **mode** is the value in the data that occurs most frequently.

Measures of spread use a single value to describe the spread of the data.

▶ The range = the highest value – the lowest value

Here is the monthly rainfall data:

	Jan	Feb	Mar	Apr	May	Jun	July	Aug	Sep	Oct	Nov	Dec
1990	78	51	60	54	55	57	45	56	68	73	78	79
2000	63	49	48	46	54	50	70	72	63	74	70	68

These are the monthly rainfall statistics:

1990
▶ The mean is 63 mm
▶ The median is 58.5 mm
▶ The range is 34 mm

2000
▶ The mean is 61 mm
▶ The median is 63 mm
▶ The range is 28 mm

You can use the mean to argue that 1990 was wetter than 2000.
You can use the median to argue that 1990 was drier than 2000.
Notice that 9 out of 12 months in 1990 were wetter than corresponding months in 2000.
It is fairer to use the mean as this uses all of the data.

You would not use the mode in this case, as there are a large number of possible values.
You could work out the modal class if the data were organised into classes.

Exercise D3.4

1 The table shows the height (in centimetres) of 15 Year 7 pupils.

150	140	157	161	157
135	144	150	147	140
165	152	150	142	139

(Source: The Census at School website:
www.censusatschool.ntu.ac.uk)

For this set of data, find:
a the mean
b the median
c the range

2 Find the median for each of these sets of data:
a Lengths in mm:
2, 13, 7, 26, 4, 9, 11
b Number of children in a family:
2, 3, 2, 4, 1, 1, 4, 3
c Temperatures in °C:
23, 13, 42, 28, 32, ⁻2
d Price of books:
£3.50, £8.99, £4.55, £7.85, £4.85, £6.99

3 Sabina collected the following data about hair colour for people in her class.

Colour	Black	Light brown	Dark brown	Blonde
Number of People	12	4	8	6

Sabina wants to find an average from this data.
a Which average can she find?
b Find the value of this average.

4 This table shows the total number of letters in 100 words selected from a book:

Word length	1	2	3	4	5	6	7	8	9	10	11	12	13
Number of words	9	8	35	21	12	9	2	3	0	0	1	0	0
Number of letters	9	18	105	84	60	54	14	24	0	0	11	0	0

The mean number of letters =

$$\frac{\text{the total number of letters}}{\text{the total number of words}}$$

a Find the mean for the data in the table.
b Find a new selection of 100 words, from a book or newspaper.
Work out the mean number of letters per word in the same way.

5 A group of students obtained these marks out of 50 in a maths test and a science test.

Maths	35	15	49	26	42	28	32	41	18
Science	31	37	29	41	35	35	38	36	32

Compare the results for maths with the results for science.
Whatever statistics you work out, explain what your calculations mean.

6 A police patrol record the speed of ten vehicles at two locations. Location A has a 30 mph speed limit, and Location B has a 50 mph speed limit. Here are their results; speeds are given in mph, to the nearest whole number.

A	29	35	42	28	32	34	37	33	38	36
B	63	74	48	51	74	60	65	59	75	63

Write a report describing the results, and comparing the speeds of the cars at each location.

This spread will show you how to:
- ▶▶ Communicate methods and results.
- ▶▶ Calculate statistics.

KEYWORDS

Statistics   Interpret

Represent   Average

The Marketing Board collected data so that they could focus visitors on the best attractions each month in Anytown.

They believe that they should promote indoor activities in a particularly rainy month and outdoor pursuits in nice weather.

They have processed, represented and interpreted the data. Now it is time to publish the findings.

▶ A statistical report should:
  - ▶ Specify the reason for the enquiry
  - ▶ Describe how the data was collected
  - ▶ Represent the data with appropriate diagrams
  - ▶ Calculate relevant statistics to summarise the data
  - ▶ Interpret the findings and justify the results
  - ▶ Consider whether any further enquiry is needed

The detailed statistical analysis covered earlier in the unit can form an appendix but must be included in the report.

Here is a small section of the report from the brochure.

The summers are longer in Anytown!

ANYTOWN is a great place to come for lazy, comfortable days in the sun. As our chart shows, you can expect at least 5 hours of sunshine each day from June right through to September. Temperatures are comfortable, with averages up to about 17 °C. This combination makes Anytown the perfect resort for a relaxed family holiday.

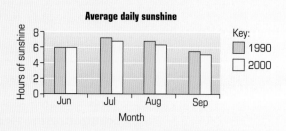

Average daily sunshine

Key:
■ 1990
□ 2000

Exercise D3.5

1 The manufacturers of Glam-Gleam toothpaste published the following advertisement in a glossy magazine:

The results speak for themselves! The results of our latest **blindfold test** show just how great the fresh taste and mighty cleaning action of *Glam-Gleam* really are! We asked 100 blindfolded volunteers to try a range of toothpastes in our laboratories, and say which one they liked best...

Glam-Gleam – the Mighty Clean!

Here are the results of the test:

Toothpaste	Votes
Glam-Gleam	21
SupaBrite	6
Pretty Pegs	28
FangTastic	32
Others	13

a Redraw the graph as a 'normal' bar chart.

b How does the chart in the advert differ from the one that you have drawn?

2 The Kitty Chunks claim appears in a newspaper advert. There are several reasons why you shouldn't just accept the claim at face value:

▶ You don't know how the survey or experiment was carried out
▶ You don't know how big the sample was
▶ Even if most cats preferred Kitty Chunks, you don't know what other food they were offered!

For each of the claims below, say whether you find the claim convincing. If you think that more information is needed, say what it is.

62% of cats prefer Kitty Chunks!

a **House Prices Soar!** As this graph shows, house prices in Smalltown are booming!

b **Customers love our service!** We asked customers to give our service a rating out of 10. The mode of the marks was a whopping 9 out of 10!

c **Fish and Chips – Britain's Favourite Meal!**

3 For each of the sets of data below, calculate the range, the mean, the median and the mode. Say which of the three different averages gives the best impression of the data, and why.

a The cost of 5 cars: £6500, £5900, £6500, £8500, £12 400

b The length (in mm) of 8 leaves: 21, 39, 48, 45, 21, 37, 52, 40

c The value of 6 old vases: £50, £120, £100, £125 000, £5, £50

d The number of slices of bread in 10 sliced loaves: 25, 29, 29, 29, 25, 25, 29, 25, 25, 29

You should know how to ...

1 Compare two simple distributions using the range and one of the mode, median or mean.

2 Explain and justify methods and conclusions.

3 Solve word problems and investigate in the context of handling data.

Check out

1 Claire and Shirley have part-time jobs in a restaurant. They record the tips they receive one evening; the data are shown in the table below.

Claire
£1.50, £2.50, £6.20, 50p, nothing, £3.50, £4.50, £2.20, £1.50, 50p, £2.50, £3.20, £1, nothing, £2, nothing

Shirley
95p, £1, £4.50, £2, £2, £3, £2.25, £1, £2.25, £2, £1.50, £1.50, £2, £1.75, £3.20, £2, £1.25, £2

Compare the tips which Shirley and Claire received; use the range, and find a suitable average.

2 The manager of restaurant in question 1 says that Shirley and Claire should share the tips equally. Do you think this is fair?
Give reasons for your answer.

3 The graph shows the average monthly temperature in Birmingham.

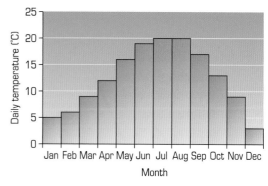

Geoff thinks it must never freeze in Birmingham as all the temperatures are above 0 °C.
Explain why he might be wrong.

This unit will show you how to:

▶▶ Understand and use the probability scale from 0 to 1.

▶▶ Find and jusify probabilities based on equally likely outcomes in simple contexts.

▶▶ Identify all the possible mutually exclusive outcomes of a single event.

▶▶ Collect data from a simple experiment and record in a frequency table.

▶▶ Estimate probabilities based on experimental data.

▶▶ Compare experimental and theoretical probabilities in simple contexts.

▶▶ Solve word problems and investigate in the context of probability.

▶▶ Identify the necessary information to solve a problem.

You can use probability to predict dice scores. If two dice landed on double six each time, you would suspect that they were 'fixed'.

Before you start

You should know how to ...

1 Write proportions as fractions.

2 Convert between fractions, decimals and percentages.

Check in

1 Write these proportions as fractions in their lowest terms

    a 15 out of 20   **b** 6 out of 15

    c 12 out of 18   **d** 45 out of 50

2 Write:

    a $\frac{4}{5}$ as a percentage

    b $\frac{7}{8}$ as a decimal

    c 0.2 as a percentage

    d 0.15 as a fraction

    e 28% as a fraction

    f 17.5% as a decimal

This spread will show you how to:
▶▶ Understand and use the probability scale from 0 to 1.
▶▶ Find and justify probabilities based on equally likely outcomes in simple contexts.
▶▶ Identify all the possible outcomes of a single event.

KEYWORDS
Certain   Outcome
Chance   Equally likely
Likelihood   Random
Probability scale

Probability is a measure of the chance of an outcome happening.
It describes the likelihood of something happening.

Probability is measured on a scale of 0 to 1. Probability that ...

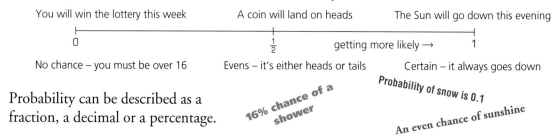

You will win the lottery this week | A coin will land on heads | The Sun will go down this evening

0 $\frac{1}{2}$ getting more likely →   1

No chance – you must be over 16 | Evens – it's either heads or tails | Certain – it always goes down

Probability can be described as a fraction, a decimal or a percentage.

16% chance of a shower

Probability of snow is 0.1

An even chance of sunshine

To **calculate** the theoretical probability of a particular event you need to identify all the possible outcomes:

▶ Probability of an event = $\dfrac{\text{number of ways the event can happen}}{\text{total number of possible outcomes}}$

This assumes all the outcomes are **equally likely**.

example

The letters of the word STATISTICS are written on tiles and put into a bag. One letter is taken out at random. What is the probability that it is:
a an S   **b** not an S   **c** a vowel?

In total there are 10 letters in the bag.

a 3 of the letters are S so the probability of an S is $\frac{3}{10}$
b 7 of the letters are not S so the probability of not an S is $\frac{7}{10}$
c 3 of the letters are vowels so the probability of a vowel is $\frac{3}{10}$

You can list and describe outcomes in various ways depending on the question.
For example:

Which tile is chosen?
There are 10 possible outcomes:

S, T, A, T, I, S, T, I, C and S

They are each equally likely to be chosen.

Is an S chosen?
There are 2 possible outcomes:

S or not S

They are not equally likely. Most of the letters are not S.

Which letter is chosen?
There are 5 possible outcomes:

S, T, A, I or C

They are not equally likely as there are more S's than I's.

Choosing a letter out of the bag is a **trial**.

You must list the outcomes carefully to be sure you have considered them all.

Exercise D4.1

1 100 raffle tickets, numbered from 1 to 100, are placed in a box, and the winning ticket is drawn out.
Mark each of these events on a copy of this probability scale.

├─┼─┼─┼─┼─┼─┼─┼─┼─┼─┤
0   1

a Ticket number 23 is chosen.
b The winning number is even.
c The winning number is between 41 and 50 (inclusive).
d The winning number is greater than 120.
e The winning number is less than 200.

2 Work out the probability of each of the events in question 1.
Give each of your answers as a:
▶ fraction
▶ decimal
▶ percentage.

3 Angela writes each of the letters of her name onto a small sticker, and puts them on the faces of an ordinary dice.

When Angela rolls the dice, what is the probability that the letter showing will be:
a A
b G
c N or G
d a vowel
e a letter which isn't A

4 A computer picks a number at random from this table.

1	2	3	4	5	6	7	8	9	10	11	12
13	14	15	16	17	18	19	20	21	22	23	24
25	26	27	28	29	30	31	32	33	34	35	36

What is the probability that the number chosen is:
a 25
b less than 20
c a multiple of 6
d a square number
e less than 50
f a prime number?

5 This table shows the data collected from a group of students:

Sex	Data of birth	Height (cm)
F	13/6/91	140
M	13/10/90	139
F	9/9/90	132
M	3/8/91	141
F	29/11/90	148
F	22/1/91	148
M	13/11/90	134
M	10/6/91	140
M	1/7/91	149
M	24/10/90	144
F	4/10/90	142
M	4/12/90	140
M	16/1/91	133
M	12/5/91	138
M	6/3/91	167
M	30/8/91	136

A student from the group is chosen at random. Find the probability that a student chosen at random is:
a male
b more than 140 cm tall
c born in 1991
d born in September
e male and less than 140 cm tall
f female and more than 140 cm tall

This spread will show you how to:
▶▶ Collect data from a simple experiment and record it in a frequency table.
▶▶ Estimate probabilities based on theoretical data.

KEYWORDS
Probability   Experiment
Outcome

Amy has to check the microchips which her company produces each day.

She carries out an **experiment** to collect some data.
She takes a batch of 50 microchips for testing. The probability of a chip being defective is supposed to be 0.1 (= 10%) or less.

▶ You can estimate the probability of an outcome using experimental data.

▶ Probability of an event
$$= \frac{\text{number of times the event occurs}}{\text{number of trials in the experiment}}$$

Experimental data is primary data as you collect it yourself.

Amy's sample contains 6 defective chips.
She estimates the probability of a chip being defective as:

Note: Testing a microchip out of the batch is a **trial**. Amy has conducted 50 trials in the experiment.

$$\frac{\text{Number of defective chips}}{\text{Total number of chips}} = \frac{6}{50} = 0.12 = 12\%$$

Amy is concerned at the high value of this estimated probability.
She decides to test some more chips to get a more reliable estimate.
She tests three more batches of 50 chips.
Her results are shown in the table:

Now her estimate of a microchip being defective is:

$$\frac{\text{Number of defective chips}}{\text{Total number of chips}} = \frac{6+3+4+5}{4 \times 50} = \frac{18}{200} = 9\%$$

Batch	Number defective
1	6
2	3
3	4
4	5

Exercise D4.2

Carry out one of the experiments described below.

Experiment A   Make a dice

You can make it an 'ordinary' cube, from a net like this:

or a triangular prism from a net like this:

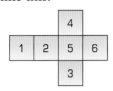

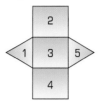

Remember that you will need to add some tabs to some of the edges so that you can stick the model together.

You can weight your dice by adding a piece of plasticine or Blu-Tak inside the shape attached to one face.

Testing your dice

Roll your dice 50 times, and keep a record of the scores in a table like this:

Score	Tally	Frequency
1		
2		
3		
4		
5		

Work out the estimated probability of each score on your dice, giving your answers as decimals. You can use the formula:

$$\text{Estimated probability} = \frac{\text{frequency}}{50}$$

Roll your dice another 50 times, and combine this set of results with your first set.
Use the combined set of 100 results to produce a better estimate for the probability of each score on your dice.

Experiment B   Make a spinner

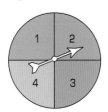

Make a spinner with an arrow. Join the arrow to the base (loosely) with a split pin. The arrow should be quite big, or it will not spin properly.
Your can weight the spinner with plasticine.
Once you have made the spinner, test it in the way described for Experiment A.

This spread will show you how to:
▶▶ Estimate probabilities based on theoretical data.
▶▶ Compare experimental and theoretical probabilities in simple contexts.

KEYWORDS
Fair	Equally likely
Spinner	Experiment
Probability	Tally

On this eight-sided, or octagonal, spinner each sector is the same shape and size.

The spinner is equally likely to land on any one of the sectors.

In theory, the probability of the spinner landing on the red sector is $\frac{1}{8} = 12.5\%$.

Rob and Maria decide to test the spinner to see whether it is fair. They collect some experimental data. They:

▶ Spin the spinner and record the colour
▶ Repeat the experiment 50 times each and keep a tally:

Colour	Rob's tally	Rob total	Maria's tally	Maria total
Black	////	4	JHt //	7
Blue	JHt /	6	///	3
Green	JHt ///	8	JHt ///	8
Orange	JHt	5	JHt /	6
Pink	////	4	JHt /	6
Purple	JHt ////	9	JHt	5
Red	JHt //	7	JHt ////	9
Yellow	JHt //	7	JHt /	6

Rob's data shows the probability of a red is $\frac{7}{50} = 14\%$
Maria's data shows the probability is $\frac{9}{50} = 18\%$
Overall the data shows the probability is $\frac{16}{100} = 16\%$

They want to investigate further but don't have time.

Rob asks his mum to perform the experiment 1000 times for him.

Maria sets up a computer simulation to perform the experiment 1000 times.

The results were:

Colour	Blue	Black	Green	Orange	Pink	Purple	Red	Yellow
Mum	125	125	125	125	125	125	125	125
Computer	118	126	123	119	118	125	152	119

Rob is suspicious – his mum's result are perfect!

Exercise D4.3

1 Ben is testing a dice to see if it is fair.
He rolls it 60 times, and gets these results:

Outcome	1	2	3	4	5	6
Frequency	13	9	12	6	10	10

Ben thinks the dice must be biased
because each number should come up 10
times.
   a Do you think that Ben is correct?
       Explain your answer.
   b How could Ben get a better idea of
       whether the dice is biased?

2 Kelly and Becky are testing a spinner to
see if it is fair.
It has 4 sections, coloured red, blue, green
and yellow.
Kelly tries the spinner 100 times, and gets
these results:

Outcome	Red	Blue	Green	Yellow
Frequency	25	20	33	22

Kelly says: 'This spinner looks biased to
me – you're much more likely to get a
green than a blue, and they should be
about the same.' What do you think?
Becky then tries the spinner 100 times.
Here are her results:

Outcome	Red	Blue	Green	Yellow
Frequency	25	28	20	27

Becky suggests they put their results
together to get a better idea of whether the
spinner is fair or biased.
Combine their results by adding the
frequencies for each outcome.
Comment on your result.

3 James is testing a dice, which he thinks
might be biased.
He rolls the dice 60 times, and gets these
results:

Outcome	1	2	3	4	5	6
Frequency	4	8	11	10	11	16

   a Work out an estimate of the
       probability of each score.
       Do you think that the dice is biased?
       Explain your answer.

James decides to collect some more data.
He rolls the dice 240 more times, and gets
these results:

Outcome	1	2	3	4	5	6
Frequency	42	29	36	33	34	66

   b Combine these two sets of results.
       Use the combined data to work out
       new estimates for the probability of
       each score on the dice.
       Do you now think that the dice is
       biased?
       Explain your answer.

4 Five teams of vets test some badgers for a
disease. The table shows their results:

Team	Number Tested	Number Infected
A	9	2
B	17	7
C	4	0
D	12	6
E	8	3

Combine the results for all 5 teams to
estimate the probability that a badger
chosen at random has the disease.

You should know how to …

1 Find and justify probabilities based on equally likely outcomes in simple contexts.

2 Understand and use the probability scale from 0 to 1.

3 Solve word problems and investigate in the context of probability.

Check out

1 When an ordinary, fair dice is rolled, what is the probability that the score obtained is:

a 6

b 7

c an even number

d a number greater than 2

e a number less than 8?

2 Mark each of the probabilities in question 1 on a probability scale.

3 In a fairground game, 5 different coloured dice are rolled, and players have to predict what all 5 scores will be.

It costs £1 to play, and you win £1000 if you guess all 5 numbers correctly.

Chris and Keith both play the game. They write down these predictions:

Dice	Keith	Chris
Blue	2	6
Red	3	6
Yellow	5	6
Green	1	6
White	4	6

Keith says to Chris: 'They're not likely to all come up with a six. You'd be better off with numbers like mine.'

Do you think that Keith is correct?

Equations and graphs

This unit will show you how to:

▶▶ Construct and solve simple linear equations with integer coefficients and the unknown on one side only using an appropriate method.

▶▶ Use simple formulae.

▶▶ Substitute positive integers into simple linear expressions and derive a formula.

▶▶ Generate sequences from practical contexts and describe the general term in simple cases.

▶▶ Express simple functions in words, then using symbols, and represent them in mappings.

▶▶ Generate coordinate pairs that satisfy a rule.

▶▶ Plot the graphs of simple linear functions.

▶▶ Recognise straight-line graphs parallel to the x-axis or y-axis.

▶▶ Solve word problems and investigate in the context of algebra.

▶▶ Identify the necessary information to solve a problem.

▶▶ Represent problems mathematically, making correct use of symbols, words, diagrams, tables and graphs.

▶▶ Present and interpret solutions in the context of the original problem.

▶▶ Explain and justify methods and conclusions.

▶▶ Suggest extensions to problems by asking 'what if …?'

£10 standing charge then 10p per minute. 2 hours and 20 minutes – that's err …

That's so easy – it's £24! Oh, better stop talking …

Reading a graph can be quicker and easier than making a calculation.

Before you start

You should know how to …

1 Plot coordinates in all four quadrants.

2 Use algebraic conventions and the order of operations.

Check in

1 Plot these points on a coordinate grid:

(⁻1, 0)   (⁻1, 2)   (⁻1, 8)

Join the points together.

Describe the line you have drawn.

2 Match each statement with the correct algebraic expression.

Statement	Expression
a 3 more than x then times 2	**A** $2x + 3$
b 3 times x then add 2	**B** $3(x + 2)$
c 2 more than x then times 3	**C** $3x + 2$
d 2 times x then add 3	**D** $2(x + 3)$

A5.1 Solving linear equations

This spread will show you how to:

▶▶ Construct and solve simple linear equations.

KEYWORDS

Equation

Solve

Solution

Marcus the Magician is performing a trick.

He puts a number into a hat without showing anyone.

The hat performs some operations.

A number comes out of the hat.

He writes an equation to describe the magic trick:

$3n + 1 = 19$ where n is the number he put in the hat.

If you solve the equation you can find the number he put into the hat.

The equation says:

Start with n	multiply it by 3	then add 1	This gives you 19
n	$3n$	$3n + 1$	$3n + 1 = 19$

To solve it you work backwards and undo the operations:

End with n	divide it by 3	subtract 1	Start with 19
6	$18 \div 3 = 6$	$19 - 1 = 18$	19

You can write it like this:

$$3n + 1 = 19$$
$$3n = 19 - 1$$
$$3n = 18$$
$$n = 18 \div 3$$
$$n = 6 \qquad \text{6 is the solution.}$$

Inverse is another word for opposite.

▶ + is the inverse of −

▶ × is the inverse of ÷

▶ **To solve an equation, work out how it is built up and then you can unravel it.**

Sometimes you need to construct an equation before you can solve it.

Marcus chooses another number.	The hat divides it by 2	Then subtracts 3.	The answer is 1. This is the equation:
n	$\frac{n}{2}$	$\frac{n}{2} - 3$	$\frac{n}{2} - 3 = 1$

Now undo it:

The number is:	multiply by 2	add 3	Start with 1
8	$4 \times 2 = 8$	$1 + 3 = 4$	1

Exercise A5.1

1 Marcus starts with 10 easy tricks.
Work out what number he put in the hat each time.

   a $2n = 18$ **b** $7x = 28$ **c** $y + 8 = 20$ **d** $m - 8 = 10$

   e $p - 6 = 6$ **f** $6 + r = 15$ **g** $a + 1\frac{1}{2} = 6$ **h** $c - 3.5 = 6.5$

   i $2.5f = 10$ **j** $\dfrac{q}{3} = 5$ **k** $1.5h = 15$ **l** $8k = 26$

2 Write an equation to describe each of Marcus's magic tricks:

   a He puts a number (n) into a hat, doubles it, adds 4 and the result is 20.
   b He puts a number (x) into a hat, mutiplies it by 4, subtracts 7 and the result is 29.
   c He puts a number (m) into a hat, multiples it by 3, subtracts 12 and the result is 0.
   d He puts a number (a) into a hat, halves it, adds 10 and the result is 17.
   e He puts a number (p) into a hat, divides it by 4, adds 5 and the result is $6\frac{1}{2}$.

3 For each question:

   ▸ construct an equation,
   ▸ work backwards to solve it.

   a Start with a, multiply by 3, add 4. The result is 46.
   b Start with b, multiply by 2, subtract 15. The result is 23.
   c Start with c, multiply by 6, add 7. The result is 61.
   d Start with d, divide by 3, subtract 5. The result is 14.
   e Start with e, divide by 5, add 3. The result is 8.2.

4 Solve each of the equations you made in question 2.
Check your answers to make sure they are correct.

5 Solve these equations.

   a $3x + 7 = 16$ **b** $4p - 3 = 33$ **c** $6t + 1 = 43$ **d** $5s - 4 = 21$

   e $2y + 7 = 12$ **f** $9s - 4 = 32$ **g** $3m - 13 = 29$ **h** $5r + 6 = 81$

   i $2q - 6 = 1$ **j** $4w + 18 = 32$ **k** $11j + 5 = 82$ **l** $2.5a + 16 = 26$

6 Copy these three lists.
Match Marcus's Magical Instructions with an algebraic equation and the correct solution.
The first one is done for you.

Instructions	Equation	Solution
Take a number, double it, add 7. The result is 43.	$2n - 7 = 43$	$n = 17$
Take a number, multiply by 7, add 2. The result is 44	$2n + 7 = 43$	$n = 25$
Take a number, multiply by 3, take 7. The result is 44	$3n - 2 = 43$	$n = 18$
Take a number, multiply by 2, take 7. The result is 43	$7n + 2 = 44$	$n = 15$
Take a number, multiply by 3, take 2. The result is 43	$3n - 7 = 44$	$n = 6$

Using formulae

This spread will show you how to:
▶▶ Substitute positive integers into simple linear equations.
▶▶ Explain the meaning of and substitute integers into formulae expressed in words.

There are 7 days in 1 week.
There are 2×7 days in 2 weeks.
There are 3×7 days in 3 weeks.
⋮   ⋮   ⋮
There are $n \times 7$ days in n weeks.

The number of days and the number of weeks can vary – they are variable.

▶ A formula is a statement that links two variables.
▶ You can write a formula in words or using symbols.
  You must describe any letters that stand for variables.

You can write:

$$\text{number of days} = 7 \times \text{number of weeks}$$
or $a = 7n$
        where a = number of days and n = number of weeks

These statements are formulae.

This formula links three variables together:

$$\text{area of a rectangle} = \text{length} \times \text{width}$$
or $A = lw$
        where A = area, l = length and w = width of rectangle

You can substitute known values into a formula to find unknown values.

example

Use the formula $A = lw$ to find:

a the area of a rectangle with length 3 m and width 2.5 m
b the length of a rectangle with area 9 cm^2 and width 2 cm
c the width of a rectangle with length 2 mm and area 11 mm^2

$\div$ is the inverse of $\times$.

a $l = 3$ m and $w = 2.5$ m,   **b** $A = 9$ cm^2 and $w = 2$ cm   **c** $l = 2$ mm and
        $A = lw$ $A = lw$ $A = 11$ mm^2
So: $A = 3 \times 2.5$ So: $9 = l \times 2$ $A = lw$
      $A = 7.5$ m^2 $9 \div 2 = l$ So: $11 = 2 \times w$
                                              $l = 4.5$ cm $11 \div 2 = w$
                                                                                  $w = 5.5$ mm

Exercise A5.2

1 Find the value of each expression when $a = 4$ and $b = 3$.
  a $2a + 3b$ **b** $b + 2a + 3b$
  c $3a - 9$ **d** $a^2 - ab$
  e $6ab$ **f** $4b + 2a$
  g $a(a - b)$ **h** $2(a + b) + b$
  i $3a \times 2b$ **j** $3(a - 3)$

2 In question 1, parts **a** and **h** have the same answer: 17.
  Consider the two expressions $2a + 3b$ and $2(a + b) + b$.
  Can you explain why they give the same answer?

3 Look for other pairs of equal answers in question 1.
  Can you explain why the expressions are the same?

4 The formula for the perimeter of this rectangle is

  $P = 2l + 2w$

  Find: **a** P if $l = 13$ cm and $w = 6$ cm
     b l if $P = 46$ cm and $w = 10$ cm
     c w if $P = 80$ cm and $l = 26$ cm

5 The formula for the area of this triangle is

  $A = \frac{1}{2}bh$

  Use the formula to find:
  a A if $b = 6$ cm and $h = 10$ cm
  b b if $A = 24$ cm^2 and $h = 8$ cm
  c h if $A = 14$ cm^2 and $b = 4$ cm

  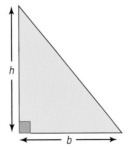

6 The distance you travel depends on your speed and
  the time taken for your journey.
  This formula links the distance travelled, speed and
  time taken for any journey:

  $s = vt$

  where s = distance, v = average speed and t = time taken.
  Use the formula to find:
  a the distance travelled (s) if $v = 60$ miles per hour and $t = 3$ hours
  b the speed (v) if $s = 120$ miles and $t = 5$ hours
  c the time taken (t) if $s = 330$ miles and $v = 60$ miles per hour

This spread will show you how to:
- ▶▶ Explain the meaning of and substitute integers into formulae expressed in words.
- ▶▶ Derive simple algebraic expressions and formulae.

KEYWORDS

Input   Polygon
Output   Perimeter
Substitute

A supermarket till has the price of everyday items already inputted.

The till uses this formula to work out the cost of these items:

cost = price of one item × number of items

The operator   ▶ inputs the number of items
               ▶ presses which item it is
               ▶ presses enter.
The machine   ▶ outputs the cost.

example

Ahmet buys 8 loaves of bread for his café.
They cost 55p each.
What is the total cost?

The operator inputs:
▶ 8
▶ Bread
▶ Enter
The machine outputs
▶ 4.40

$$\text{cost} = \text{number of items} \times \text{price of one item}$$
$$= \quad 8 \quad \times \quad 55\text{p}$$
$$= £4.40$$

You can make up formulae to describe everyday situations.
You should substitute known values into your formula to check it works!

example

Karl is planning his garden.
He wants a rectangular lawn edged with 1 metre square paving stones.
The cost of the paving stones depends on the size of the lawn.
Write a formula for the number of stones he will need if his lawn is 2 metres wide.

First draw a sketch:

The edge of the lawn is the perimeter:
length + width + length + width

The width is 2 m.
The length is not given so call it x metres.

The number of paving stones is $x + 2 + x + 2 + 4 = 2x + 8$ stones
Let the number of paving stones be N.

The formula is $N = 2x + 8$ stones

This includes 4 stones for the corners!

Exercise A5.3

1 Ahmet pays his waiters £4.30 per hour.
  a Write a formula to work out how much a waiter gets paid per week.
    Use: w = wages per week
           n = number of hours worked
           p = amount paid per hour.
  b If a waiter works 45 hours in one week, how much will he be paid?

2 In a mixed bag, there are red, green, black, yellow and purple sweets.
  Using x to stand for the number of yellow sweets, answer these questions.
  a There are twice as many black sweets as yellow sweets.
    How many black sweets are there?
  b There are two less red sweets than yellow sweets.
    How many red sweets are there?
  c There are half as many purple sweets as yellow sweets.
    How many purple sweets are there?
  d There are 5 more green sweets than purple sweets.
    Write an expression for the number of green sweets.
  e How many sweets are there altogether in the bag?
    Write your answer as simply as possible.

3 At the start of the week, Ms. Take, the maths teacher, opened two boxes of pencils and
  three packets of rulers for students to borrow.
  a Copy and complete the table below to show what happened to the rulers and pencils
    during the week (in algebra of course!)

Day	What happend to rulers and pencils?		Number of pencils	Number of rulers
Start of Monday	Opened	2 boxes of n pencils 3 packs of m rulers	$2n$	$3m$
End of Monday	Lost Lost	2 pencils 4 rulers	$2n - 2$	
End of Tuesday	Lost Lost	3 more pencils no more rulers		
End of Wednesday	Found Lost	1 pencil 2 more rulers		
End of Thursday	Lost Lost	8 more pencils 11 more rulers		$3m - 17$
End of Friday	Lost Lost	3 more pencils 1 more ruler		

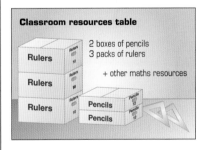

Classroom resources table

2 boxes of pencils
3 packs of rulers

+ other maths resources

Rulers
Rulers
Rulers
Pencils
Pencils

  b There are 12 pencils in a full box and 10 rulers in a pack.
    How many pencils and rulers were left at the end of the week?
  c At the end of the following week, Ms. Take had $(n + 3)$ pencils and $(2m - 6)$ rulers left.
    How many of each were there?

This spread will show you how to:
▶▶ Generate sequences from simple practical contexts.
▶▶ Begin to find a simple rule for the *n*th term of some simple sequences.

KEYWORDS
Continue   Sequence
*n*th term   Substitute
Rule

Here is a pattern of dots:

Once you can see how the pattern grows you can continue the pattern.
The pattern grows by adding 2 dots each time:

To find the 20 th or 100 th term or pattern in the sequence, you could:

▶ draw 20 or 100 patterns
▶ add 2 to the first pattern 19 or 99 times
▶ use a formula linking the term number with the number of dots.

To find the formula you find the number of dots for the *n*th term.
First you put the results you know in a table like this:

Term number	1	2	3	4	5	...	*n*
Number of dots	4	6	8	10	12	...	

The pattern goes up in 2s so you compare the number of dots with the multiples of 2.

Term number	1	2	3	4	5	...	*n*
Number of dots	4	6	8	10	12	...	
Multiples of 2	2	4	6	8	10	...	$2n$

The number of dots is 2 more than the multiples of 2:

Term number	1	2	3	4	5	...	*n*
Number of dots	4	6	8	10	12	...	
Multiples of 2	2	4	6	8	10	...	$2n$
Multiples of 2 + 2	4	6	8	10	12	...	$2n + 2$

The general rule for the sequence is $d = 2n + 2$
where d is the number of dots and n is the term number.

Check your rule by substituting known values.

▶ You can use a formula to describe the *n*th term of a sequence.
  ▶ Describe the steps the sequence grows in.
  ▶ Compare the results to multiples of the steps.

Exercise A5.4

For questions 1 to 5:
- ▶ copy the patterns and draw the next pattern
- ▶ copy and complete the table of results
- ▶ work out the general rule for the sequence

1

Pattern no.	1	2	3	4	5	...	n
No. of lines							
Multiples of 4							

2

Pattern no.	1	2	3	4	5	...	n
No. of lines							
Multiples of ?							

3

Pattern no.	1	2	3	4	5	...	n
No. of lines							
Multiples of ?							

4

Pattern no.	1	2	3	4	5	...	n
No. of lines							
Multiples of ?							

5

Pattern no.	1	2	3	4	5	...	n
No. of lines							
No. of dots							
Multiples of 2							
Lines							
Dots							

6 The general rules in the table are incorrect.
Find the correct rules. Explain why the reason given is incorrect.

	Sequence	nth term	Reason
a	4, 6, 8, 10 ...	$2n$	because it is the 2 times table (multiples of 2)
b	5, 8, 11, 14, ...	$5n + 3$	starts at 5 and goes up 3 every time
c	90, 80, 70, 60, ...	$10n - 100$	goes down 10 every time from 100
d	1, 4, 9, 16, 25	$3n + 2$	goes up 3 and then 2 more every time

Spot the function

This spread will show you how to:
- ▶▶ Draw simple mapping diagrams.
- ▶▶ Given inputs and outputs, find the function.
- ▶▶ Begin to recognise some properties of simple functions.

KEYWORDS

Function   Mapping
Input   Output

Marcus the Magician is changing his trick!

He shows the number that goes into the hat.

The hat performs a function at the touch of his wand.

He shows the number that comes out of the hat.

The trick is to work out what operations the hat performs.

The trick maps 3 onto 6.
You can show this using a mapping diagram: 3 6

A trick that maps 3 onto 6 is 'add 3' or + 3.

> There are other 'tricks' that could map 3 onto 6. Can you think of any?

▶ A **function** maps one value onto another.

example

Find a function for each of these mappings:

a   2 ➡ 9   b   9 ➡ 5
c   12 ➡ 24   d   12 ➡ 6

....

a $2 + 7 = 9$ so the function is $+ 7$ b $9 - 5 = 4$ so the function is $- 5$
c $12 + 12 = 24$ so the function is $+ 12$ d   The function could be:
     or an alternative function is $\times 2$ $\div 2$ or $- 6$ or $\times \frac{1}{2}$

Marcus puts the numbers 1 to 4 into the hat and touches the hat with his wand twice.
Here are the output numbers:

Input		Output	Multiples of 3	Multiples of 3 – 2
1	➡	1	3	1
2	➡	4	6	4
3	➡	7	9	7
4	➡	10	12	10

The output numbers go up in 3s so compare them with multiples of 3.   The function is '× 3 then – 2'.

You can write: input $\times 3 - 2 =$ output
or $3x - 2 = y$ where x is the input and y is the output.

Exercise A5.5

1 Find two different function rules for each of these machines:

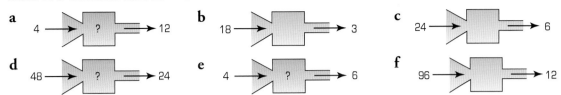

a 4 → ? → 12

b 18 → → 3

c 24 → → 6

d 48 → ? → 24

e 4 → ? → 6

f 96 → → 12

2 For each of these double function machines, find the outputs:

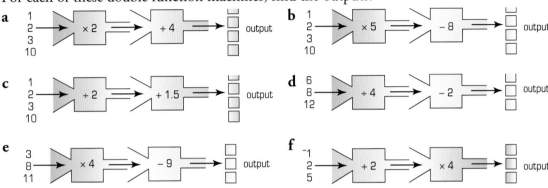

a 1, 2, 3, 10 → × 2 → + 4 → output

b 1, 2, 3, 10 → × 5 → − 8 → output

c 1, 2, 3, 10 → ÷ 2 → + 1.5 → output

d 6, 8, 12 → ÷ 4 → − 2 → output

e 3, 8, 11 → × 4 → − 9 → output

f −1, 2, 5 → + 2 → × 4 → output

3 For each of these double function machines, find the inputs:

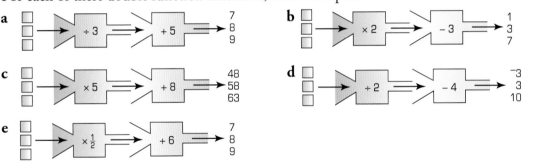

a → ÷ 3 → + 5 → 7, 8, 9

b → × 2 → − 3 → 1, 3, 7

c → × 5 → + 8 → 48, 58, 63

d → ÷ 2 → − 4 → −3, 3, 10

e → × ½ → + 6 → 7, 8, 9

4 Find the missing functions for each of these machines:

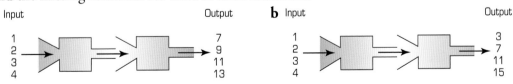

a Input 1, 2, 3, 4 → → → Output 7, 9, 11, 13

b Input 1, 2, 3, 4 → → → Output 3, 7, 11, 15

5 For the function machines in question 4, write down the output if the input is x.

6 Marcus's secret

Marcus is a great magician because he can find a second way to complete a trick.
Find alternative functions to give the same values on these machines.

a 1, 2, 3, 4 → + 2 → × 2 → 6, 8, 10, 12

b 1, 2, 3, 4 → × 3 → + 9 → 12, 15, 18, 21

227

A5.6 Graphs of functions

KEYWORDS
Coordinate pair
Function   Input
Predict   Output
Straight-line graph

Marcus the Magician puts the numbers 1 to 4 into the hat.
He touches it twice with his wand.
The mapping diagram shows the numbers that come out of the hat:

Input		Output	Multiples of 4
1	⟹	1	4
2	⟹	5	8
3	⟹	9	12
4	⟹	13	16

▶ The output numbers go up in 4s so the function will be × 4
▶ The output numbers are 3 less than the multiples of 4 so the function is: output = input × 4 – 3
   or: $y = 4x - 3$
   where x is the input and y is the output.

You can use the function $y = 4x - 3$ to find an output value for a given input value:
When the input is 7:
$$x = 7$$
so $y = 4 \times 7 - 3 = 25$

The input and output values form a pair:

Input	Output		Pair
1	1	⟹	(1, 1)
2	5	⟹	(2, 5)
3	9	⟹	(3, 9)
4	13	⟹	(4, 13)

You can plot the pairs on a coordinate grid:

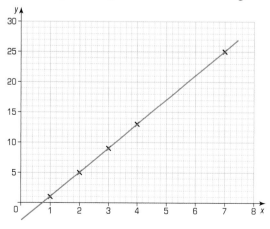

You can join the points together to make a straight line.
If you continue the line you can see that an input of 7 gives an output of 25.

▶ You can plot mappings on a coordinate grid.
   This will help you to spot patterns and make predictions.

Exercise A5.6

1 Copy and complete the mapping diagram, and write down the coordinate pairs. Plot these pairs on a coordinate grid and join the points to form a straight line.

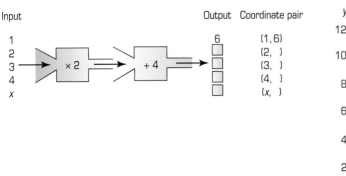

Output Coordinate pair

(1, 6)
(2,)
(3,)
(4,)
(x,)

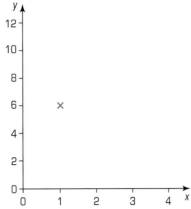

2 ▶ Copy and complete each mapping diagram.
 ▶ List the pairs formed and plot them on a coordinate grid.
 ▶ Join each set of a points to make a straight line.

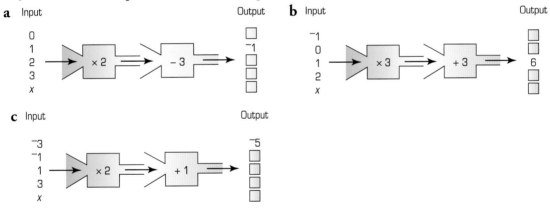

a Input   Output   **b** Input   Output

0   ⁻1
1   ⁻1   0
2   × 2   − 3   1   × 3   + 3   6
3   2
x   x

c Input   Output

⁻3   ⁻5
⁻1
1   × 2   + 1
3
x

3 For this mapping diagram, when the input is *x*, the output is $3x - 2$.

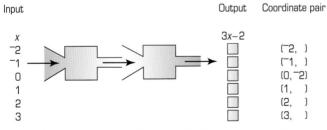

Input   Output   Coordinate pair

x   3x−2
⁻2   (⁻2,)
⁻1   (⁻1,)
0   (0, ⁻2)
1   (1,)
2   (2,)
3   (3,)

Copy the function machine and the mapping diagram.
a Write the functions in the function machine.
b Complete the mapping diagram.
c Plot the coordinate pairs on a grid.
d Join the points to make the straight-line graph of $y = 3x - 2$.

This spread will show you how to:

⏩ Generate and plot pairs of coordinates that satisfy a simple linear relationship.

⏩ Begin to consider the features of graphs of simple linear functions.

▶ **A graph shows a relationship between variables.**

These coordinates join to make a straight-line graph:

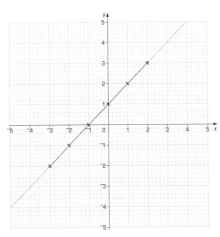

If you extend the line you can see that ($^-$4, $^-$3) and (3, 4) are also on the line.

The line goes on for ever, in both directions.
The red part is a line segment – a part of the line.

The coordinate pairs form a straight line.
The variables *input* and *output* have a **linear relationship**.

▶ **Points that lie on a straight line have a linear relationship.**

This function relates two variables, x and y:
$y = 3x - 2$

This is a table of values.

To see the relationship you:

1 Generate pairs of coordinates:
  ▶ choose values for x
  ▶ find corresponding values for y
  ▶ write the pairs as coordinates.

x	1	2	3
y	$3 \times 1 - 2 = 1$	$3 \times 2 - 2 = 4$	$3 \times 3 - 2 = 7$
	(1, 1)	(2, 4)	(3, 7)

2 Plot the points and join them up.

3 Describe the relationship – it is linear.

4 Check your line:
  (4, 10) should satisfy $y = 3x - 2$
  When $x = 4$, $y = 3 \times 4 - 2 = 10$

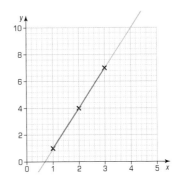

Exercise A5.7

1 a Copy and complete this table of values to satisfy the rule $y = x + 3$

x	$^-3$	$^-2$	$^-1$	0	1	2	3
$y = x + 3$			2				

  b List the coordinate pairs and plot them on a grid.
    Join up the plotted points to form a straight line.
  c Use your line to find the value of y when $x = 1.5$

2 Copy and complete the table of values from $x = ^-3$ to $^+3$ for each of these equations:

a $y = 2x + 1$

x	$^-3$	$^-2$	$^-1$	0	1	2	3
$y = 2x + 1$							

b $y = x - 1$

x	$^-3$	$^-2$	$^-1$	0	1	2	3
$y = x - 1$							

c $y = 5 - x$

x	$^-3$	$^-2$	$^-1$	0	1	2	3
$y =$							

For each equation:
▶ List the coordinate pairs.
▶ Plot them on a grid.
▶ Draw a line through each set of points.

3 The graph shows the line for the equation $y = 3$
The line connects all the points where y is 3.
  a On a copy of the grid, draw the lines for $y = 4$
    and $y = ^-2$
  b On the same grid, plot the points (3, 2) and
    (3, $^-2$) and join them with a straight line.
    This is the line $x = 3$ as it connects all the points
    where x is 3.

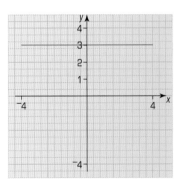

4 Copy this grid.
  a Draw in the lines where $y = 6$ and $y = ^-2$
  b Draw in the line for the equation $y = 2x + 1$
    (from question **2a**)
  c Draw in the line for the equation $y = 2x + 4$
  What shape have you made between all the lines?

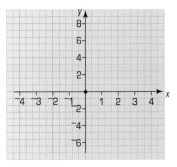

Linear graphs

This spread will show you how to:

▶▶ Begin to consider the features of graphs of simple linear functions.

▶▶ Recognise that equations of the form $y = mx$ correspond to straight-line graphs through the origin.

KEYWORDS

x-coordinate   Equation
Graph   Origin
Function   Axes

Here are the graphs of some linear functions:

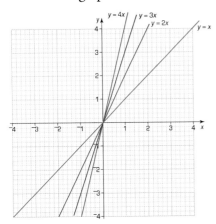

The graphs of the functions make a pattern.
They all pass through the origin but get steeper as the multipliers get bigger.

The functions have similar equations:

$y = x$
$y = 2x$
$y = 3x$
$y = 4x$

The bigger the number the steeper the line.

The y-coordinate is a multiple of the x-coordinate.
In general, $y = mx$ (where m stands for multiple).

▶ Graphs of the form $y = mx$:
   ▶ pass through the origin (0, 0)
   ▶ get steeper as m gets bigger.

The graph of $y = 3 - x$ shows a downward-sloping line:

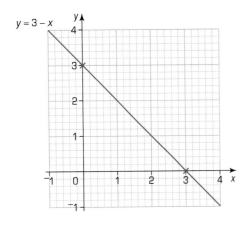

The only points shown are where the line crosses the coordinate axes:

On the x-axis, $y = 0$ so $3 - x = 0$ and $x = 3$
On the y-axis, $x = 0$ so $3 - 0 = y$ and $y = 3$

▶ **You only need to plot two points to specify a straight line.**

It is useful to use a third point as a check.

Exercise A5.8

1 These two graphs look different, but have very similar equations.

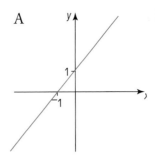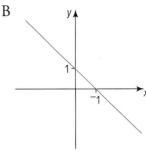

a Write down two similarities between the graphs.

b Write down the main difference.

c The equations for the graphs are $y = 1 - x$ and $y = 1 + x$. Match each equation with its graph.

d How is the difference you wrote in part **b** shown in the equations?

2 This is a graph of $y = 3 + x$

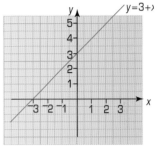

a Copy the graph accurately.

b Draw in the line for the equation $y = 3 - x$ on the same axes.

c Look at the two lines you have drawn. Describe one similarity and one difference.

3 On a grid, draw the lines for the equations $y = 1 + 2x$ and $y = 1 - 2x$

What are the coordinates of the point where the lines intersect?

4 This is the line for the equation $y = x$

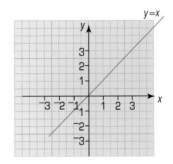

a Copy the grid and the line.

b Draw in the lines for the equations $y = x + 3$ and $y = x - 2$

c What can you say about the three lines?

d Comment on the points where each of the lines intersects the y-axis.

5 On a grid, sketch lines for the equations:

$y = \frac{1}{2}x$ $y = \frac{1}{2}x + 2$ $y = \frac{1}{2}x - 4$ $y = \frac{1}{2}x + \frac{1}{2}$

What can you say about all four lines?

Describe the similarities and differences.

6 The grid shows the graph of $y = x^2 + 2$.

The smooth curve is called a parabola.

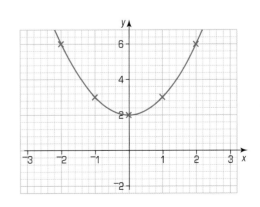

Copy the graph onto graph paper.

On your graph, plot the graphs with equations:

a $y = x^2$

b $y = x^2 - 1$.

Comment on the graphs and their equations.

You should know how to ...

1 Construct and solve simple linear equations.

2 Find the nth term of a simple sequence.

3 Plot the graphs of simple linear functions.

4 Solve word problems and investigate in context of algebra.

5 Explain and justify methods and conclusions.

Check out

1 Solve these equations:

  a $5 + n = 11$

  b $2n + 5 = 11$

  c $3n - 1 = 11$

  d $\frac{(n + 12)}{2} = 11$

2 For this sequence:

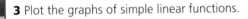

  a Draw the next two patterns.

  b Copy and complete the table:

Term	1	2	3	4	5
Number of squares	3	5	7		

  c Find the nth term of the sequence.

3 Draw the graph of $y = 3x + 2$ for the values of x from $^-3$ to 3.

4 Here are the equations of three straight-line graphs:

  A: $y = 2x - 1$ **B**: $y = 3 - x$ **C**: $2y = x + 1$

For each of these coordinate pairs, decide which, if any, of the lines they lie on:

$(^-1, 0)$ $(0, 3)$ $(1, 1)$
$(2, 5)$ $(3, 0)$ $(3, 5)$

5 Use algebra to justify your answers to question 4.

5 Polygons

This unit will show you how to:

- Begin to identify and use angle, side and symmetry properties of triangles and quadrilaterals.
- Solve geometrical problems involving properties of triangles and quadrilaterals.
- Use step-by-step deduction and explain reasoning with diagrams and text.
- Recognise and visualise transformations and symmetries.
- Use a ruler and protractor to construct a triangle given two sides and the included angle (SAS) or two angles and the included side (ASA).
- Use a ruler and protractor to construct simple nets of 3-D shapes.
- Solve word problems and investigate in the context of shape and space.
- Explain and justify methods and conclusions.
- Begin to generalise and to understand the significance of a counter-example.

Islamic design uses geometrical shapes to beautiful effect.

Before you start

You should know how to ...

1 Use conventions for labelling shapes.

2 Use a protractor to draw angles.

Check in

1 Write down the size of the given angle in these shapes:

a AB̂C

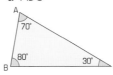

b Q̂

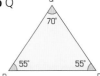

2 Draw angles of :

a 73°   **b** 171°

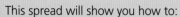

This spread will show you how to:
- ⏩ Construct lines, angles and shapes.
- ⏩ Use accurately the notation and labelling conventions for lines, angles and shapes.

KEYWORDS

Line   Protractor
Construct   Ruler
Draw   Sketch

You can construct a triangle using a ruler, protractor and compasses.

example

Construct triangle ABC with AB = 3 cm, BC = 2.5 cm and B̂ = 28°.
What is the length of AC?

Sketch the shape.   Draw the base AB.   Measure angle B.   Mark point C.

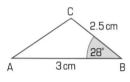
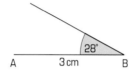
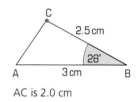

AC is 2.0 cm

example

Construct triangle PQR with P̂ = 80°, Q̂ = 65° and PQ = 3 cm.

First make a sketch.   Measure P̂ and draw   Measure Q̂ and draw   The lines join at R.
Draw the base PQ.   the line.   the line.

Check your drawing: R̂ should be 35°

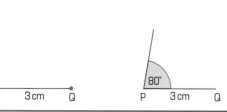
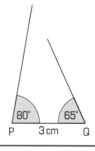

▶ You can construct a triangle when you know:
   ▶ two angles and the included side (ASA) or
   ▶ two sides and the included angle (SAS).

You need to know these facts to ensure your triangle is unique.

Triangle XYZ has X = 80°, Y = 90° and YZ = 4 cm.
These triangles satisfy the information.

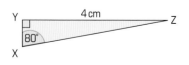
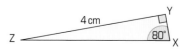

Exercise S5.1

1 Make accurate drawings of these triangles:

a

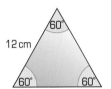

3 cm

4 cm

b

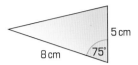

5 cm

8 cm   75°

c

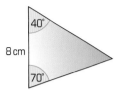

40°

8 cm

70°

d

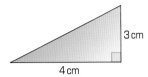

60°

12 cm

60°   60°

e

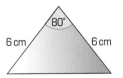

80°

6 cm   6 cm

f

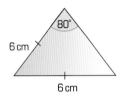

80°

6 cm

6 cm

2 Construct these triangles where possible.

    a triangle LMN with L = 56°, M = 87° and LM = 5 cm

    b triangle PQR with PQ = 8 cm, QR = 6 cm and Q = 90°

    c triangle XYZ with X = 30°, Y = 90° and YZ = 6 cm

    d triangle ABC with A = 40°, AB = 4 cm and BC = 9 cm

    e an isosceles triangle with an angle of 100° and the equal sides 6 cm

    Explain, with reasons, which triangles are unique.

> Sketch each triangle first.

3 **a** Construct an equilateral triangle of side 6 cm.

    b Construct an identical equilateral triangle on one of the sides of the first triangle.
        The two triangles will share a common side.

    c Describe your resulting shape.

4 **a** Construct triangle ABC where AC = 5 cm, CAB = 45° and AB = 4 cm.

    b Now construct an identical triangle so that the two triangles share side AB.
        Describe the resulting shape.

    c Repeat the construction so that the two triangles share side AC.

    d Repeat the construction so that the two triangles share side BC.

This spread will show you how to:
▶▶ Construct lines, angles and shapes.
▶▶ Use accurately the notation and labelling conventions for lines, angles and shapes.

KEYWORDS
Triangle   Congruent
Quadrilateral Construct
Base   Sketch

You can make a quadrilateral using two triangles:

These isosceles triangles fit to make a rhombus.

These scalene triangles make an irregular quadrilateral.

You can construct a quadrilateral using a ruler, protractor and compasses.

example

Construct a parallelogram PQRS with
▶ sides PQ = 3 cm and QR = 2 cm and
▶ angle PQR = 55°.

Sketch the shape first – it's important that you can see all the information you need:

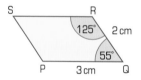

$180° - 55° = 125°$ so QR̂S = 125°

1 Draw the base, PQ = 3 cm   **2** Use a protractor to mark the angle 55°   **3** Mark R 2 cm along the line

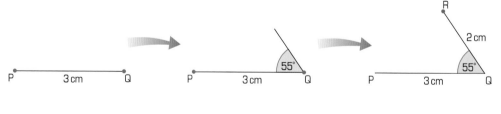

6 Now check SP is 2 cm   **5** Mark S 3 cm along   **4** The obtuse angle QRS is 125°

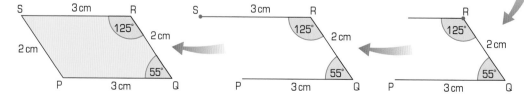

238

Exercise S5.2

1 Make accurate drawings of these quadrilaterals.

a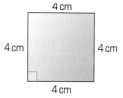

b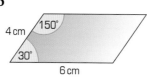

c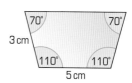

d

e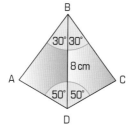

f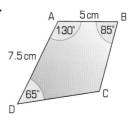

2 Construct a parallelogram ABCD where AB = 8 cm, BC = 5 cm and BÂD = 60°.
Use the properties of a parallelogram to find the other angles.

3 Construct a rhombus PQRS with sides 6 cm, and angle PQ̂R = 35°.
Use the properties of a rhombus to find the other angles.

4 Construct these quadrilaterals ABCD and then name them.
Sketch them first!
  a AD = 8 cm, BÂD = 70°, AD̂C = 70°, AB = 5 cm, CD = 5 cm
  b All sides 5 cm, Â = 110°
  c AD = 8 cm, Â = 70°, D̂ = 110°, AB = 5 cm, DC = 5 cm
  d DB̂C = DB̂A = 60°, BD̂A = BD̂C = 20°, BD = 6 cm
  e DB̂C = BD̂C = BD̂A = DB̂A = 45°, BD = 6 cm
Are your constructions unique? Give reasons for your answers.

5 A regular shape has all its sides and angles equal.
  a Construct this regular pentagon:

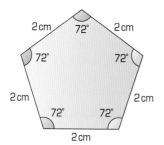

  b This regular hexagon is made from six equilateral triangles:

Construct a regular hexagon with side 4 cm.

S5.3 Constructing 3-D shapes

This spread will show you how to:
- ▶▶ Construct solid shapes.
- ▶▶ Use a ruler and protractor to construct simple nets.

KEYWORDS

3-D	Vertex
Solid	Net
Face	Base
Edge	

This solid is a tetrahedron.
It is a pyramid with all faces equilateral triangles.

It has 4 faces, 6 edges and 4 vertices.

You can open out the box and lay it flat.
How it looks when it's flat depends on how you open it ...

like this: or like this:

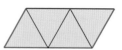

You can see there are 4 faces.   The colours show which edges fit together.

▶ A flat shape that folds up to make a 3-D shape is called
  a **net**.
▶ To construct a 3-D shape you construct a net for it then
  fold it up.

To make the edges stick
together you include flaps!

example

Sketch the net of a square-based pyramid.
What information do you need to construct the net accurately?

Imagine laying the box flat:
You need to know:

▶ the length of the side of the square base, *b*
▶ and the angle *a* between the base and the sloping sides
▶ the length of the sloping sides, *c*.

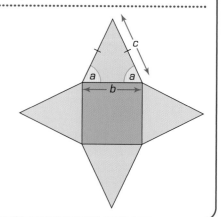

Exercise S5.3

1 Sketch a net for each of these boxes.

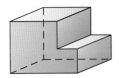  

2 This is the net of a 2-D shape.
Name the shape and construct the net.

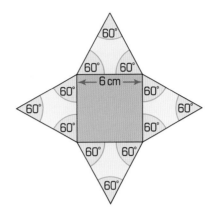

3 Match these nets to their solid shapes:

a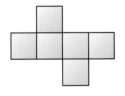

b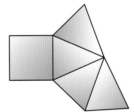

c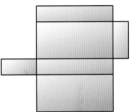

d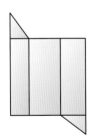

e

f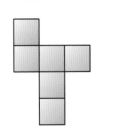

4 Construct accurate nets for these solids.

a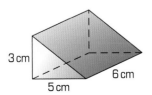

b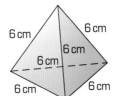

c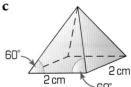

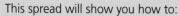

S5.4 Properties of triangles and quadrilaterals

This spread will show you how to:

▶▶ Identify parallel and perpendicular lines.

▶▶ Identify and use the geometric properties of triangles, quadrilaterals and other polygons to solve problems.

▶▶ Explain and justify inferences and deductions using mathematical reasoning.

KEYWORDS

Adjacent   Intersect
Opposite   Parallel
Perpendicular   Symmetry
Quadrilateral   Triangle

You can describe a shape by its properties.
To give a full description you identify as many properties as you can.

Here is some of the language you need to use:

▶ Sides – opposite, adjacent, equal, parallel, perpendicular, diagonal, bisect
▶ Angles – acute, obtuse, reflex, right
▶ Symmetries – order of rotational symmetry, line of reflection symmetry

To describe this triangle you would say:

There are 3 sides.

One angle is 90 degrees.

Two sides are equal so it is isosceles.
It has 1 line of symmetry.

The triangle is a right-angled isosceles triangle.

To describe this square you would say:

All sides and angles equal.

Adjacent sides perpendicular.

Opposite sides parallel.
These marks show parallel lines. →

Symmetries:
4 lines of symmetry
order of rotational symmetry is 4.

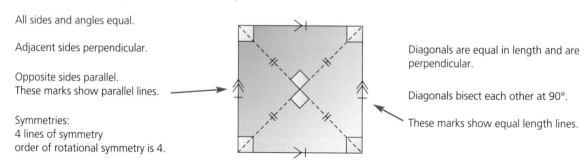

Diagonals are equal in length and are perpendicular.

Diagonals bisect each other at 90°.

These marks show equal length lines.

You can use the properties of shapes to solve problems.

example

Can you draw a triangle with interior angles 123°, 96° and 31°?

....

The interior angles in a triangle add to 180°.
These angles add to 250° so the angles cannot form a triangle.

Exercise S5.4

1 In each question, sketch a quadrilateral with the given symmetry properties:

   a at least one line of symmetry

   b at least one line of symmetry but no rotational symmetry

   c at least one line of symmetry but no rotational symmetry and a reflex angle

   For each of your sketches:

   ▶ name the shape

   ▶ describe its side and angle properties

2 Start with a 4 × 2 rectangle.

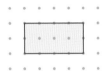

   Cut it once to make two new shapes:

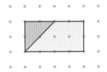

   What other shapes can you make with one cut?

   Name each shape you can make and describe their side, angle and symmetry properties.

3 For each of these statements, say whether it is true or false.

   Justify your answers.

   a Any quadrilateral with 4 equal sides must be a square.

   b A triangle can have a reflex angle.

   c A triangle can have two obtuse angles.

   d All squares are rectangles.

   e A rectangle has 4 lines of symmetry.

   f Rectangles with the same area have the same perimeter.

4 Draw any quadrilateral.

   ▶ Mark the midpoints of each side and join them up.

   ▶ Describe the new shape.

   Repeat for other quadrilaterals.

   Describe what happens.

5 On a 3 × 3 pinboard, make as many different shapes as you can.

   Name each shape and describe its side, angle and symmetry properties.

> For example:
>
>
>
> This is a right-angled isosceles triangle.
> It has 2 equal sides and 2 equal angles and 1 line of symmetry.

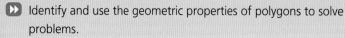

S5.5 Properties of polygons

This spread will show you how to:

▶▶ Identify and use the geometric properties of polygons to solve problems.

▶▶ Recognise and visualise symmetries of 2-D shapes.

KEYWORDS

Polygon   Rotation

Concave   Reflection

Convex

▶ A polygon is a shape with straight sides.

▶ In any polygon: number of sides = number of angles.

Some polygons have special names:

3 sides	4 sides	5 sides	6 sides
triangle	**quadrilateral**	**pentagon**	**hexagon**

A **concave** polygon has at least one reflex angle: A **convex** polygon has no reflex angles:

▶ Regular polygons have all sides and all angles equal.

This is a regular hexagon:
It has 6 sides and angles equal.

It has 6 lines of symmetry:

and rotational symmetry of order 6:

  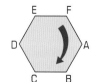

▶ A regular n-sided polygon has n lines of symmetry and order of symmetry n.

Exercise S5.5

1 a Sketch triangles with different numbers of lines of symmetry?

b Repeat part **a** for quadrilaterals then pentagons then hexagons.

Copy and complete this table for your answers. Write Yes or No in each box.

	Number of lines of symmetry								
	0	1	2	3	4	5	6	7	8
Triangles									
Quadrilaterals									
Pentagons									
Hexagons									

c Is there a connection between the number of sides of a shape and the number of lines of symmetry it can have? Justify your answer.

2 The table contains an incomplete description of a parallelogram and a rectangle.
Copy the table.
List any other shapes that fit each description.

Description	Other examples
Rectangle 4 sides and 4 right angles	
Parallelogram 2 sets of parallel sides	

3 Justify your answers to these questions:

a Can shapes have all angles equal but *not* all sides equal?

b Name a shape with all sides equal but *not* all angles equal.

c Are all shapes with equal sides regular?

d Is a rectangle a regular shape?

4 Copy this Venn diagram.
Put all the 2-D shapes you know in the correct places.

> **Hint:** Shapes with different sides and angles go outside the loops.

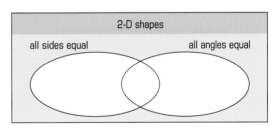

What is the collective name for the shapes in the overlap?

5 What shape can also be described as:

a a rectangle with equal sides

b a rhombus with equal angles

c a parallelogram with equal sides but unequal angles

d a parallelogram with equal angles but unequal sides?

▶ **The angles in a triangle add to 180°.**

You can use this fact to find the angle sum of any polygon.
Split the polygon into triangles like this:

Draw all the diagonals from one vertex:

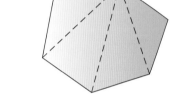

The polygon is now split into triangles:

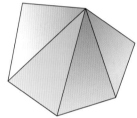

There are 4 triangles in a hexagon.
The angles of a hexagon add to $4 \times 180° = 720°$

Tessellations
Whether a polygon will tessellate depends on its angles.
Polygons that **tessellate** fit together with no gaps or overlaps.
This is a tessellation of octagons and squares.

These are two different tessellations.

▶ Tessellations are produced when congruent shapes fit together without any gaps or overlaps.

Congruent shapes are exactly the same shape and size.

A shape that is rotated, reflected or translated produces a congruent image which may tessellate:

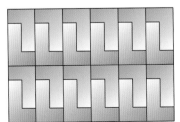

Exercise S5.6

1 For each of these patterns, say whether it is a tessellation:

a

b

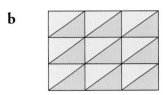

2 Which of these shapes tessellate?
Make copies to help you.

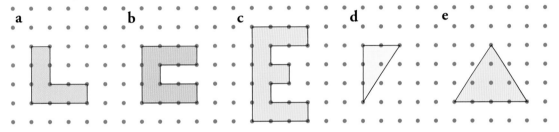

a   **b**   **c**   **d**   **e**

3 An enlargement is the same shape as the original shape
but larger.
Show how each shape tessellates to make an enlargement.
The first one is done for you:

> Make copies of the shape to try
> out different tessellations.

a

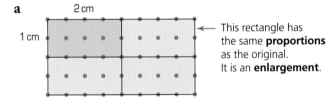

← This rectangle has
the same **proportions**
as the original.
It is an **enlargement**.

b   **c**

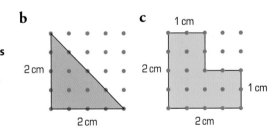

4 Draw a 3 by 3 square on squared paper.
Mark on the diagonals.
Cut out the square and cut along the diagonals to make four congruent triangles.
  a What shapes can you make from joining two of the triangles?
  Draw them and name them.
  b What shapes can you make from joining three of the triangles?
  Draw them and name them.
  c What shapes can you make from joining all of the triangles?
  Draw them and name them.

5 Without measuring, write down the sum of the interior angles for each shape you made in
question 4.

Summary

You should know how to ...

1 Identify and use properties of triangles, quadrilaterals and other polygons to solve problems.

2 Explain and justify methods and conclusions.

3 Solve word problems and investigate in the context of shape and space.

Check out

1 A regular pentagon can be dissected into three pieces:

   a Name the three triangles formed. Be as specific as possible.

   b Copy the pentagon and cut out the triangles. Use two or three of the triangles to make as many different shapes as you can. The edges must fit together exactly on your shapes. Sketch and name each shape you draw.

2 Explain why:

   a a triangle can never have a reflex angle

   b it is always possible to make an isosceles triangle from two congruent right-angled triangles.

3 The diagram shows two shapes that fit together.

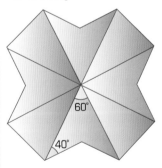

   a Name the two shapes. Be as specific as possible.

   b Use the given angles to find all the other angles in each shape.

add, addition
N1.2, N1.3, N1.5

Addition is the sum of two numbers or quantities.

adjacent (side)
S3.3, S5.4

Adjacent sides are next to each other and are joined by a common vertex.

algebra
A1.6, A2.1, A2.2

Algebra is the branch of mathematics where symbols or letters are used to represent numbers.

amount
N4.2, N5.8

Amount means total.

angle: acute, obtuse, right, reflex
S2.1, S3.1

An angle is formed when two straight lines cross or meet each other at a point. The size of an angle is measured by the amount one line has been turned in relation to the other.

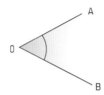

An acute angle is less than 90°.

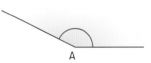

An obtuse angle is more than 90° but less than 180°.

A right angle is a quarter of a turn, or 90°.

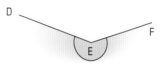

A reflex angle is more than 180° but less than 360°.

angles at a point
S2.2, S3.1

Angles at a point add up to 360°.

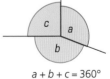

$a + b + c = 360°$

angles on a straight line
S2.2, S3.1

Angles on a straight line add up to 180°.

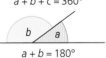

$a + b = 180°$

approximate, approximately
N1.5, N1.6, N3.4, N3.5, N3.6, N3.7, N5.1

An approximate value is a value that is close to the actual value of a number.

approximately equal to (≈)
N3.4, N3.5, N5.4

Approximately equal to means almost the same size.

area: square millimetre, square centimetre, square metre, square kilometre
N2.5, S1.1, S1.2, S1.3, A3.1

The area of a surface is a measure of its size.

Glossary

average
D1.1, D1.2, D3.4, D3.5

An average is a representative value of a set of data.

axis of symmetry
S4.1, S4.2

An axis of symmetry of a shape is a line about which the shape can be folded so that one half fits exactly on top of the other half.

axis, axes
A5.8

An axis is one of the lines used to locate a point in a coordinate system.

bar chart
D1.3, D2.4, D2.5, D3.2, D3.3

A bar chart is a diagram that uses rectangles of equal width to display data. The frequency is given by the height of the rectangle.

bar-line graph
D2.4

A bar-line graph is a diagram that uses lines to display data. The lengths of the lines are proportional to the frequencies.

base (of plane shape or solid)
S1.2, S1.4, S3.5, S5.2, S5.3

The lower horizontal edge of a plane shape is usually called the base. Similarly, the base of a solid is its lower face.

base

between
N5.1

Between means in the space bounded by two limits.

brackets
A4.3, N3.2, N3.8

Operations within brackets should be carried out first.

calculate, calculation
N1.3

Calculate means work out using a mathematical procedure.

calculator: clear, display, enter, key, memory
N1.6, N3.8

You can use a calculator to perform calculations.

cancel, cancellation
N2.2, N2.4, N2.6, N4.1, N4.5

A fraction is cancelled down by dividing the numerator and denominator by a common factor.

For example, $\dfrac{24}{40} \underset{\div 8}{\overset{\div 8}{=}} \dfrac{3}{5}$

capacity: litre
S1.3

Capacity is a measure of the amount of liquid a 3-D shape will hold.

centre of rotation
S4.4

The centre of rotation is the fixed point about which a rotation takes place.

certain
D1.4, D4.1

An event that is certain will definitely happen.

chance
D1.4, D4.1

Chance is the probability of something happening.

class interval
D2.3

A class interval is a group that you put data into to make it easier to handle.

common factor
N4.5

A common factor is a factor of two or more numbers. For example, 2 is a common factor of 4 and 10.

commutative

An operation is commutative if the order of combining two objects does not matter. For example, addition is commutative as $4 + 3 = 3 + 4$, but subtraction is not commutative because $4 - 3 \neq 3 - 4$.

compare
N1.1, N4.3, N4.5, N5.6

Compare means to assess the similarity of.

complement
N1.3, N1.4

In addition, a number and its complement have a given total. For example, 13 is the complement to 20 of 7.

concave
S3.2, S5.5

A concave shape bends inwards. A concave polygon has at least one interior angle greater than 180°.

This is a concave quadrilateral.

congruent
S4.2, S4.3, S4.4, S4.6, S5.2, S5.6

Congruent shapes are exactly the same shape and size.

consecutive
A1.1, A2.3, N3.4

Consecutive means following on in order.
For example 2, 3 and 4 are consecutive integers.

construct
S3.4, S5.1, S5.2

To construct means to draw a line, angle or shape accurately.

continue
A1.2, A5.4

Continue means carry on.

convert
N2.3, N2.4, N2.6, N3.1, N4.1, N5.7

Convert means to change.

convex
S3.2, S5.5

Convex means bending outwards. A convex polygon has no interior angles greater than 180°.

This is a convex quadrilateral.

coordinate pair
A3.5, A5.6

A coordinate pair is a pair of numbers that give the position of a point on a coordinate grid.
For example, (3, 2) means 3 units across and 2 units up.

coordinate point
A5.7

A coordinate point is the point described by a coordinate pair.

coordinates
A3.5, A3.6, S4.3

Coordinates are the numbers that make up a coordinate pair.

data
D1.1, D2.1

Data are pieces of information.

data collection sheet
D2.2, D3.1

A data collection sheet is a sheet used to collect data. It is sometimes a list of questions with tick boxes for collecting answers.

decimal fraction
N1.5, N2.4

A decimal fraction shows part of a whole represented as tenths, hundredths, thousandths and so on.
For example, 0.65 and 0.3 are decimal fractions.

Glossary

decimal number
N4.1, N5.7, N5.8

A decimal number is a number written using base 10 notation.

decimal place (d.p.)
N1.1, N3.5, N3.7, N5.1

Each column after the decimal point is called a decimal place.
For example, 0.65 has two decimal places (2 d.p.)

degree (°)
S2.1

A degree is a measure of turn. There are 360° in a full turn.

denominator
N2.1, N2.2

The denominator is the bottom number in a fraction. It shows how many parts there are in total.

diagonal
S3.2

A diagonal of a polygon is a line joining any two vertices but not forming a side.

This is a diagonal.

difference
N1.2, N1.4

You find the difference between two amounts by subtracting one from the other.

digit
N1.1, N5.1

A digit is any of the numbers 0, 1, 2, 3, 4, 5, 6, 7, 8, 9.

direction
S2.3

The direction is the orientation of a line in space.

distance
S1.1, S1.2

The distance between two points is the length of the line that joins them.

divide, division
N2.1, N2.5, N3.1, N3.6, N3.7

Divide (÷) means share equally.

divisible, divisibility
N5.3

A whole number is divisible by another if there is no remainder left.

divisor
N3.6

The divisor is the number that does the dividing.
For example, in 14 ÷ 2 = 7 the divisor is 2.

double, halve

Double means multiply by two. Halve means divide by two.

draw
S2.1, S5.1

Draw means create a picture or diagram

edge (of solid)
S1.4, S3.5, S5.3

An edge is a line along which two faces of a solid meet.

equal (sides, angles)
S3.3

Equal sides are the same length. Equal angles are the same size.

edge

equally likely
D1.5, D4.1, D4.3

Events are equally likely if they have the same probability.

equals (=)
A2.5, A3.4, A4.1

Equals means having exactly the same value or size.

equation
A3.4, A4.1, A4.2, A4.4, A5.1

An equation is a statement linking two expressions that have the same value.

equation (of a graph)
A3.5, A3.6, A5.8

An equation is a statement using an = sign to link two expressions.

equivalent, equivalence
N2.2, N2.3, N2.4, N2.5, N2.6,
N4.1, N4.2, N4.3, N5.6

Equivalent fractions are fractions with the same value.

estimate
N1.5, N5.8, D1.6

An estimate is an approximate answer.

evaluate
A2.4

Evaluate means find the value of an expression.

exact, exactly

N5.5

Exact means completely accurate.
For example, three divides into six exactly.

experiment
D1.6, D2.1, D4.2, D4.3

An experiment is a test or investigation to gather evidence for or against a theory.

expression
A1.6, A2.1, A2.2, A2.3, A2.4,
A3.3, A4.1, A4.3, A4.4, A5.2

An expression is a collection of numbers and symbols linked by operations but not including an equals sign.

face
S1.4, S3.5, S5.3

A face is a flat surface of a solid.

face

factor
N5.3, A3.1, A3.2, S1.1

A factor is a number that divides exactly into another number.
For example, 3 and 7 are factors of 21.

fair
D1.6, D4.3

In a fair experiment there is no bias towards any particular outcome.

finite
A1.1

A finite sequence has a definite beginning and end.

fraction
N2.1, N2.2, N2.4, N2.5, N2.6,
N3.7, N4.1, N4.2, N4.3, N5.7, N5.8

A fraction is a way of describing a part of a whole.
For example $\frac{2}{5}$ of the shape shown is red.

frequency
D1.1, D1.6, D2.2, D2.3

Frequency is the number of times something occurs.

frequency diagram
D2.4, D2.5

A frequency diagram uses bars to display grouped data. The height of each bar gives the frequency of the group, and there is no space between the bars.

function
A1.4, A1.5, A1.6, A3.4,
A5.5, A5.6, A5.8

A function is a rule.
For example, $+ 2$, $- 3$, $\times 4$ and $\div 5$ are all functions.

function machine
A1.4, A1.5

A function machine links an input value to an output value by performing a function.

generalise
A3.3

Generalise means formulate a general statement or rule.

generate
A1.2, A5.7

Generate means produce.

Glossary

graph
A3.6, A5.7, A5.8

A graph is a diagram that shows a relationship between variables.

greater than (>)
N5.6, N5.8

Greater than means more than.
For example 4 > 3.

grid
S2.3

A grid is a repeated geometrical pattern used as a background to plot coordinate points. It is usually squared.

height, high
S1.2

Height is the vertical distance from the base to the top of a shape.

highest common factor (HCF)
N5.2

The highest common factor is the largest factor that is common to two or more numbers.
For example, the HCF of 12 and 8 is 4.

horizontal
A4.2

Horizontal means flat and level with the ground.

hundredth
N1.1

A hundredth is 1 out of 100.
For example 0.05 has 5 hundredths.

impossible
D1.4

An event is impossible if it definitely cannot happen.

improper fraction
N2.3

An improper fraction is a fraction where the numerator is greater than the denominator. For example, $\frac{8}{5}$ is an improper fraction.

increase, decrease
N4.4

Increase means make greater. Decrease means make less.

infinite
A1.1

An infinite sequence has no definite end.

input, output
A1.4, A1.5, A2.5, A3.4,
A5.3, A5.5, A5.6

Input is data fed into a machine or process. Output is the data produced by a machine or process.

integer
N1.2, N2.5

An integer is a positive or negative whole number (including zero).
The integers are: ..., ⁻3, ⁻2, ⁻1, 0, 1, 2, 3, ...

interpret
N3.8, D2.5, D3.3, D3.5

You interpret data whenever you make sense of it.

intersect, intersection
S2.3, S5.4

Two lines intersect at the point, or points, that they cross.

intersection

interval
D2.4

An interval is the size of a class or group in a frequency table.

inverse
N3.3

An inverse operation has the opposite effect to the original operation. For example, multiplication is the inverse of division.

label
D2.4

A label is a description of a diagram or object.

length: millimetre, centimetre, metre, kilometre; mile, foot, inch
S1.1, S1.3

Length is a measure of distance. It is often used to describe one dimension of a shape.

less than (<)
N5.6, N5.8

Less than means smaller than.
For example, 3 is less than 4, or 3 < 4.

likelihood
D4.1

Likelihood is the probability of an event happening.

likely
D1.4, D1.6

An event is likely if it will happen more often than not.

line of symmetry
S4.2, S4.5

A line of symmetry is a line about which a 2-D shape can be folded so that one half of the shape fits exactly on the other half.

line symmetry

A shape has line symmetry if it has a line of symmetry.

line
S5.1

A line joins two points and has zero thickness.

lowest common multiple (LCM)
N5.2, N5.6

The lowest common multiple is the smallest multiple that is common to two or more numbers.
For example the LCM of 4 and 6 is 12.

lowest terms
N2.2, N2.4

A fraction is in its lowest terms when the numerator and denominator have no common factors.

mapping
A1.5, A3.4, A5.5

A mapping is a rule that can be applied to a set of numbers to give another set of numbers.

mass: gram, kilogram; ounce, pound
S1.3

Mass is a measure of the weight of an object.

mean
D1.2, D3.4

The mean is an average value found by adding all the data values and dividing by the number of pieces of data.

measure
S2.1, S3.1, S3.4

When you measure something you find the size of it.

median
D1.1, D3.4

The median is an average which is the middle value when the data is arranged in size order.

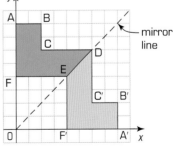

mirror line
S4.1, S4.2

A mirror line is a line or axis of symmetry.

mixed number
N2.3

A mixed number has a whole number part and a fraction part.
For example, $3\frac{1}{2}$ is a mixed number.

modal class
D1.1, D3.4

The modal class is the most commonly occurring class when the data is grouped. It is the class with the highest frequency.

mode
D1.1, D3.4

The mode is an average which is the data value that occurs most often.

multiple
N3.6, N5.5, A3.1, A3.3

A multiple of an integer is the product of that integer and any other.
For example, these are multiples of 6: $6 \times 4 = 24$ and $6 \times 12 = 72$.

Glossary

multiply, multiplication
N3.1, N5.3, N5.4

Multiplication is the operation of combining two numbers or quantities to form a product.

nearest
N5.1, N5.5

Nearest means the closest value.

negative
N1.2, N1.3, N1.6

A negative number is a number less than zero.

net
S1.4, S5.3

A net is a 2-D arrangement that can be folded to form a solid shape.

nth term
A3.3, A3.4, A5.4

The nth term is the general term of a sequence.

numerator
N2.1, N2.2

The numerator is the top number in a fraction. It shows how many parts you are dealing with.

object, image
S4.1, S4.2, S4.3

The object is the original shape before a transformation. An image is the same shape after a transformation.

operation

An operation is a rule for processing numbers or objects. The basic operations are addition, subtraction, multiplication and division.

opposite (sides, angles)
S3.3, S5.4

Opposite means across from.

The red side is opposite the red angle.

order
N1.1

To order means to arrange according to size or importance.

order of operations
N3.2

The conventional order of operations is:
brackets first,
then division and multiplication,
then addition and subtraction.

order of rotation symmetry

The order of rotation symmetry is the number of times that a shape will fit on to itself during a full turn.

origin
A5.8, S2.3

The origin is the point where the x- and y-axes cross, that is (0, 0).

outcome
D1.5, D1.6, D4.1, D4.2

An outcome is the result of a trial or experiment.

parallel
S2.2, S3.3, S5.4

Two lines that always stay the same distance apart are parallel. Parallel lines never cross or meet.

partition; part
N1.4, N2.1, N3.3, N3.4, N5.3, A4.3

To partition means to split a number into smaller amounts, or parts. For example, 57 could be split into 50 + 7, or 40 + 17.

percentage (%)
N2.6, N4.1, N4.2, N4.3, N5.7, N5.8

A percentage is a fraction expressed as the number of parts per hundred.

perimeter
A2.1, A5.3, S1.1, S1.2

The perimeter of a shape is the distance around it. It is the total length of the edges.

perpendicular
S2.2, S3.3, S5.4

Two lines are perpendicular to each other if they meet at a right angle.

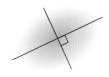

pie chart
D1.3, D2.4, D2.5, D3.2

A pie chart uses a circle to display data. The angle at the centre of a sector is proportional to the frequency.

place value
N1.1, N3.1

The place value is the value of a digit in a decimal number.
For example, in 3.65 the digit 6 has a value of 6 tenths.

polygon: pentagon, hexagon, octagon

A polygon is a closed shape with three or more straight edges.

A pentagon has five sides.

A hexagon has six sides.

An octagon has eight sides.

positive
N1.2, N1.3

A positive number is greater than zero.

predict
A1.3, A3.3, A5.6

Predict means forecast in advance.

prime
N5.2, A3.1

A prime number is a number that has exactly two different factors.

probability
D1.4, D1.5, D4.2, D4.3

Probability is a measure of how likely an event is.

probability scale
D4.1

A probability scale is a line numbered 0 to 1 or 0% to 100% on which you place an event based on its probability.

product
N3.4, N5.2, A3.1

The product is the result of a multiplication.

proportion
N4.3, N4.4, N4.5

Proportion compares the size of a part to the size of a whole. You can express a proportion as a fraction, decimal or percentage.

protractor (angle measurer)
S2.1, S3.1, S3.4, S5.1

A protractor is an instrument for measuring angles in degrees.

quadrant
S2.3

A coordinate grid is divided into four quadrants by the *x*- and *y*-axes.

quadrilateral: kite, parallelogram, rectangle, rhombus, square, trapezium
S2.3, S3.2, S3.3, S5.2, S5.4

A quadrilateral is a polygon with four sides.

rectangle

parallelogram

kite

All angles are right angles. Opposite sides equal.

Two pairs of parallel sides.

Two pairs of adjacent sides equal. No interior angle greater than 180°.

rhombus

square

trapezium

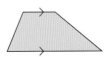

All sides the same length. Opposite angles equal.

All sides and angles equal.

One pair of parallel sides.

Glossary

questionnaire
D2.2

A questionnaire is a list of questions used to gather information in a survey.

quotient
N3.6, N5.5

A quotient is the result of a division.
For example, the quotient of $12 \div 5$ is $2\frac{2}{5}$, or 2.4.

random
D4.1

A selection is random if each object or number is equally likely to be chosen.

range
D1.1, D2.2, D2.3, D3.4

The range is the difference between the largest and smallest values in a set of data.

ratio
N4.5

Ratio compares the size of one part with the size of another part.

reflect, reflection
S4.2, S4.6, S5.5, S5.6

A reflection is a transformation in which corresponding points in the object and the image are the same distance from the mirror line.

reflection symmetry
S4.1, S4.5, S4.6

A shape has reflection symmetry if it has a line of symmetry.

regular

A regular polygon has equal sides and equal angles.

relationship
A3.5, A5.7

A relationship is a link between objects or numbers.

remainder
N3.6, N3.7, N5.2, N5.5

A remainder is the amount left over when one quantity is exactly divided by another. For example, $9 \div 4 = 2$ remainder 1.

represent
D3.2, D3.3, D3.4, D3.5

You represent data whenever you display it in the form of a diagram.

rotate, rotation
S4.4, S4.5, S4.6, S5.5, S5.6

A rotation is a transformation in which every point in the object turns through the same angle relative to a fixed point.

rotation symmetry
S4.5

A shape has rotation symmetry if when turned it fits onto itself more than once during a full turn.

round
N1.6, N3.4, N3.5, N5.1, N5.5

You round a number by expressing it to a given degree of accuracy. For example, 639 is 600 to the nearest 100 and 640 to the nearest 10.
To round to one decimal place means to round to the nearest tenth. For example 12.47 is 12.5 to 1 d.p.

rule
A1.1, A1.2, A1.3, A1.4, A5.4

A rule describes the link between objects or numbers. For example, the rule linking 2 and 6 may be +4 or ×3.

ruler
S3.4, S5.1

A ruler is an instrument for measuring lengths.

sequence
A1.1, A1.2, A1.3, A3.2, A3.3, A5.4

A sequence is a set of numbers or objects that follow a rule.

shape
S3.2

A shape is made by a line or lines drawn on a surface, or by putting surfaces together.

side (of 2-D shape)
S2.1

A side is a line segment joining vertices.

sign
N2.3

A sign is a symbol used to denote an operation.

significant
N1.1

The first non-zero digit in a number is the most significant figure. For example, the most significant figure in 207 is the 2, which represents 200.

simplest form
N2.2, N4.5

A fraction (or ratio) is in its simplest form when the numerator and denominator (or parts of the ratio) have no common factors.
For example, $\frac{3}{5}$ is expressed in its simplest form.

simplify
A2.3

To simplify an expression you gather all like terms together into a single term.

sketch
S3.4, S5.1, S5.2

A sketch shows the general shape of a graph or diagram.

solid (3-D) shape: cube, cuboid, prism, pyramid, square-based pyramid, tetrahedron
S1.4, S3.5, S5.3

A solid is a shape formed in three-dimensional space.

cube

six square faces

cuboid

six rectangular faces

prism

the end faces are constant

pyramid

the faces meet at a common vertex

tetrahedron

all the faces are equilateral triangles

square-based pyramid

the base is a square

solution (of an equation)
A5.1

The solution of an equation is the value of the variable that makes the equation true.

solve (an equation)
A4.1, A4.2, A4.4, A5.1

To solve an equation you need to find the value of the variable that will make the equation true.

spin, spinner
D1.5, D4.3

A spinner is an instrument for creating random outcomes, usually in probability experiments.

square number, squared
N3.2, A2.4, A3.1, A3.2

If you multiply a number by itself the result is a square number.
For example 25 is a square number because $5^2 = 5 \times 5 = 25$.

square root
A3.2

A square root is a number that when multiplied by itself is equal to a given number. For example $\sqrt{25} = 5$, because $5 \times 5 = 25$.

statistic, statistics
D1.3, D3.4, D3.5

Statistics is the collection, display and analysis of information.

Glossary

straight-line graph
A3.6, A5.7

When coordinate points lie in a straight line they form a straight-line graph. It is the graph of a linear equation.

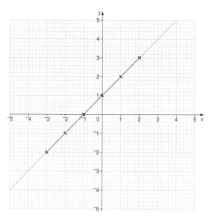

substitute
A2.4, A5.2, A5.3, A5.4

When you substitute you replace part of an expression with a value.

subtract, subtraction
N1.2, N1.3, N1.5, N3.3, N3.6, N5.5

Subtraction is the operation that finds the difference in size between two numbers.

sum
D1.2

The sum is the total and is the result of an addition.

surface, surface area
S1.4

The surface area of a solid is the total area of its faces.

survey
D2.1, D2.2

A survey is an investigation to find information.

symbol
A2.3, A2.4, A5.2

A symbol is a letter, number or other mark that represents a number or an operation.

symmetrical
S4.5, S5.4

A shape is symmetrical if it is unchanged after a rotation or reflection.

table
D2.3

A table is an arrangement of information, numbers or letters usually in rows and columns.

tally
D2.3, D4.3

You use a tally mark to represent an object when you collect data. Tally marks are usually made in groups of five to make it easier to count them.

temperature: degrees Celsius, degrees Fahrenheit

Temperature is a measure of how hot something is.

tenth
N1.1

A tenth is 1 out of 10 or $\frac{1}{10}$.
For example 0.5 has 5 tenths.

term
A1.1, A1.2, A1.3, A1.6,
A2.2, A4.2, A4.4

A term is a number or object in a sequence. It is also part of an expression.

thousandth
N3.1

A thousandth is 1 out of 1000 or $\frac{1}{1000}$.
For example, 0.002 has 2 thousandths.

three-dimensional (3-D)
S3.5, S5.3

Any solid shape is three-dimensional.

total
N1.4

The total is the result of an addition.

transformation
S4.1, S4.6

A transformation moves a shape from one place to another.

translate, translation
S4.3, S4.6, S5.6

A translation is a transformation in which every point in an object moves the same distance and direction. It is a sliding movement.

triangle: equilateral, isosceles, scalene, right-angled
S1.2, S3.2, S3.3, S5.2, S5.4, S5.6

A triangle is a polygon with three sides.

equilateral

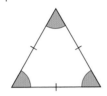

three equal sides

isosceles

two equal sides

scalene

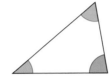

no equal sides

right-angled

one angle is 90°

triangular number
A3.2

A triangular number is the number of dots in a triangular pattern:
The numbers form the sequence
1, 3, 6, 10, 15, 21, 28 ...

two-dimensional (2-D)
S3.2

A flat shape has two dimensions, length and width or base and height.

unknown
A1.2, A2.1, A2.2, A2.3, A4.1, A4.2, A4.4, A5.2

An unknown is a variable. You can often find its value by solving an equation.

value
A1.6, A3.5, A3.6, A4.2, A4.4, A5.2

The value is the amount an expression or variable is worth.

variable
A1.6, A2.4, A2.5, A5.2, A5.7

A variable is a symbol that can take a range of values.

vertex, vertices
S1.4, S2.1, S3.1, S3.5, S5.3

A vertex of a shape is a point at which two or more edges meet.

vertex

vertical
A4.2

Vertical means straight up and down.

Glossary

vertically opposite angles
S2.2

When two straight lines cross they form two pairs of equal angles called vertically opposite angles.

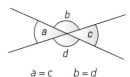

$a = c$ $b = d$

whole
N2.1

The whole is the full amount.

width
S1.1, S1.3

Width is a dimension of an object describing how wide it is.

x-axis, y-axis
A2.2, S2.3

On a coordinate grid, the x-axis is usually the horizontal axis and the y-axis is usually the vertical axis.

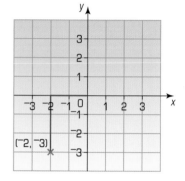

x-coordinate, y-coordinate
A5.8, S2.3

The x-coordinate is the distance along the x-axis.
The y-coordinate is the distance along the y-axis.
For example, (⁻2, ⁻3) is ⁻2 along the x-axis and ⁻3 along the y-axis.

zero
N3.1

Zero is nought or nothing.
A zero place holder is used to show the place value of other digits in a number. For example, in 1056 the 0 allows the 1 to stand for 1 thousand. If it wasn't there the number would be 156 and the 1 would stand for 1 hundred.

A1 Check in

1 a 2, 5, 8, 11, 14, 17
  b 20, 16, 12, 8, 4, 0
  c 10, 9.5, 9, 8.5, 8, 7.5
  d 3, 2.9, 2.8, 2.7, 2.6, 2.5

2 a 27 b 32 c 42 d 63
  e 9 f 6 g 7 h 6
  i 4 j 9

A1 Check out

1 a 18, 23, 28; starts at 3, goes up by 5; 48
  b 14, 18, 22; starts at 2, goes up by 4; 38
  c 9, 6, 3; starts at 18, goes down by 3; -9
  d 32, 64, 128; starts at 2, doubles each time; 1024
  e 12, 15, 18; starts at 3, goes up by 3; 30 matches

2 a 11, $x + 3$ b 3, $x - 5$ c 16, $2x$
  d 2, $x/4$ e 19, $2x + 3$ f 20, $3x - 4$

N1 Check in

1 a i Thirteen thousand, two hundred and six
    ii One hundred and thirty thousand, two hundred and six
  b i 400 008
    ii 408 000

2 a 172 b 17

3 a 4599 b 1189

N1 Check out

1 a 7.1 b 11.3

2 a $^-10$ b 9 c $^-21$ d 9.5

3 a 35.96 b 45.68

4 a £67.58
  b £2.45
  c Rows are: $^-2$, 5, $^-3$; $^-1$, 0, 1; 3, $^-5$, 2

S1 Check in

2 8 cm^2

S1 Check out

3 c 4 cm square
4 a 1600 cm^2
  b 900 000 cm^2
  c 562.5

N2 Check in

1 a One fifth
  b Three fifths
  c Two thirds
  d Three tenths
2 a $\frac{2}{5}$ **b** $\frac{3}{8}$ **c** $\frac{1}{3}$ **d** $\frac{7}{10}$
3 a 1, 2   **b** 1, 3   **c** 1, 2
  d 1, 2, 5, 10

N2 Check out

1 a i $\frac{3}{4}$ **ii** $7\frac{1}{5}$
  b 24
2 Fraction: $\frac{9}{20}$, $\frac{8}{25}$, $1\frac{2}{5}$
  Decimal: 0.45, 0.32, 1.4
  Percentage: 45%, 32%, 140%
3 a 1.2 **b** $10\frac{1}{5}$ **c** £24 **d** 90 sheep
4 15% of 240 = 36

1 **a** 1, 2, 3, 6, 7, 7, 8
  b 0.6, 0.8, 1.2, 1.2, 1.3, 1.4, 1.5, 1.9
2 $\frac{3}{5}$
3 **a** 50% **b** 25% **c** 30% **d** 70%

1 **a** Median = 9.5
  b Modal mark = 8
  c Mean mark = 10.8
  d Range = 21
  e Frequencies: 1, 11, 4, 3, 1
    The modal class is 6 – 10.
2 0.1, 0.5, 0.01, 1, 0.8, 0
3 **a** 24 **b** 4 **c** $\frac{1}{2}$

1 **a** $t + 9$ **b** $m - 6$ **c** $2n$
2 **a** 14 **b** 13 **c** 6

2 **a** $6w$ **b** $2pq$ **c** $6ab$
  d $5vw$ **e** $2pq$
3 **a** $5p + 1$ **b** $5x + y$ **c** $4d$
  d $3t + 3s$ **e** $15x + 8y$
  f $5a - 3b + 3$
4 **a** 1 **b** 6 **c** 14 **d** 14

S2 Check in

1 a Kite b Parallelogram
2 b Pentagon

S2 Check out

2 a $a = 118°$
  b $b = 110°$
  c $c = 60°$
  d $d = 30°$
  e $e = 45°$
  f $f = 30°$

D2 Check in

1 a 19, 23, 24, 24, 29, 34, 41, 43, 82
  b 0.3, 1.6, 3.2, 4.0, 4.11, 5, 7
2 3, 4, 5, 19, 4, 109, 4

D2 Check out

1 The chart does not show the number of goals scored by the opposing team.
  You can conclude that the team scored more goals at home than away.

N3 Check in

1 **a** 56 **b** 54 **c** 40 **d** 42
e 3 **f** 6 **g** 9 **h** 8

2 Four and thirty-two hundredths; thirteen and seven hundredths

3 6, 12, 18, 24

N3 Check out

1 **a** False; $(7 + 2) \times 3$
b True **c** False; $14 \div (2 + 5) \times 6$

2 **a** 146 **b** 120.4 **c** 29.12 **d** 3712
e 47.38 **f** 1.64 **g** 0.9 **h** 13.4

4 **a** **i** 4.8 cm **ii** 600 mm
iii 0.04284 km
b **i** 3.3 kg **ii** 15.8 m

5 **a** ÷ **b** + **c** − **d** ÷

A3 Check in

1 Vertical line, $x = 3$

2 3, 5, 7, 9, 11

A3 Check out

1 **a** 0, 4, 8, 12 **b** $4n - 4$
c (1, 0), (2, 4), (3, 8), (4, 12)
e $y = 4x - 4$

2 **a** $y = {}^{-}1, 0, 1, 2, 3$
c (1, 0)

3 No, $53 = 52 + 1$

1 **a** Trapezium   **b** Rhombus
2 **a** 62°   **b** 291°
3 **a** $4a$ **b** $6b$ **c** 3
   d $3d + 2e$

1 **a** $a = 56°$, $b = 68°$
   b $c = 50°$, $d = 65°$
2 **a** Top and bottom parallel, none perpendicular
   b Vertical sides are parallel and each of these is perpendicular to top
4 No, angle sum >180°

1 Fraction: $\frac{3}{4}$, $\frac{3}{5}$, $\frac{1}{5}$
   Decimal: 0.75, 0.6, 0.2
   Percentage: 75%, 60%, 20%
2 **a** $\frac{1}{3}$ **b** $\frac{3}{8}$ **c** $\frac{2}{9}$
3 **a** £34   **b** £444   **c** £187.50

1 **a** 0.39, 0.4, $\frac{3}{7}$, 43%, $\frac{9}{20}$
   b 14%
   c £1984
   d **i** True   **ii** True   **iii** False
3 **a** £960, £1600, £2240
   b $\frac{1}{3}$
   c 46.7%
   d $\frac{1}{5}$
4 **a** 300   **b** 200   **c** 150

A4 Check in

1 a $x + 1$ **b** $n - 2$ **c** $3f$

   d $\dfrac{r}{2}$ **e** $m - n$ **f** $b + c$

   g $\dfrac{x}{y}$ **h** n^2

2 a $4a\cdot$ **b** $6b$ **c** $3c$

   d $2d$ **e** $3e + 2$ **f** $f + 12$

   g xy

A4 Check out

1 a $10 - x$ **b** $2n + 6$ **c** $\dfrac{m}{2} + 7$

   d $3p + 5$ **e** $2x - 3$ **f** $2(y + 6)$

   g $\dfrac{(n-3)}{2}$ **h** $\frac{1}{2}(2t + 5)$

2 a $6, x = 4$ **b** $+, y = 17$

   c $2 + h = 9$ so $9 - 2 = h, h = 7$

   d $2, m = 16$

   e $\dfrac{n}{3} = 5$ so $5 \times 3 = n, n = 15$

   f $c, c = 1.8$

   g $5 - 3 = n, n = 2$

   h $12 + 6 = b, b = 18$

3 a $5n + 3 = 8, n = 1$

   b $3n - 10 = 8, n = 6$

   c $\dfrac{n}{2} + 3 = 8, n = 10$

4 20

S4 Check in

1 $(3, {}^{-}2)$

2 a Right-angled isosceles triangle

   b Isosceles trapezium

   c Parallelogram

   d Right-angled kite

S4 Check out

2 Possible shapes with congruent triangles: hexagon, pentagon, isosceles trapezium, isosceles triangle, equilateral triangle

   Possible shapes with non-congruent triangles: quadrilateral, pentagon, hexagon, scalene triangle, right-angled triangle, isosceles triangle, trapezium

1 **a** 23   **b** 0.6   **c** 179
2 **a** 30 cm   **b** 14 m   **c** 0.423 litres
   d 0.068 kg
3 **a** 256 apples   **b** 105.6 m

1 **a** Fraction: $\frac{27}{100}$, $\frac{3}{8}$, $\frac{2}{5}$, $1\frac{1}{4}$
     Decimal: 0.27, 0.375, 0.4, 1.25
     Percentage: 27%, 37.5%, 40%, 125%
   c £3.75
2 **a** 48.33   **b** 3385.2   **c** 139.16
   d 45   **e** 12.4   **f** 23.68
5 **a** £270
   c The property will be worth
     $1.1^5 = 1.61051$ times more, which is
     61% more.
6 Both the same.

1 35.2, 52, 52.1, 52.9, 53.92
2 **a** 4.3   **b** 12.6   **c** 123.5
   d 8.04   **e** 0.51   **f** 5.0

1 Claire: Range = £6.20, mean = £1.98,
   median = £1.75, mode = nothing
   Shirley: Range = £3.55, mean = £2.01,
   median = £2, mode = £2
   Comparing the ranges, Claire's tips are
   more variable. The median is the most
   suitable average to use (Claire's mode is too
   low and her mean too high).
2 On average, Shirley's tips are higher. In view
   of the statistics, Shirley may prefer not to
   share tips, as this will benefit Claire.
3 The monthly average is over 0°C but
   individual days may be less than 0°C.

1 **a** $\frac{3}{4}$ **b** $\frac{2}{5}$ **c** $\frac{2}{3}$ **d** $\frac{9}{10}$

2 **a** 80% **b** 0.875 **c** 20% **d** $\frac{3}{20}$

e $\frac{7}{25}$ **f** 0.175

1 **a** $\frac{1}{6}$ **b** 0 **c** $\frac{3}{6} = \frac{1}{2}$ **d** $\frac{4}{6} = \frac{2}{3}$ **e** 1

3 Keith is incorrect. Each time a fair dice is rolled, any number is equally likely to come up.

1 Vertical line, $x = -1$

2 **a** $2(x + 3)$ **b** $3x + 2$ **c** $3(x + 2)$

d $2x + 3$

1 **a** $n = 11 - 5 = 6$

b $2n = 11 - 5$

$2n = 6$

$n = 6 \div 2 = 3$

c $3n = 11 + 1$

$3n = 12$

$n = 12 \div 3 = 4$

d $n + 12 = 11 \times 2$

$n + 12 = 22$

$n = 22 - 12 = 10$

2 **b** 9, 11

c $2n + 1$

4 $(^-1, 0)$ lies on line C

$(0, 3)$ lies on line B

$(1, 1)$ lies on lines A and C

$(2, 5)$ does not lie on any of the lines

$(3, 0)$ lies on line B

$(3, 5)$ lies on line A

1 a 80°   **b** 70°

1 a Three isosceles triangles
2 a A reflex angle is more than 180°, so the angle sum would be more than 180°.
  b One pair of equal sides are joined, one pair make the base of the new triangle and the other pair make two equal sides of the new triangle.
3 isosceles triangle 30°, 75°, 75°
arrowhead 60°, 40°, 40°, 220°

Index

Index

Index